The design, installation, commissioning and maintenance of fire detection and fire alarm systems

A guide to BS Code 5839-1

The design, installation, commissioning and maintenance of fire detection and fire alarm systems

A guide to BS Code 5839-1

Colin S. Todd

Business
Information

First edition published by CMP Information Ltd in 2003

Second edition published by BSI in 2006

This new edition first published in 2008

by
BSI
389 Chiswick High Road
London W4 4AL

Typeset in Century Schoolbook by Monolith
Printed in Great Britain by the MFK Group, Stevenage

British Library Cataloguing in Publication Data
A catalogue record for this book is available from the British Library

ISBN 978 0 580 63098 9

Dedicated to my children, Keith, Jayne and Fiona, all of whom make me proud every day. And to Karen for her undying love and support.

Contents

About the author

Colin Todd MSc, FIFireE, FBEng, MIRM, MSFPE, C.Phys, FInstP, C.Eng, FIEE graduated from Edinburgh University with an honours degree in Physics. He then undertook a one year Master's degree in Fire Safety Engineering, developing a specific interest in quantitative assessment of risk, mathematical modelling and systems engineering.

In 1975, he joined the captive insurance company of Unilever Ltd. As a member of the risk management section, he carried out regular fire surveys of Unilever premises and was responsible for providing in-house advice on loss prevention matters. He later joined the technical department of the Fire Offices' Committee (FOC), which dealt with the preparation of codes and standards on fire protection and approvals of fire protection equipment. With the FOC he specialized in electrical matters, and was responsible for assessing the suitability of fire alarm equipment for FOC approval. During this time, he represented the FOC on national committees including those of BSI. (The FOC was later incorporated into the Loss Prevention Council and, subsequently, the Building Research Establishment.)

Colin Todd is a chartered engineer and a Fellow of the Institution of Electrical Engineers, the Institute of Physics, the Association of Building Engineers and the Institution of Fire Engineers. He is a corporate member of the Institute of Risk Management and the Society of Fire Protection Engineers. He is also a standards associate of the British Standards Society.

As the final President of the UK Chapter of the Society of Fire Protection Engineers, he was instrumental in the merger between that organization and the Society of Fire Safety Engineers to form the Institute of Fire Safety, which subsequently became the Engineering Council Division of the Institution of Fire Engineers (IFE). He is a member of the Board of the Division and a member of the Division's Membership Committee, which for many years he chaired. The Division is empowered to award engineering qualifications, including chartered engineer, to suitably qualified fire safety engineers. He is also a member of the IFE Board, where he holds the responsibility for technical issues. He serves on a number of British Standards Committees, including those concerned with fire detection and fire alarm systems. He also represents the Confederation of British Industry on Expert Group A of the Loss Prevention Certification Board, which is responsible for the development of approval schemes for all aspects of automatic fire alarm equipment.

Colin's consulting practice, C.S. Todd & Associates Ltd, is independently certificated by the National Security Inspectorate (NSI) for the design and verification of fire detection and alarm systems under the British Approvals for Fire Equipment (BAFE) SP203 Scheme for fire alarm specialists. The practice was the first independent consulting practice to receive this certification.

Foreword

This book follows on from two previous guides to BS 5839-1:2002 written by Colin Todd and published in 2003 and 2006. Since publication of these earlier guides, some amendments have been made to the code, while fire safety legislation in Great Britain has been subject to radical change.

The advice provided by BS 5839-1:2002, the British Standard code of practice for fire detection and fire alarm systems, is presented in the form of explanatory information followed by specific recommendations. The explanatory information helps readers to understand the rationale behind the recommendations. This book serves to further that understanding. It is not a replacement for the code.

This guide not only explains the code, it also provides extensive information regarding issues that have to be considered when designing, installing and commissioning a fire detection and fire alarm system. It could be considered as a course textbook for all those concerned with fire detection and fire alarm systems, including users, regulators and those who approve fire detection and fire alarm systems.

The guide benefits from the fact that Colin Todd was contracted by BSI to produce the draft for the 2002 version of BS 5839-1. In preparing that draft, Colin consulted various interested parties. It also benefits from the fact that Colin is a member of the BSI technical subcommittee (FSH/12/1), responsible for the code, and of its parent committee FSH/12. He was involved in the committee discussions that took place before the 2002 version of the code was published and in those before each of the amendments to the code were made.

J.W. Northey
Chairman, BSI Technical Committees FSH/12 and FSH/12/1

1. Introduction

The aim of this book is to provide guidance on the current version of BS 5839-1, which was published at the end of 2002, with subsequent amendments in 2004, and most recently, in April 2008. The code, which, as one part of the BS 5839 suite of codes and standards, bears the generic heading *'Fire detection and fire alarm systems for buildings'*, is entitled *'Code of practice for system design, installation, commissioning and maintenance'*. As such, the code represents the universal 'Bible' for those involved in the design, installation, commissioning, maintenance and use of fire detection and fire alarm systems in the United Kingdom.

Compliance with the code is very commonly required by building control bodies throughout the United Kingdom (although, in Scotland, fire alarm systems are only required by the relevant building regulations in specific occupancies), fire and rescue authorities and other authorities who may enforce provisions for fire safety in certain occupancies (e.g. housing authorities in the case of houses in multiple occupation, or Health and Safety Executive for construction sites). Frequently, property insurers also require automatic fire detection systems complying with the recommendations of the code, or are prepared to take account of such systems in their underwriting considerations, provided the system complies with the code.

Consulting engineers also commonly demand compliance with the code, often as part of the electrical specification for a building. However, under the 2002 version of BS 5839-1, a simple reference to the code, along with siting of devices on associated drawings, does not, by itself, constitute design of the system, as that term is defined in the code. Whereas, under previous versions of the code, there could be some ambiguity as to whether some aspects of design were the responsibility of the specifier, the supplier of the equipment, or the installer, the scope and duties of the 'designer' under the 2002 version of the code are much clearer, thereby, hopefully, resulting in less contract disputes if systems are found to fall short of compliance with the code. Experience shows, nevertheless, that there is still an educational process required before the identity and role of the 'the designer' is fully understood by all relevant parties.

This guide is less detailed than the equivalent guide to the 1988 version of the code. The reason for this is that the 2002 version now contains substantial explanatory text that provides background information on the reason for the majority of the recommendations made within the code. Moreover, the 'unbundling' of the explanatory text and the recommendations within the code, effectively makes the explanatory text, referred to in the code as 'Commentary', a form of guide to the recommendations of the code. Although, inevitably, some of the contents of this guide will virtually repeat parts of the commentary within the code, the intention of this guide is not merely to pull together such explanatory text into a single document. Instead, the guide is intended to provide readers with guidance on practical application of the recommendations in a variety of situations, taking into account the insight to the recommendations provided by the commentary. Thus, this guide is not a substitute for the code itself, but should be read in conjunction with the code.

The guide should not be regarded as offering any final authoritative interpretation on any recommendations of the code, although it is hoped that the opinions expressed are an accurate reflection of the relevant BSI technical committee's intent when the code was published. If it is essential to obtain a definitive interpretation, such as in the event of a dispute, advice may be sought from BSI, which will refer the matter to the relevant committee. Ultimately, the final arbiter in such a dispute can, however, only be the courts. Hopefully, the 2002 version of BS 5839-1 will be sufficiently less ambiguous and clearer than previous versions that the need for such interpretations, and the occurrence of disputes, will be uncommon. To further assist users in interpretation, BSI intends, in the future, to publish a series of interpretations given in response to queries put to the technical committee (rather like FAQs on internet websites). This new information will be published as PD 6531, most likely within the next two years.

In 2006, there were radical changes to fire safety legislation in Great Britain, with greater responsibility placed on those who employ people to work in, and/or have control over, buildings to ensure the adequacy of fire precautions in the buildings for which they are responsible. More specifically, suitable and sufficient fire risk assessments need to be carried out by all such dutyholders.

There is a compelling logic in this approach to fire safety, and it has already led to a much more flexible and pragmatic approach to the formulation of appropriate 'recipes' for fire safety in buildings. There is no doubt that this has led to enhanced recognition of automatic fire detection as one of the ingredients in the recipe. Whereas, traditionally, different components of fire protection were thought to be watertight compartments, each considered separately and independently of the others, the modern and more holistic approach to fire safety recognizes the influence that the presence of automatic fire detection can have on the level of safety afforded occupants of a building, sometimes resulting in the possibility to relax requirements in respect of other fire precautions. This recognition will be even more explicit after the future publication of a new comprehensive guide to the design of fire precautions in buildings, in the form of BS 9999.

This modern approach to fire safety is clearly acknowledged and well recognized within BS 5839-1 (as amended). On this basis, it is reasonable to assert that the 2002 version of the code constitutes an important member of the suite of codes and standards on which fire safety in the twenty-first century is based. Already, the original version of the code has been subject to two amendments, necessitating this third edition of this guide. These factors, coupled with the rate at which fire detection technology advances, make it unlikely that the 2002 code and this current edition of the guide will have the 14-year life of their predecessors.

2. History of fire alarm installation codes

General

The earliest codes of practice for the installation of automatic fire detection and alarm systems were those produced by the then Fire Offices' Committee (FOC). The 'Committee' comprised representatives of most of the major fire insurers in the United Kingdom, and the 'rules' of the FOC were associated with fire insurance underwriting considerations.

The FOC was constituted to represent fire insurers' interests, after insurers suffered numerous severe fire losses in the latter part of the nineteenth century, particularly in London wharfs and warehouses. Although the FOC became well known throughout the world as a fire protection approvals and code producing body, its principal raison d'être was to set minimum rates or 'tariffs' for different classes of trade. Insurance premium discounts could be offered to clients who installed adequate fire protection measures, whereas premium penalties could be imposed for risks that had adverse features.

In order to ensure that the fire protection systems for which premium discounts could be offered were reliable and effective, it was necessary for the FOC to enter the business of approving equipment; the first heat detector (known then as an 'approved thermostat') was approved around the turn of the century. It was, however, also necessary to develop 'rules' for the installation of the fire protection equipment. Thus, the earliest automatic fire detection codes of practice in the United Kingdom were associated with protection of property, rather than safety of life.

Although simple, electrical, manual fire alarm systems became well recognized as essential for protection of occupants of buildings, it was to be many decades before automatic fire detection became recognized in the same light. Automatic detection tended to be regarded as insufficiently reliable, or unnecessary, for protection of life. As recently as the 1970s, guidance that supported the (now repealed) Fire Precautions Act 1971, in respect of certification of hotels and boarding houses under the Act, advised that a manual fire alarm system was sufficient and that automatic fire detection might only be necessary to compensate for shortcomings in structural fire protection measures, such as means of escape. (Even today, it is, very occasionally, possible to find a hotel or boarding house that has no, or very little, automatic fire detection, having been certificated under the Fire Precautions Act in the 1970s. However, such a situation would not meet the standards now applicable in England and Wales under the Regulatory Reform (Fire Safety) Order 2005*. Shortcomings in fire detection should be identified by the fire risk assessment required by this legislation and should be acted upon by the relevant dutyholder (normally the employer)).

1951 code: CP 327.404/402/501

The British Standards Institution (BSI) first produced a code of practice (CP 327.404/402/501) in 1951. This code of practice was based on the FOC rules and, indeed, reference to these rules, and more particularly, the FOC list of approved equipment, was frequently made in situations in which the role of the automatic fire detection system did relate to life safety, rather than the property protection objective for which the rules and the approved list were published.

1972 code: CP 1019

The FOC continued to publish their rules, and both these rules and the BSI code appeared to stand the test of time, in that a new version of the BSI code did not appear until 1972, when it was published as CP 1019. Arguably, it was only then that the specialist nature of fire alarm systems was recognized within BSI, in that, whereas CP 327 comprised a series of codes of practice for telecommunications facilities, sound distribution, clock systems and fire alarms, CP 1019 was a code of practice dedicated to the installation and servicing of electrical fire alarm systems.

---

* and equivalent legislation in Scotland and Northern Ireland.

Systems designed and installed in accordance with CP 1019 still exist today, but, as they will be over 30 years old, they will be coming to the end of their natural life, particularly if they incorporate automatic detectors. Although these systems might continue to satisfy the requirements of legislation, it is likely that they would fall significantly short of satisfying the recommendations of any subsequent version of BS 5839-1. For example, CP 1019 contained no quantitative recommendations regarding sound pressure levels of alarm signals; it was merely required that there be at least two sounders inside the building and, in the case of a system incorporating automatic fire detectors, an additional sounder outside the building. With regard to audibility, the recommendation was that the type, number and location of alarm sounders should be such that the alarm was distinct from the background noise in every part of the premises.

None of the wiring used in a CP 1019 system needed to be fire resisting, and the wiring to fire alarm sounders did not need to be monitored. For small manual systems, a single power supply was satisfactory, and it is only with the publication of the 2002 version of BS 5839-1 that this recommendation, which continued to appear within the earlier versions of BS 5839-1, has been withdrawn. However, such systems do not meet current legislation, as they contravene the requirements of the Health and Safety (Safety Signs and Signals) Regulations 1996** (see Chapter 21).

The fact that CP 1019 had a lifetime of only eight years before it was completely revised and published as BS 5839-1, compared with the 21-year life of its predecessor, is a reflection of the speed with which developments were occurring in the field of fire detection and alarm systems (and electronics generally). Equally, a number of concepts that, today, we regard as 'modern' were addressed in CP 1019.

For example, the forerunner of the modern 'voice alarm system', which now warrants its own dedicated code of practice (BS 5839-8[1]) warranted a subclause in CP 1019, which addressed the subject of 'audible alarms provided by public address equipment'. Similarly, two-stage alarms were addressed, albeit that this subject warranted only a single sentence. Moreover, some of the concepts, and even the detailed text, incorporated within BS 5839-1:2002 are identical to specific clauses of CP 1019; an example concerns the use of mains powered sounders to reinforce the primary fire alarm sounders in areas with high ambient noise levels.

** and equivalent legislation in Northern Ireland.

[1] BS 5839-8:1998, *Fire detection and alarm systems for buildings – Code of practice for the design, installation and servicing of voice alarm systems.* In 2008, BS 5839-8:1998 will be superseded by BS 5839-8:2008.

There was an implication in CP 1019 that manual fire alarm systems were provided to satisfy legislation and that automatic fire detectors were purely provided for property protection. This principle arose from the attitudes to automatic fire detection described above and the fact that CP 1019 was based on the fire insurers' FOC rules. Thus, CP 1019 'allowed' manual call points to be incorporated within automatic fire detection systems, but, if automatic fire detection was installed, compliance with CP 1019 demanded that every portion of the building should be covered, other than small lavatories, which could rely on detection within any common lobby serving them; this reflected insurers' attitudes that manual call points did not contribute to property protection and that partial coverage by automatic fire detection was not recognized as a valid principle for fire insurance purposes.

BS 5839-1:1980

BS 5839-1 was first published in 1980 as a revision of CP 1019. For the first time, the 1980 code was produced by a fire standards committee within BSI, as opposed to a more general electrical engineering committee. Although, on the face of it, this first version of BS 5839-1 had the same eight-year life as its predecessor, in fact the 1980 code was amended five times, in some cases quite fundamentally, between 1980 and 1984.

Unlike CP 1019, BS 5839-1 drew a significant distinction between systems intended for the protection of life and those for the protection of property. The role of automatic fire detection, particularly for protection of escape routes, was acknowledged. For property protection, the code still encouraged protection of all parts of the premises with automatic detectors. However, for the first time, it was acknowledged that a lower standard of protection, by installation of detectors in high risk areas only, could still be worthwhile. However, a 'health warning' was included to draw attention to the fact that such an installation would be unlikely to satisfy the requirements of fire insurers.

Another major difference between BS 5839-1 and CP 1019 was that the use of telephones for initiating a fire alarm signal within a building was no longer recommended; such an arrangement, whereby the fire alarm signal was given by dialling a predetermined number on a telephone, was acceptable under CP 1019.

Also, other important changes from CP 1019 (either in the first published version of BS 5839-1 or as it was ultimately amended by 1984) included a distinction between cables that were permissible if operation during a fire were required and cables permissible where prolonged operation during a fire was not required. In the former case, which would apply to, for example, alarm sounder circuits, PVC insulated cables in steel conduit were no longer acceptable without additional fire protection (e.g. by chasing into walls or protection by fire-resisting construction). PVC insulated cables in rigid PVC conduits did not require such additional protection, as it was considered that greater thermal insulation would be provided to the cables.

Another new principle introduced within the first version of BS 5839-1 was a need to avoid total loss of the fire alarm signal throughout a building in the event that fire results in a short circuit of a sounder circuit at a single point in the building. The intent of this recommendation, which is discussed further in Chapter 11, was widely misunderstood, to the extent that, even today, this issue is probably the most misunderstood aspect of fire alarm design practice.

For the first time, quantitative guidance was given on sound pressure levels within BS 5839-1. It was no longer adequate to offer the fire officer a tour of the building and hope that the fire alarm signal would be sufficiently audible to him. The recommendation for a minimum sound pressure level of 65 dB(A), or 5 dB(A) above background noise, and 75 dB(A) at the bedhead in sleeping risks, was introduced.

A very important development in the world of fire protection was also reflected for the first time in BS 5839-1:1980, namely the self-contained domestic smoke alarm. An amendment to the original 1980 code gave important advice on the use of domestic smoke alarms that is still valid today. Indeed, recommendations for the installation of at least two smoke alarms in a two-storey house, and for the interconnection of smoke alarms, exceeded the first 'official' recommendations produced by the Home Office around eight years later. It is interesting to note that it was then not until 1992 that the original guidance was 'rediscovered' or at least recirculated, in the guidance that supported the Building Regulations 1991 in England and Wales, by which time, sadly, deaths had occurred in two-storey dwellings 'protected' by the single smoke alarm that Home Office guidance suggested would be acceptable on the basis that it was better than nothing.

In 1982, during the early life of BS 5839-1:1980, the first addressable systems, in which each detector was separately identifiable at the control and indicating equipment, appeared on the UK market. Since these had not been anticipated when the 1980 code was written, it did not adequately cater for such systems. These 'new generation' systems gave rise to new perplexities in terms of compliance with the letter, or at least the spirit, of the code. Particular issues included zonal indication;

some people claimed that, since a text display of the identity and location of each detector could be given at the control and indicating equipment, conventional zone indicators were unnecessary.

Another issue was tolerance to fault conditions, particularly short circuits. The large number of devices that could now be connected on a single circuit created the potential for areas larger than that of the conventional zone to lose protection in the event of a single fault. This led to the introduction of short-circuit isolators, but perplexity regarding the number and location of isolators remained.

This situation was merely a reflection of the fact that codes of practice do not lead technology, but merely endeavour to articulate good custom and practice in the use of existing technology. There is, therefore, always a 'phase angle' between technology and the codes of practice that describe recognized good practice in its use. However, if one examines some of the addressable systems installed between 1982 and 1988 today, it can well be the case that the systems do not comply with the 1980 code for reasons described above, while, equally, they do not comply with the 1988 code, as the recommendations of that code could not have been anticipated at the time of their installation.

BS 5839-1: 1988

When the code was revised in 1988, account was taken of addressable systems, but all recommendations of the code could be applied to both conventional and addressable systems. Indeed, generally, the view was taken that the introduction of addressable systems, while providing many benefits, should not significantly increase the vulnerability of the system to faults. Hence, for example, the 1988 code recommended that, in the event of a single fault condition, the area throughout which protection was disabled should not exceed the maximum permitted for a single zone. This is, of course, inherently true in the case of a conventional system, in which a circuit and a zone are synonymous, but necessitated the provision of short circuit isolators at zone boundaries (but not necessarily every zone boundary in the case of small zones) in the case of addressable systems.

The slower speed of microprocessors in those days could mean something of a delay between manual call point or detector operation and the operation of fire alarm sounders, particularly in systems in which, to minimize false alarms, devices were polled several times to confirm their alarm status before a fire alarm signal was given. While a short delay between operation of a fire detector and the sounding of the alarm was not significant (and, indeed, was already permitted by the standards of the day), concern was expressed regarding possible delays between operation of a manual call point and the sounding of the fire alarm. The concern did not relate to the overall evacuation time, but in the confusion that could result if someone operated a manual call point and the system appeared not to operate.

If, for example, a light switch were operated but the lights did not come on for 10 seconds, long before that period had expired it would be considered that the light was inoperative. Given that, in an emergency, time appears to pass more slowly, on perception that a manual call point was inoperative, a person might follow some inappropriate course of action. Particular concern was expressed regarding certain occupancies, such as hospitals. Whereas, in other occupancies, it would be reasonable to assume that, having operated a manual call point, a person would evacuate the building, in hospitals staff are trained to raise the alarm and then begin movement of patients. If the fire alarm system were considered to be inoperative, a nurse might well move further from the patients who need assistance in order to raise the alarm by other means.

After much debate of this subject, the technical committee responsible for the code decided that, while not wishing to penalize new technology, there was a need to limit the delay between operation of a manual call point and the sounding of alarm devices in, at least, the zone of origin (which would then be audible to anyone operating the manual call point). In order to minimize the effect of this recommendation on systems already in the marketplace at the time, a maximum delay of eight seconds was recommended in the 1988 code; this figure was based on the maximum time delay that was known to occur with systems already on the market. However, the code gave notice that this period would be reduced to three seconds from 1 January 1990.

This three-second period remained somewhat controversial throughout the 1990s, at least within the European Standards forum. Some European countries saw no good reason for imposing such a short period for the maximum permissible delay. The result was that, when the European product standard for control and indicating equipment, BS EN 54-2, was published in the UK in 1998, a maximum time delay of 10 seconds was permitted (a retrograde step in the opinion of the author).

This presented a dilemma when the code was further revised in 2002. Should the code concede that a 10-second delay was permissible, particularly as a fundamental principle of European standardization is that barriers to trade between European countries should not be permitted by national codes (unless strictly necessary on the grounds of safety)? Alternatively, should the maximum delay of three seconds be so sacrosanct as to create a situation in which products complying with the European Standard adopted in the UK, and, therefore, possibly even third-party certificated in accordance with the standard, could not be used in installations complying with BS 5839-1?

Ultimately, it was agreed that the maximum period of three seconds should remain within BS 5839-1:2002, but in conjunction with 'a health warning' that BS EN 54-2 permits a delay of 10 seconds. As a compromise, the code advises that a delay of between three seconds and 10 seconds may be acceptable, but only with the agreement of the relevant enforcing authority and the recording of the delay as a variation in the completion certificate.

By 1988, there was much greater use of automatic fire detection for protection of life, particularly in premises in which people sleep. The original principle for certification of hotels under the Fire Precautions Act, that a manual fire alarm system was sufficient, had evolved into a requirement that, in the event of a fire within, say, a hotel bedroom, automatic fire detection should give a sufficiently early warning for those beyond the room of fire origin to make their escape before smoke from the fire made escape routes impassable. In practice, this 'escape route protection' translated into the installation of smoke detectors within escape routes, such as corridors and staircases.

Around the mid 1980s, however, the Home Office began to question whether the objective described above was adequately achieved by the installation of smoke detectors in escape routes only. This led to very elegant research work by the then Fire Research Station, involving full-scale fire tests in a rig that simulated a hotel corridor with bedrooms opening into it.

The research showed that, under certain conditions (but only certain conditions), it was possible that, when a fire occurred in a bedroom, smoke could smoke log the corridor, precluding escape by those beyond the room of fire origin, before detection by smoke detectors in the corridor, spaced at the normally specified intervals for these detectors. This research was taken into account in the 1988 code, which introduced the concept of the type L3 ('escape route protection') system. In this system, detectors are installed not only within the escape routes, but also all rooms opening onto escape routes.

The purpose of the L3 system was to provide a specification for automatic fire detection in circumstances in which the detection was required to protect sleeping occupants under legislation, particularly the (now repealed) Fire Precautions Act (i.e. in hotels and boarding houses). It was appreciated that the L3 system would represent a considerably increased cost, compared with the provision of detection purely in escape routes. However, as the research showed that, in the specific conditions of the research set-up, up to nine minutes' extra time for escape could be achieved, simply by installing heat detectors within the bedrooms, the additional cost associated with this greatly increased level of protection was considered justifiable.

As much of the smoke that created the problem within the corridor arose from pyrolysis of the timber of the bedroom door, rather than from the hot buoyant products of the fire, the objective, in the L3 system, was to give a warning before the door itself was under severe attack by fire. The BSI technical committee considered that this could be easily achieved by the use of either a heat or smoke detector, as even a heat detector would provide a generous time for escape before the timber at the head of a timber door was undergoing pyrolysis. Moreover, for the purposes of this objective, the exact location of the detector was not critical.

Accordingly, the 1988 code introduced the principle that, for 'escape route protection' with the objective defined above, the detectors in rooms opening onto escape routes could be either heat detectors or smoke detectors, and that the detector need not be ceiling mounted, but could be mounted, for example, on the wall close to the door. The latter installation practice was permitted for ease of installation, thereby minimizing the cost impact of the enhanced, and more expensive, protection recommended.

Unfortunately, when the 1988 code was published, many fire authorities throughout the UK totally misunderstood the concept of the L3 system. Many fire officers assumed that the new requirements for fire detectors within rooms opening onto escape routes (which became a requirement for certification of hotels and boarding houses under the Fire Precautions Act) were intended to protect the sleeping occupant in the room of fire origin. In effect, they thought that the objective of the automatic fire detection in sleeping risks had changed. In fact, the 'goalposts had not moved' in any way; the intention of legislation and the L3 system described in BS 5839-1 was still only to protect those beyond the room of fire origin.

Based on this misconception, many fire authorities rejected the idea of heat detectors within bedrooms. Fire officers began to impose requirements for smoke detectors in all hotel bedrooms in the case of new applications for certification under the Fire Precautions Act (and, sometimes, even when material alterations were carried out to existing hotels). It was not until 1991 that definitive guidance on this issue was produced by the Home Office/Scottish Office in the form of what was commonly known as the 'Purple Guide', which provided guidance to fire and rescue authorities on the fire precautions that should be required as a prerequisite of certification of hotels and boarding houses under the Fire Precautions Act.

The 'Purple Guide' advised that the detectors installed in hotel bedrooms should be heat detectors in the case of hotel bedrooms that are to be occupied by one or two persons; this was to avoid the much higher incidence of false alarms associated with smoke detectors. The guidance did, however, advise that it was reasonable to expect smoke detectors in accommodation provided specifically for disabled persons or elderly people, who may need assistance in case of fire, dormitory accommodation for a large number of people, or other circumstances in which there might be a high probability of ignition. Unfortunately, by the time this guidance was produced, many fire authorities were entrenched in their policy of requiring smoke detectors in hotel bedrooms. A number of fire and rescue authorities even suggested that the Home Office were in error in their interpretation of BS 5839-1.

Some of the confusion arose from the fact that the 'Purple Guide' also recommended that the automatic fire detection and alarm system be a type L2 system. The new L2 system, first defined in the 1988 code, was, by definition, equivalent to an L3 system with the addition of fire detection in areas in which the normal occupants are especially vulnerable to fire starting in their vicinity and areas with a high probability of ignition, such that fire could spread to affect the building's occupants. The guidance on the L2 system also stated that, in the case of sleeping accommodation, any smoke detectors in the room should be sited in accordance with normal recommendations, rather than be, for example, wall-mounted. It was argued by some fire and rescue authorities that the L2 designation, in conjunction with the above advice, supported their requirements for smoke detectors in bedrooms.

In fact, the code also advised that a reference to a type L2 system was virtually meaningless unless the party specifying L2 clarified the areas to be protected by detectors, over and above the areas that would require protection in a type L3 system. In effect, the Home Office had followed this advice perfectly by specifying that smoke detection should be installed in certain rooms, such as those used by disabled people. In effect, the detectors in these rooms were 'L2' detectors, while the heat detectors installed in other bedrooms were part of the basic L3 system. Ultimately, the issue of interpretation of the code was referred to the BSI technical committee, who confirmed that there was no anomaly between the guidance contained in the 'Purple Guide' and the recommendations of BS 5839-1; the Home Office had fully understood the concept behind type L3 and type L2 systems (which is hardly surprising, since they had funded the research that led to the need for the L3 concept).

At the time of writing, this issue remains, if anything, even more controversial under the new fire safety legislation that came into effect in Great Britain in 2006. In England and Wales, sector-specific guidance on the Regulatory Reform (Fire Safety) Order 2005 is produced by Communities and Local Government (CLG). One specific guide deals with sleeping accommodation. Unfortunately, that guidance is far from definitive in terms of the types of detector that should be installed in the bedrooms of hotels, boarding houses, hostels and similar premises, abdicating responsibility for such a decision to the findings of the fire risk assessment. The 'suggested' standard of protection for such premises is Category L2.

However, BS 5839-1 advises that any specification of Category L2 needs to include details of those areas of the building that are to be protected; the CLG guide is silent on this matter. The reference to Category L2 simply means that the system should satisfy the recommendations for a Category L3 system, with the additional objective of affording early warning of fire in specified areas of high fire hazard level and/or high fire risk.

Category L3 can be satisfied with heat, smoke, carbon monoxide or multi-sensor fire detectors in rooms opening onto escape routes. Without further information, the CLG guidance is, therefore, too vague for consistent interpretation.

Some enforcing authorities in England and Wales take the view that legislation now demands protection of an individual(s) within the bedroom of fire origin, using the powers of enforcement to require the originally acceptable heat detectors to be changed to smoke detectors. Others endeavour to persuade upgrading of this nature, but see no reason to enforce such a change, unless as compensation for some other shortcoming. Yet others, see no shortcoming in existing provision of heat detectors in accordance with original practice.

In Scotland, Scottish Government sector-specific guidance on the equivalent Scottish legislation (the Fire (Scotland) Act 2005 in conjunction with the Fire Safety (Scotland) Regulations 2006) takes the form, in the case of sleeping accommodation, of two guides, one dealing with small premises, while another deals with medium-sized and large premises. The former guide, which is applicable to, for example, a small boarding house, unequivocally recommends smoke detectors in bedrooms. The guide for medium and large premises provides excellent discussion regarding the different types of detector, but, as in the case of the CLG guide, relies solely on a reference to a Category L2 system, without further detailed advice on how this should be interpreted. Equally, in the experience of the author, Scottish fire and rescue authorities tend to adopt a pragmatic approach to the matter in the case of existing premises.

Of course, BS 5839-1 simply sets out a menu of systems from which enforcing authorities can select the system of their choice. The code does not provide recommendations on the nature of the protection that should be provided in any specific occupancy, although, in the 2002 version, an informative annex comments that, in the bedroom areas of hotels and hostels, the design requirements are usually based on the recommendations for a Category L3 system. No amendment to this information has been considered necessary by the introduction of new fire safety legislation in 2006.

In general, the recommendations in the 2002 code on protection of escape routes remain consistent with those in the 1988 code. However, endeavours have been made to further explain and clarify the concept of escape route protection. In addition, a minor relaxation from the recommendation to install detectors in rooms opening onto escape routes is given in the case of short corridors that are separated from other sections of the escape routes by fire resisting construction.

Returning to other, and less controversial, new aspects introduced into the code in 1988, the code, for the first time, provided recommendations on radio-linked systems in which, at that time, fire detectors and manual call points could be linked to control and indicating equipment by radio, rather than wiring. At the time in question, it appeared to the BSI technical committee that only one commercially available system was used in significant numbers. Accordingly, on the basis that 'if it isn't broken, don't fix it', the recommendations for radio-linked systems in the 1988 code were based on the design of that particular system. Thus, for example, the recommendation in the 1988 code that sounder circuits in radio-linked systems should be 'hard wired', rather than 'wireless', simply arose from the fact that, as the one major commercially available system did not use radio-linked sounders, there was no need to consider these or make recommendations for them.

In the 1988 code, all advice on domestic smoke alarms was removed. Instead, as an appendix to the code, the Home Departments' *Smoke alarms in the home*[2] booklet was reproduced. It is this booklet that suggested that one smoke alarm might be sufficient – guidance that

---

[2] This booklet was produced by the Home Office/Scottish Home and Health Department/Northern Ireland Office in 1988.

was, happily, subsequently reversed again, in the case of houses of two or more storeys, as discussed earlier in this chapter.

By 1988, the increase in the use of automatic fire detection had led to a commensurate increase in the number of false alarms. Accordingly, the 1988 code gave more detailed recommendations on the avoidance of false alarms. An entire clause of the code was devoted to this subject.

BS 5839-1:2002

By 2002, the 1988 code was rapidly becoming out of touch with the latest technology and with custom and practice. In addition, the lack of clarity of some recommendations, to the extent that what was, or was not, a positive recommendation could be difficult to determine, coupled with the somewhat theoretical discussions in some clauses, were creating problems.

Installations were difficult to audit under certification schemes for designers and contractors, such as the BRE Certification LPS 1014 scheme and the BAFE modular schemes, the latter of which were launched in 2002. The 1988 code could also be quite difficult for small contractors to implement, in view of some of the difficulties described above. It was therefore found that, in installation audits by certification bodies, many conscientious contractors, striving hard to comply with the recommendations of the code, fell short of compliance, sometimes as a result of recommendations that were tucked away within somewhat academic discussion of matters, such as stratification of smoke.

In addition, by 2002, the role of automatic fire detection in fire engineering solutions was well recognized and, in a less sophisticated manner, as a need identified in the fire risk assessments that were, by then, required under legislation. However, the 1988 code, and its five system 'types', were insufficiently flexible to cater for the 'tailor-made' use of fire detection associated with these modern concepts.

However, perhaps the greatest shortcoming of the 1988 code was that it did not adequately reflect the manner in which fire alarm contracts operate. The 1988 code was written around a mythical organization or character, known as 'the installer'. Certification of the completed installation rested, according to the code, with the commissioning engineer of the installer.

In practice, many fire alarm systems are designed by consulting engineers, rather than by the installer, particularly in the case of large new building projects. The installer is often an electrical contractor, whose sole role is to install the system in accordance with the requirements of the designer. Under these circumstances, the commissioning engineer may be employed by the manufacturer or supplier of the fire alarm equipment, who is contracted purely to supply and commission the equipment.

In the situation described above, it is entirely unreasonable to expect the commissioning engineer to certificate that the design and installation of the system complies in full with all recommendations of the code of practice. Moreover, it may be beyond the ability of the commissioning engineer to carry out this task, since he/she is not a design engineer. This has led to widespread complaints that BS 5839-1 certificates were meaningless. While this is quite a valid complaint, it is understandable as to how this situation has arisen.

The 2002 code was drafted by consultants, acting under contract to BSI. The consultants were tasked with drafting a code that would take account of advances in technology, but that was simpler than the 1988 code. Part of this simplification was to comprise removal of unnecessary explanatory text, so that the code was 'user-friendly', albeit that the consultants were instructed to identify any explanations that remained necessary. There was also a requirement to take account of the many new European standards for fire alarm products, which had been published subsequent to 1988. Account was also to be taken of interpretations given by the BSI technical committee on various clauses of the 1988 code, all of which had been published in the form of PD 6531.[3] In addition, recognition of the need for risk assessment and the importance of performance based requirements was necessary.

The brief to the consultants from BSI also required additional, or more comprehensive, guidance on a number of matters, particularly false alarms, but also including servicing and maintenance. Most difficult and controversial of all, the consultants were to take up a well-known 'poison chalice' by reviewing the guidance given on cables.

A debate had raged for many years on the subject of the fire resisting cables used in fire alarm systems. As a result of this, a BSI working group had determined that two different 'grades' of fire resisting cable were necessary. The consultants were tasked with making proposals as to the circumstances in which each grade would be appropriate; specifically, there was a need for proposals as to the circumstances in which only the 'enhanced' grade of fire resisting cables should be recommended.

---

[3] PD 6531: 1997, *Queries and interpretations on BS 5839: Parts 1 and 4 (as amended)*.

In order to address these requirements, the new code was, for the first time, written in 'practice specification' format. The format of the 2002 code is discussed in the next chapter of this guide.

The 2002 code also addresses at least four technologies that first became available, or, at least, became much more common, since the publication of the 1988 code. These include carbon monoxide fire detectors, video smoke detection and multi-sensor detection. In addition, an interesting new clause within the code deals with fire warning systems for deaf people. This clause is an important step forward in making buildings safer for use by deaf people.

An important intention for the 2002 code is that it should much better reflect the manner in which fire alarm contracts operate. Accordingly, the code gives recognition to the various parties involved in the contract, namely the designer or specifier, the installer, the commissioning engineers, the maintenance organization and the user. Separate recommendations are given for each of these parties.

The term system 'type' has now been replaced by the term system 'category'. (The term 'type' is somewhat imprecise, as a reference to system type could relate to whether the system is conventional or addressable, smoke detection or heat detection, etc.) In addition, two new system 'categories' were introduced, namely the L4 system and L5 system. These are discussed in a later chapter of this guide.

In the revision of the code, no existing recommendation was considered as sacrosanct. All existing recommendations were carefully reviewed, and, if considered appropriate, modified. Thus, the 2002 code contains a number of quite detailed technical changes, including a change (generally an increase, but under some circumstances, a minor decrease) in the maximum distance anyone should have to travel to reach the nearest break glass call point.

Flexibility has also been given in the sound pressure levels produced by the system, with a small reduction in the minimum sound pressure level in the case of stairways, small rooms and 'specific points of limited extent'. Recommendations for standby battery capacity have been simplified, resulting in a reduction in the minimum capacity recommended in some cases. The maximum period between service visits has also been increased, subject to determination that it is appropriate to do so on the basis of a risk assessment.

The issue of fire resistance of cables was addressed by a new recommendation that all cables used within the fire alarm system, including those carrying the mains supply, should be fire resisting, while specific situations in which only cables of enhanced fire resistance should be used are identified.

Perhaps one of the most important changes in the 2002 code is the much greater significance attached to avoidance of false alarms. Substantial hopes have been pinned on the 2002 code to make a major impact on the number of false alarms that are generated by automatic fire detection and alarm systems. In the year 2000, over 250,000 false alarms were generated by fire alarm systems, and this is no longer regarded as acceptable by central government, fire and rescue authorities and users of fire detection and alarm systems.

The 2002 code imposes a 'cradle to grave' responsibility for limitation of false alarms on all parties. The major responsibility for avoidance of false alarms is imposed on the designer. However, the installer has a minor role to play. The commissioning engineer has an important role to play in checking that the installed system is likely to be satisfactory in its immunity to false alarms. The user is expected to manage the building and the system properly in order to minimize false alarms. When the system is serviced, under the code, it is the responsibility of the servicing organization to monitor the false alarm record and to provide suitable advice where appropriate. New benchmark figures for anticipated and acceptable rates of false alarms were incorporated within the 2002 code.

Whereas, in the 1988 code, false alarms warranted a single clause within one section of the code, in the 2002 code one entire section of the seven sections into which the code is divided is devoted purely to the matter of limitation of false alarms. The code stresses the importance for the designer and the commissioning engineer to consider fully the recommendations contained in this section of the code.

A major change in philosophy towards automatic transmission of fire alarm signals to the fire and rescue service can be found in the 2002 version of the code. Previous versions of the code have provided information on methods for transmitting fire alarm signals from protected premises to the fire and rescue service, although the very detailed information contained in the 1980 code was not included within the 1988 code.

However, no previous version of the code has positively recommended whether, in fact, there is any need to transmit signals automatically to the fire and rescue service or an alarm receiving centre (ARC). The 2002 code takes a completely different approach. In the 2002 code, it is recognized that, if the objective of the system is property protection, unless the premises are continuously manned on a 24-hour basis, the objective will not be achieved unless there is automatic transmission of signals to the fire and rescue service (normally via an ARC). Thus, the code recommends that all Category P systems have a facility for automatic transmission of signals to the fire and rescue service, unless the premises are continuously manned. Failure to provide such a facility in a Category P system is, therefore, a variation from the recommendations of the code, which would need to be agreed with the interested parties and recorded as a variation in the relevant certificate (see Chapter 8).

In general, the safety of occupants of buildings should not depend on intervention by the fire and rescue service (other than in special cases, such as hospitals). Thus, in general, BS 5839-1 does not regard facilities for automatic transmission of fire alarm signals to the fire and rescue service as absolutely essential in a Category L system. Similar comments apply, of course, to a Category M system, since the system cannot generate an alarm signal unless someone is there to operate a break glass call point; this person can then ensure that the fire and rescue service are summoned.

An exception, however, occurs in certain non-domestic premises in multiple occupation, such as an office building with numerous tenants, a small business park, or some retail parks. If such premises are served by a single fire alarm system, BS 5839-1 recommends that this system should have the facility for automatic transmission of signals to the fire and rescue service, unless there are reliable arrangements for summoning the fire and rescue service when the system operates. The problem does not arise in the case of manual fire alarm systems for the reasons already stated. However, if there is automatic fire detection, the operation of a fire detector in the occupied premises of one occupier might well affect the safety of other occupiers, none of whom might regard it as their responsibility to summon the fire and rescue service when the fire alarm system operates as a result of a fire alarm signal that does not emanate from their own premises. Thus, in these circumstances, there may be a need for transmission of fire alarm signals to the fire and rescue service via automatic means.

There is no doubt that the 2002 code of practice was revolutionary in many respects, as it incorporated numerous new ideas that should result in more reliable and trouble-free installations that more closely comply with both the intent and the letter of the code than has previously been the case.

However, the extensive nature of the changes incorporated within the 2002 code were such that, since 2002, new ambiguities and perplexities have come to light. As a result of these, the code was first amended in December 2004. Although most of the amendments made were minor, or even editorial, the number of amendments was such that, rather than issuing an amendment slip, the code was reprinted to incorporate the amendments. A further amendment was made in April 2008 as a result of, in 2007, the five-yearly review that all British Standards undergo. Again, although in principle, the changes made were primarily editorial, some of these amendments contain important amplification or clarification of advice, albeit no major changes to specific recommendations. The April 2008 amendment also updates references to fire safety legislation. Users of the code can confirm that they are using the correct version by looking at the front cover; at the top right-hand corner, the title BS 5839-1:2002 is qualified with the addition '+A2:2008'.

If users of any code consider that an amendment to a code or standard may be necessary, or that some clarification may be required, it is always worthwhile writing to the BSI committee responsible for its production, in this case, committee FSH/12/1. All such comments, whether from a major installer, a small electrical contractor, a single independent consultant or whoever, are always given serious consideration, and it is from such comments that codes of practice sometimes develop and keep pace with custom and practice. As asserted in the previous chapter, it can reasonably be anticipated that the 2002 code, at least in its present form, will have a shorter lifetime than its predecessors. At the time of writing, it is anticipated that a number of clarifications will be published as a new version of PD 6531, now that those clarifications that required minor amendment of the code have been completed.

3. The format and layout of the code

The format

BS 5839-1 is set out in 'practice specification' format. In this format, each clause begins with a 'Commentary', followed by the recommendations themselves. To distinguish between the commentary and the recommendations, the commentary is written in italics, while the recommendations are written in normal standard roman text.

The purpose of the commentary is to provide background information on the principles associated with the topic that is the subject matter of the clause in question. It is written in something of a narrative style and contains no specific or positive recommendations. Thus, for example, to avoid confusion, the word 'should' is not used in the commentary as this verb is reserved for the recommendations; rather, the wording used contains phrases such as, 'always needs to be subject to consideration', 'it needs to be ensured', 'it is appropriate', etc.

For the designer or contractor who wishes, simply, to comply with the recommendations of the code and is not concerned with the whys and wherefores of the underlying philosophy, there should be absolutely no need to read any of the commentary. Similarly, if anybody, such as an enforcing authority, third-party certification body or representative of the user or purchaser, is carrying out an audit of compliance with the code, the audit should only be against the recommendations of the code and not the commentary. In this sense, compliance with the commentary does not arise.

The commentary is, however, useful for those who want a greater insight into the recommendations. Such insight might be necessary in situations in which strict compliance with the recommendations is difficult, but there is a desire still to meet the spirit of the recommendations. Thus, in considering whether a 'variation' from the recommendations of the code is acceptable, reference may need to be made to the commentary. ('Variations' were described as 'deviations' in the 1988 version of the code.)

Turning to the recommendations themselves, these are relatively short in the 2002 code and, for ease of reference, each recommendation is numbered. This assists those who wish to create checklists for compliance with the code and to refer to a specific recommendation when highlighting any area of non-compliance.

Layout of the code

The code is divided into seven main sections, followed by a number of annexes. The seven sections bear the following titles:

- Section 1. General;
- Section 2. Design considerations;
- Section 3. Limitation of false alarms;
- Section 4. Installation;
- Section 5. Commissioning and handover;
- Section 6. Maintenance;
- Section 7. User responsibilities.

Section 1 (General) should be read by all users of the code, as the information in this section is aimed at all interested parties, namely the designer, installer, commissioning engineer, maintenance engineer and the purchaser or user. In effect, Section 1 sets the scene for the fire alarm contract.

In both length and importance, Section 2 of the code (Design considerations) is by far the most significant. It is aimed at a party described as the designer, and there is no doubt that the designer's duties under the code are quite onerous. Whereas, under previous versions of the code, a party might claim to be the designer, simply by referring to the system type (now system 'category'), specification of certain (usually electrical engineering) parameters, such as cable type, and siting devices on drawings, as we shall see throughout the chapters of this guide, this alone would not satisfy the duties described for the 'designer' defined in BS 5839-1. Indeed, by definition, the designer described in the 2002 code is responsible for ensuring that system design complies with all the very many detailed recommendations of Section 2 of the code.

Section 3 (Limitation of false alarms) is dedicated solely to the subject of limiting the number of false alarms that the system is likely to generate throughout its lifetime. It is no accident that this section immediately follows the section on design, as the view taken in the drafting of BS 5839-1 is that the principal duty for avoidance or limitation of false alarms rests, initially at least, with the system designer. However, both Section 2 and subsequent sections of the code all make reference to Section 3, necessitating that this section should, at least to some extent, be read by all the interested parties who need to read Section 1.

Section 4 (Installation) is very short. Indeed, in terms of number of pages, it represents only 2% of the code. This reflects the fact that all that the code expects of the installer is that he/she complies with the requirements specified by the designer and follows good installation practices of the type described in BS 7671[4] (IEE Wiring Regulations).

Section 5 (Commissioning and handover) is concerned with the processes that occur after completion of installation work. Thus, this section deals with commissioning, acceptance by the user or purchaser and the (optional) process of verification. Verification is a new concept introduced in the 2002 code, and is discussed further in Chapter 32.

Section 6 (Maintenance) provides recommendations for maintenance of the system. In the context of the code, maintenance includes routine testing of the system, periodic servicing of the system and various forms of 'non-routine' attention (including repair, investigation and action on false alarms, action after a fire, and action after a long period of non-occupation of the building).

Section 7 (User responsibilities) is aimed specifically at the user to whom the system is, ultimately, handed over. It provides guidance for all those charged with looking after the fire alarm system and, therefore, responsible for arranging testing, servicing or service contracts, action when false alarms occur, etc.

The contents of each of these sections is discussed on a clause-by-clause basis in Chapter 5, which also provides information on the six annexes. At this stage, it should be noted that some of these annexes are indicated in the code as normative, which means that compliance with the code involves compliance with these annexes; they, therefore, add to or amplify the firm recommendations contained within the code.

---

[4] BS 7671 *Requirements for electrical installations. IEE Wiring Regulations.* (When BS 5839-1 was published in 2002, the current edition of the IEE Wiring Regulations was the 16th edition. This has now been replaced by the 17th edition.)

Other annexes are indicated as informative, in which case 'compliance' with these annexes does not arise. In effect, these annexes constitute guidance that is supplementary to the recommendations of the code and that, therefore, may, or may not, be relevant to any particular installation.

4. Scope of BS 5839-1:2002

Although the generic title of BS 5839 has traditionally been 'Fire detection and alarm systems for buildings', this has been changed to 'Fire detection and fire alarm systems for buildings' in the 2002 version of BS 5839-1. Moreover, the scope of BS 5839-1 is stated to be the planning, design, installation, commissioning and maintenance of fire detection and fire alarm systems in and around buildings, other than dwellings. There are two important implications of the minor change of title and this very first sentence of the code.

First, contrary to the possible implication of the traditional generic title, the code does not just deal with systems that include automatic fire detection; manual fire alarm systems, in which an alarm of fire can only be raised by operation of a break glass call point, are fully recognized under the code. As we have seen in Chapter 2, this has, of course, always been the case, and the fact is well known to anyone with a reasonable knowledge of the code. However, the traditional title of the code has been known to cause confusion, particularly when reference is made to it without a reference to system category (previously known as system 'type' in BS 5839-1:1988); a requirement for a system complying with BS 5839-1 has, on occasions, been considered to mean a system incorporating automatic fire detection. However, the changed generic title and the scope of BS 5839-1:2002 makes it clear that the systems to which the code applies range from those comprising only one or two manual call points and sounders to complex networked systems that do incorporate a large number of automatic fire detectors, etc.

The second implication of the information provided in the first sentence of the code is that, again contrary to the generic title of BS 5839, the code can be applied to systems 'around buildings' (i.e. in the open air). Such systems include, for example, those protecting open air storage of flammable liquids.

Systems installed in dwellings are outside the scope of BS 5839-1 because they are the subject of an entirely separate code of practice, namely BS 5839-6.[5] However, while the latter code is appropriate for systems protecting houses in multiple occupation that take the form of a number of self contained units, BS 5839-1 would be the appropriate code for, for example, hostels, even though these are regarded as houses in multiple occupation under the Housing Acts in England and Wales. Moreover, for very large dwellings and all houses in multiple occupation other than those akin to the size of a normal single family dwelling house, BS 5839-6 advocates a system that is, in effect, one complying with almost all the recommendations of BS 5839-1.

It is not within the scope of BS 5839-1 to recommend whether, in the case of any particular building, a fire alarm system is necessary or, even if it is necessary, the category of system that should be installed. This is a matter for legislation, enforcing authorities, other interested parties (such as fire insurers and building occupiers or owners) and other codes of practice dealing more generally with the subject of fire safety, such as those forming the various parts of BS 5588.[6] However, purely for information, an informative annex does provide information on the categories of system that are typically installed in various types of premises. For example, in the case of common places of work, such as offices, shops, factories, warehouses and restaurants, the code advises that a Category M (i.e. manual) fire alarm system normally satisfies the requirements of legislation, but is, however, often combined with a Category P (automatic fire detection) system to satisfy the requirements of insurers, as company policy for protection of assets, or to protect against business interruption.

Often, fire detection and fire alarm systems are interfaced with other fire protection systems and equipment. Such other systems and equipment include automatic fire extinguishing systems, smoke control systems, and, for example, magnetic door holders that, on operation of the fire alarm system, allow fire resisting doors to self-close automatically. Often, there is also an interface between the fire alarm system and other building services, so that, for example, HVAC systems shut down, stop recirculation of air or shunt extracted air to atmosphere rather than recirculate it. It is also very common for lifts to ground automatically on operation of the fire alarm system. Indeed, in some

---

[5] BS 5839-6:2004, *Fire detection and fire alarm systems for buildings — Code of practice for the design, installation and maintenance of fire detection and fire alarm systems in dwellings.*

[6] BS 5588, *Fire precautions in the design, construction and use of buildings.* (To be replaced in due course, with the exception of Part 1 of BS 5588, by BS 9999).

premises, the prime purpose of any automatic fire detection present in the building is to operate other fire protection facilities, such as a smoke control system, rather than to give a warning of fire per se, which can sometimes be achieved adequately with a manual fire alarm system.

Fire detection and fire alarm systems that are capable of providing signals to initiate the operation of other systems and facilities come within the scope of BS 5839-1. However, the code does not apply to the other systems and equipment, nor does it apply to the circuits used to interface between the fire detection and fire alarm system and other systems. However, a completely separate suite of codes of practice, published as various parts of BS 7273, does deal with this matter. Any special requirements associated with the operation of other systems (e.g. the siting of smoke detectors used to trigger the automatic closing of fire doors and shutters) are, therefore, outside the scope of BS 5839-1.

In 2007, a new part (Part 4) of BS 7273 was published; this deals with the interface between fire detection and fire alarm systems and door release mechanisms. As such, it deals with the interface between fire alarm systems and:

- devices that cause held-open fire doors to close (e.g. magnetic hold-open devices and acoustically or radio-linked hold open devices).
- devices that release electronically locked doors (e.g. solenoid locks or magnetic locks).
- powered sliding doors on means of escape (which are normally required to remain permanently open in the event of fire).

On the other hand, some fire extinguishing systems have what the code describes as a 'secondary alarm function'. The most obvious of these is an automatic sprinkler system; although the purpose of the system is to control or extinguish a fire, each head may be regarded as a point type heat detector. It is common practice, therefore, to capitalize on the fire detection function of the system to initiate a fire alarm signal in the building. If the building's fire alarm system has a facility for transmission of alarm signals to an alarm receiving centre (ARC), a fire alarm signal is also transmitted to the ARC. This is normally achieved by connecting a pressure switch, in the pipework serving the sprinkler system's hydraulic water gong, as a trigger device on a detection zone of the fire alarm system. Less commonly, a flow switch may be used as the trigger device, but, arguably, a flow switch is less reliable and flow switches are normally only used to provide supplementary indication if there is a need, in the case of a large sprinkler installation, to provide an indication of the area or floor in which sprinkler heads are operating.

The scope of BS 5839-1 extends to the use of signals of the type described above as one initiating element of the fire alarm system. Thus, it would be expected that the relevant clauses of the code would apply to the fire resistance and monitoring of the wiring to the pressure or flow switch.

In many complex buildings, such as shopping complexes, airport terminals and large public assembly buildings, a voice alarm system is used to give warnings of fire. Indeed, the use of a voice alarm system may be specifically recommended by the relevant part of BS 5588 or may be required to support a phased evacuation arrangement. The voice alarm system itself would be outside the scope of BS 5839-1, as an entirely independent code of practice, BS 5839-8,[7] applies to voice alarm systems. The recommendations of that code of practice would, however, address the interface between the fire detection and fire alarm system and the voice alarm system, as well as dealing with other measures to ensure adequate integration of the two systems (e.g. display of voice alarm fault warnings at the fire alarm control equipment).

Systems in which the fire alarm system is integrated with systems other than voice alarms are not within the scope of BS 5839-1. This does not imply that such systems are not acceptable, but merely that suitable recommendations are not contained within BS 5839-1. However, BS 7807 deals with such systems, in which, for example, the fire alarm system may be integrated with a security monitoring system. (BS 7807 will be withdrawn during 2008, in favour of a European code of practice.)

In some special applications or occupancies, the recommendations of BS 5839-1 may need to be modified, even though, generally, the fire alarm system in the premises in question would be intended to comply with the code. The code, itself, gives two particular examples of such a situation.

The first relates to fire detection and fire alarm systems in electronic data processing installations and similar critical electronic equipment rooms. The code points out that BS 6266 provides recommendations for the fire detection and fire alarm systems in such cases, over and above the recommendations of BS 5839-1. BS 6266 is not, primarily, a fire detection and fire alarm system code of practice, but is a general code of practice dealing with fire protection of critical electronic equipment installations.

---

[7] BS 5839-8:1998, *Fire detection and alarm systems for buildings — Code of practice for the design, installation and servicing of voice alarm systems.* In 2008, BS 5839-8:1998 will be superseded by BS 5839-8:2008.

Prior to 2002, the scope of BS 6266 related purely to systems in electronic data processing installations (i.e. computer rooms). However, traditionally, the greatly increased density of automatic fire detectors used in such installations had also been used for protection of critical electronic installations that did not involve data processing (e.g. electronic communications facilities, electronic production control facilities, etc.); in these cases, the density of detector spacing recommended in BS 6266 had been used. In recognition of this, the scope of the 2002 revision of BS 6266 extends to all critical electronic equipment installations, rather than the narrower scope of previous versions of that code.

Automatic fire detection and alarm systems in hospitals are designed in accordance with HTM 05-03 Part B,[8] rather than BS 5839-1. This is recognized in BS 5839-1, which, therefore, points the reader towards HTM 05-03 Part B in the case of fire detection and fire alarm systems in hospitals. However, in practice, the recommendations of HTM 05-03 Part B are based on the recommendations of BS 5839-1 for a Category L1 system, with some variations from the recommendations of BS 5839-1. Thus, HTM 05-03 Part B cannot really be used without substantial reference to BS 5839-1. Moreover, the 2002 version of BS 5839-1 does consider the special requirements of hospitals, so that, for example, the code acknowledges that different minimum sound pressure levels apply to alarm signals and refers the reader to HTM 05-03 Part B for advice on these.

In addition to these explicit examples of situations in which BS 5839-1 defers to other codes of practice, in some situations a part of BS 7273 may override the recommendations of BS 5839-1. For example, in some situations, BS 7273-4 recommends closer spacing of smoke detectors in corridors than recommended by BS 5839-1, if the detectors are used to trigger release of fire doors.

It is made clear in the code that its recommendations apply to at least any new work involved in extending or altering existing systems. There can, in practice, sometimes be an element of difficulty in determining how to deal with alterations to, or more particularly, extensions to, an existing installation designed in accordance with a previous code, such as CP 1019 or BS 5839-1:1980. At one extreme, it would not be reasonable to expect a complete new fire alarm installation to be installed, simply because a few detectors are added to a very old installation. At the other extreme, it would, arguably, be equally unreasonable to double the size

---

[8] HTM 05-03 Part B, *Alarm and detection systems*. Published by the Department of Health in England and Wales. (In Scotland, the relevant code of practice is SHTM 82 published by NHS Scotland.)

of a CP 1019 installation if existing premises doubled in size; under these circumstances, a complete new BS 5839-1:2002 installation would probably be appropriate.

In practice, many extensions to existing installations fall between these two extremes, and there is, probably, no right or wrong answer as to the point at which a decision should be made to install a complete new system. The dilemma associated with alterations and extensions to existing systems is recognized in the code, which acknowledges that the extended or altered system might not, overall, comply with the recommendations of the code.

The code points out that certain other systems or facilities are outside its scope. These include mechanically operated sounders (e.g. rotary gongs), which may be suitable for some very small premises, the public emergency call system (i.e. the 999 or 112 system) and audible or visual way-guidance systems. Audible way-guidance takes the form of 'sound beacons', which, by various methods, can attract those evacuating a building to the fire exits. However, while the code acknowledges the existence of such systems, since they are only complementary to the automatic fire detection and alarm system they are regarded by the code as outside the scope of its recommendations. (These systems are, however, the subject of a separate code of practice, namely BS 8456.[9] Since they are, however, not a form of fire warning, but a means for way-guidance to indicate escape routes, this code of practice is the responsibility of an emergency lighting committee in BSI.)

---

[9] BS 8456:2005, *Code of practice for design and installation of directional sounder evacuation systems*.

5. Contents of the code

As discussed in Chapter 3, the code is divided into seven sections, namely:

- Section 1. General;
- Section 2. Design considerations;
- Section 3. Limitation of false alarms;
- Section 4. Installation;
- Section 5. Commissioning and handover;
- Section 6. Maintenance;
- Section 7. User responsibilities.

Seven annexes provide further information or recommendations on a number of specific issues.

These seven sections are subdivided into a total of 48 clauses, which are briefly reviewed, along with the seven annexes, below, highlighting important aspects that will be discussed in subsequent chapters of this guide.

Section 1 – General

1   Scope

The scope of the code was discussed in the previous chapter. The important point is that the systems covered by the code include, in effect, all fire alarm systems, whether manual or incorporating automatic fire detection, other than those in dwellings.

2   Normative references

Normative references are basically other standards and codes providing requirements or recommendations that should be followed. Most, but not all, of these are BSI publications.

If, in the code, a normative reference includes a date, only the edition of that date applies (together with any amendments to the reference that had been made prior to the publication of BS 5839-1). If the reference is undated in the code, the latest edition of the document applies, together with any amendments.

In fact, most of the normative references in the code are undated, which means that, over a period of time, the recommendations of the code could change subtly, because of changes to the recommendations or requirements contained in normative references. An example of this arises as the result of the revision of BS 7671 (IEE Wiring Regulations). It is, therefore, important that users of the code ensure that they refer to the latest version of undated normative references.

3   Terms and definitions

Clause 3 defines 63 terms used in BS 5839-1 *as they are to be understood for the purpose of interpreting the code*. In addition to these explicitly defined terms, the definitions contained in BS EN ISO 13943 apply; this international standard contains a vocabulary of terms used within the field of fire safety.

4   Need for a fire alarm system

This short clause provides some outline advice on the basis on which a need for a fire alarm system is determined and the references that should be made in respect of further guidance.

5   Categories of system

This clause formally defines eight 'categories' of system. The system category defines whether the system should be purely manual or whether it should comprise, or incorporate, automatic fire detection. In the latter case, the system category defines the extent of the automatic fire detection and its purpose (life safety or property protection).

Five of the categories described incorporate, or comprise, automatic fire detection for the purpose of life safety, while two categories relate to property protection. The eighth category is a manual system, and incorporates no automatic fire detection.

Categories of system are discussed in Chapter 7 of this guide.

6 Exchange of information and definition of responsibilities

This clause considers the consultations that should take place between each of the interested parties and the responsibilities that should be defined, prior to placing an order for a system.

7 Variations from the recommendations of this standard

This important clause introduces the concept of 'variations', (previously described in the 1988 version of the code as 'deviations'). In short, a variation is an intentional departure from the recommendations of the code in a particular installation. Variations are discussed in Chapter 8 of this guide.

Section 2 – Design considerations

Whereas the previous section should be read by all interested parties who need to use the code, the clauses within Section 2 are directed towards 'the designer'. Indeed, with an element of tautology, the designer is defined in the code as the person or organization taking responsibility for the work outlined in Section 2 of the code.

8 Relationship between system category and areas protected

In effect, this clause takes forward the concept of system categories and, other than in the case of a Category M system, relates these to the rooms or areas that should be protected by automatic fire detection. Consideration is also given to the type of automatic fire detection that should be installed (e.g. heat, smoke, combustion gas, or multi-sensor detectors).

9   Actuation of other fire protection systems or safety facilities

This clause is very short, since the actuation of other fire protection systems or safety facilities is outside the scope of the code. The prime purpose of the clause is to refer the reader to other codes and to ensure that the interconnection of the fire alarm system to another system does not impair the reliability of the fire alarm system to give warning in the event of fire. Thus, it would be a misconception to assume that reference should be made to BS 5839-1 for information on, for example, the siting of smoke detectors that are provided purely for the specific purpose of, say, causing the automatic closure of fire resisting doors or shutters. (This is addressed in BS 7273-4.[10])

10   Systems in explosive gas or dust atmospheres

This clause is the shortest in the code and simply refers the reader to the relevant European standards on these matters.

11   System components

This clause is primarily a list of product standards, to which the various components of the system (e.g. manual call points, various types of fire detector, control and indicating equipment, power supply equipment, cables, etc.) should comply. In the majority of cases, these are the relevant parts of BS EN 54.[11]

12   Monitoring, integrity and reliability of circuits external to control equipment

This is the first 'meaty' clause of the code. The recommendations of the clause are subdivided into those concerned with fault monitoring and those concerned with system integrity. The purpose of the clause is to ensure that the probability of faults that could prevent the system from giving a fire warning is minimized and that, when such faults occur, or work on the system occurs, the extent and duration of the impairment of the system is limited.

---

[10] BS 7273-4:2007, *Code of practice for the operation of fire protection measures – Actuation of release mechanisms for doors.*

[11] BS EN 54, *Fire detection and fire alarm systems.*

Within this clause are, arguably, the recommendations of the code that have been most misunderstood within previous versions of the code, namely those relating to the principle whereby, in the event of fire damage to a sounder circuit, a limited audible warning can still be given at a single point in the building. In order to amplify and clarify this recommendation, the code contains two relevant diagrams.

13 Detection zones

In previous versions of the code 'detection zones' were merely referred to as 'zones'. In the 2002 code, the adjective 'detection' is intended to distinguish these zones from 'alarm zones'. While some of the recommendations of this clause are applicable to all detection zones (i.e. those containing either manual call points or automatic detectors or both), separate recommendations are given for detection zones that contain only manual call points, detection zones that contain non-addressable automatic fire detectors and those containing addressable automatic fire detectors.

One parameter that may limit the size of a detection zone is the 'search distance' (see Chapter 12 of this guide). This concept, which was first introduced in the 1988 code, has been commonly misunderstood. Accordingly, a diagram within this clause assists in the understanding of search distance.

14 Alarm zones

Alarm zones were a new concept introduced into the 2002 code. By definition, an alarm zone is a geographical subdivision of the protected premises, in which the fire alarm warning can be given separately, and independently, of a fire alarm warning in any other alarm zone. The code provides some simple recommendations concerning the subdivision of the premises into alarm zones. The need for this will, of course, not occur in premises in which single phase evacuation is used (i.e. all areas of the building are evacuated simultaneously).

15 Communication with the fire service

This clause highlights the importance of rapid summoning of the fire and rescue service on every occasion that the fire alarm system operates, unless, in order to avoid false alarms being passed to the fire and rescue service, filtering arrangements are appropriate (see Chapter 25). In previous versions of BS 5839-1, means for automatic transmission of fire alarm signals to the fire and rescue service were discussed and, if such facilities for automatic transmission were provided, recommendations were given.

However, as well as providing recommendations to ensure the early summoning of the fire and rescue service and the reliability of automatic transmission facilities, the 2002 code, for the first time, makes recommendations regarding the circumstances in which automatic transmission facilities positively *should* be provided. These are discussed in Chapter 13 of this guide.

16 Audible alarm signals

The prime purpose of this clause is to set minimum sound pressure levels for the audible fire alarm signal. Guidance is given on a minimum sound pressure level for all buildings, but with an increased sound pressure level for bedrooms in premises in which people sleep. A new feature in the 2002 code is a small relaxation in minimum sound pressure level for stairways, small cellular rooms and very limited areas. Separate recommendations are given for hospitals and residential care premises. In the former case, reference is made to HTM 05-03 Part B,[12] whereas, in the latter case, minimum sound pressure level in bedrooms depends on whether or not the alarm is intended to arouse the occupants or whether reliance is placed on staff for this purpose.

Guidance is also given in this clause on the practical measurement of sound pressure level. This guidance is quite important, as, according to whether or not it is adopted, a system may 'pass' or 'fail' compliance with the code.

17 Visual alarm signals

This clause is analogous to the previous clause, but relates to practical considerations in the siting and performance of visual alarm signals. Generally, of course, visual alarm signals are only used to supplement audible alarm signals, primarily in areas of high ambient noise level,

---

[12] HTM 05-03 Part B, *Alarm and detection systems*. Published by the Department of Health in England and Wales. (In Scotland, the relevant code of practice is SHTM 82 published by NHS Scotland.)

where ear defenders may be used. However, the guidance given in this clause would also be applicable to situations in which visual alarm signals are used to warn deaf people of fire or where the disturbance of an audible warning is undesirable (e.g. television and radio studios, cinemas, theatres and hospital operating theatres). (At the time of writing, the Loss Prevention Certification Board (part of BRE Certification) are preparing a new code of practice on visual alarm devices, to supplement the guidance in BS 5839-1.)

18   Fire alarm warnings for people with impaired hearing

Given the need to make all buildings accessible and usable by disabled people, this is a very important clause of the code, which was first introduced in the 2002 version. The majority of the recommendations in this clause are concerned with systems that use vibrating pagers to warn deaf and hard of hearing people of fire. The purpose of the clause is to ensure that such an arrangement has, as far as practicable, a similar degree of reliability and integrity to the audible fire warning facilities provided for people with normal hearing. It is important to note that, in the case of vibrating pager systems, the recommendations of this clause are supplemented by the recommendations given in Annex C of the code.

19   Staged fire alarms

This clause deals with fire alarm systems in which the initial warning of fire is given only in a restricted area, or is even restricted to key staff, but can be extended in further stages so that, ultimately, all occupants of the premises are given an evacuation signal. Thus, the clause deals with both systems that can give what is normally described as a two-stage alarm and those that have a facility for a 'staff alarm'. In the latter case, the warning of fire is restricted to key staff, either so that they can prepare for an evacuation or can investigate to determine whether the incident is a false alarm. Staff alarm arrangements are becoming increasingly common to avoid unnecessary summoning of the fire and rescue service to false alarms.

20 Manual call points

This clause recommends the type of call points that should be used in all premises, and it provides recommendations for the location and siting of manual call points. Recommendations are also given for the maximum delay that should occur between operation of a manual call point and the sounding of the fire alarm signal within the detection zone in which the manual call point is located.

This clause also introduces the suggestion that, in public car parks, where there is a risk of malicious operation of call points, an emergency voice communication system (e.g. an intercom system) might be used as a means of raising the alarm, rather than manual call points. Such systems should comply with BS 5839-9.[13]

21 Types of fire detector and their selection

This clause 'sets out the stall' of automatic fire detectors that may be used in a system (i.e. heat detectors, smoke detectors, combustion gas detectors, flame detectors and multi-sensor fire detectors). The principle of operation of each type of detector is briefly examined and there is considerable discussion regarding the factors to consider in selection of detector type. This is, possibly, the most textbook-type clause of the code, and, therefore, the commentary is considerably longer than the recommendations. However, recommendations are given regarding the situations in which the various types of detector should, or should not, be used.

22 Spacing and siting of automatic fire detectors

This very lengthy clause provides all the detail required by the designer regarding the spacing of automatic fire detectors and their siting, particularly siting in relation to physical features of the building, such as structural beams, partitions, etc. Special guidance is given for what has become a common perplexity, namely the siting and arrangement of detectors in 'honeycomb' ceilings and between structural joists and beams. Maximum ceiling heights at which the various types of fire detector should be used are also given.

---

[13] BS 5839-9:2003, *Fire detection and fire alarm systems for buildings – Code of practice for the design, installation, commissioning and maintenance of emergency voice communication systems.*

23 Control and indicating equipment

This clause provides recommendations for the indicating facilities that should be provided, the siting of control and indicating equipment and the environment in which the equipment should be sited.

24 Networked systems

This clause considers a number of special recommendations that apply when a number of fire alarm panels are 'networked' together. The recommendations that apply depend on whether the resulting networked system is, in effect, a single fire alarm system with outstations or a number of separate fire alarm systems reporting back to a single point.

25 Power supplies

It is a common misconception that the 230 V mains power supply for the system is not actually part of the fire alarm system, but is simply a local mains supply within the building. Clause 25 of the code makes it very clear that this is incorrect, and it provides a considerable number of recommendations that apply specifically to the mains power supply.

Equally, the clause provides guidance on standby power supplies (i.e. batteries), and gives recommendations for the duration for which the standby supplies should be capable of operating the system. The actual method by which the capacity should be calculated from the recommended duration is given in a normative annex, which forms part of the code, thereby ensuring that all designers adopt the same approach in the determination of the appropriate battery size.

26 Cables, wiring and other interconnections

The prime purpose of the recommendations in this clause is to ensure that the cable type and installation methodology is suitable to maintain the integrity of the fire alarm system for a sufficient duration in the event of fire. In order to achieve this, various recommendations in respect of installation practice are contained within this clause.

However, the overwhelmingly most important matter addressed by this clause is that of the fire resistance of the cable itself. Two different performance levels for fire resisting cables are described, thereby defining two 'grades' of fire resisting cable ('standard' and 'enhanced').

Having defined these grades of fire resistance, the recommendations of this clause include a description of the situations in which only the enhanced grade of fire resisting cable should be used.

27 Radio-linked systems

This clause provides recommendations for systems in which manual call points, detectors and sounders may be linked to control equipment by radio, rather than by wiring. A recommendation is also made in respect of the standard to which radio-linked systems should comply.

28 Electromagnetic compatibility

This clause provides some basic recommendations designed to ensure that the fire alarm system is not unduly prone to malperformance or failure as a result of electromagnetic interference.

29 Electrical safety

This clause provides recommendations in respect of matters such as earthing and avoidance of electric shock to people from the fire alarm system.

Section 3 – Limitation of false alarms

This is a very important section of the code, which follows on naturally from the section concerned with design, as the code places the primary responsibility on avoidance of false alarms on the designer of the system. However, the majority of Section 3 should be read by all parties involved in the system, from the person who first specifies that a system should be provided through to the system designer, the installer (to a much lesser extent), the commissioning engineer, the maintenance organization and the actual user of the system. It is intended that this 'cradle-to-grave' approach to limitation of false alarms, within the 2002 code, will, over the next few years, make a major impact on what remains, at the time of writing, an unacceptable rate of false alarms from automatic fire detection and alarm systems.

30 Responsibility for limitation of false alarms

It is this clause that places the various responsibilities on all the relevant parties, as described above. In the case of those responsible for servicing the system, a responsibility to carry out a preliminary investigation arises if, on inspection of records, it is determined that the rate of false alarms exceeds a level specified within the clause.

31 Categories of false alarms

This clause acknowledges that false alarms do not emanate solely (or even primarily) from equipment faults. Four categories of false alarm are defined, only one of which relates to faults in equipment.

If the matter of false alarms is to be tackled successfully, on a global basis or specific installation basis, it is necessary for a universal language to be adopted in respect of the nature of false alarms; this is the significance of clause 31 of the code.

The only recommendation within this clause relates to recording of the category of false alarm by users.

32 Acceptable rate of false alarms

This is a very important clause within Section 3 of the code. It acknowledges the fact that no installation will be entirely immune from false alarms. Having done so, it then offers benchmarks against which the rate of false alarms generated by any particular system can be judged as acceptable or not.

Since the number of false alarms is likely to be directly proportional to the number of automatic fire detectors, the benchmark rates are expressed in units of one false alarm per specified number of detectors per annum. An in-depth investigation is recommended if specified benchmarks are exceeded.

It should also be noted, at this stage, that, within a previous clause (clause 30), the commentary asserts that systems that produce unacceptably high rates of false alarms need to be regarded as not complying with BS 5839-1; such non-compliance could have implications, of course, in respect of legal liability, insurance and civil liability. It is clause 32 that, no doubt, would be used as the basis for any associated assertion that the rate of false alarms was unacceptable. Such an assertion might conceivably be regarded by an enforcing authority as a breach of the Regulatory Reform (Fire Safety) Order in England and Wales*.

33 Causes of false alarms

The commentary within this clause provides information on recognized causes of false alarms and recommends that those responsible for specification, design, commissioning or maintenance of fire alarms should be conversant with them.

34 Design process for limitation of false alarms

This clause is aimed particularly at the system designer. It makes recommendations for formal consideration of the potential for false alarms at the design stage, with appropriate review and, if necessary, suitable modification of the design, prior to its completion.

35 Measures to limit false alarms

This clause provides all parties with specific and practical measures that should be taken to avoid false alarms from both manual call points and automatic fire detectors. As well as considering the selection and siting of these devices, recommendations are provided for suitable selection of system type (e.g. analogue or multi-sensor), protection against electromagnetic interference, performance monitoring of newly commissioned systems and measures to filter out false alarms (e.g. by a 'staff alarm' arrangement). The clause also acknowledges the importance of suitable servicing and maintenance of the system.

Section 4 – Installation

This section is the shortest in the code, reflecting the fact that the role of the installer is simply to install the system in accordance with the requirements of the designer and with recognized good installation practices, such as those embodied in BS 7671 (IEE Wiring Regulations).

---

* and equivalent legislation in Scotland and Northern Ireland.

36 Responsibility of installer

Notwithstanding the principal duties and role of the installer, as described above, this clause recommends that the installer give consideration to certain basic recommendations contained within Section 2 of the code.

37 Installation practices and workmanship

This clause recommends a number of basic good installation practices in conjunction with those contained within BS 7671.

38 Inspection and testing of wiring

This clause sets out the tests that should be carried out on completion of wiring, or sections of wiring, by the installer. It should be noted that further tests will, of course, be carried out as part of the commissioning process, but these are described in Section 5 of the code (see below).

Section 5 – Commissioning and handover

39 Commissioning

This clause provides quite detailed information on the inspection and testing that should be carried out by the commissioning engineer to ensure that the entire system operates satisfactorily.

40 Documentation

This clause provides details on the documentation that should be provided to the purchaser or user of the system. The clause resides within Section 5, as the code considers that it is the responsibility of the commissioning engineer to check that either the documentation has been provided to the relevant parties or that absent documentation is identified for appropriate action.

41 Certification

This clause makes recommendations for the provision of certificates of design, installation, commissioning and, if appropriate, verification.

42 Acceptance

Perhaps the greatest importance of this clause is the acknowledgement, by the existence of the clause, that acceptance of the system by the purchaser (or representative of the purchaser) should be a formal process. Recommendations regarding matters that the purchaser should ensure are satisfactory, prior to acceptance, are given. The signing of an acceptance certificate by the purchaser is recommended.

43 Verification

This clause introduces the concept of verification of compliance with the code. It should be noted that compliance with BS 5839-1 does not, in itself, necessitate verification, but the code advocates that a separate verification process be carried out if a purchaser or user considers that, as a result of division of responsibility for the design, supply, installation and commissioning processes, there is significant potential for the installed system to deviate from the recommendations of the code. Recommendations in respect of the verification process are given.

Section 6 – Maintenance

In the context of the code, maintenance is defined as the work of inspection, servicing and repair necessary in order to maintain the efficient operation of the installed system.

44 Routine testing

This clause provides recommendations for weekly testing by the user and, if appropriate and relevant, monthly testing of automatically started emergency generators and inspection of vented batteries.

45 Inspection and servicing

This clause provides recommendations on the frequency at which the system should be serviced and the work that should be carried out during servicing.

46 Non-routine attention

This clause provides recommendations for special inspection on appointment of a new servicing organization, arrangements for repair of faults or damage, the recommendations that are applicable to modification work, recommendations to address an unacceptable rate of false alarms, recommendations for inspection and test of the system following any fire, and for inspection and test of the system following long periods of disconnection.

Section 7 – User responsibilities

This section is directed specifically to the end user of the system.

47 Responsible person

This clause recommends that a single, nan.ed responsible person be appointed to supervise all matters pertaining to the fire alarm system. The duties of this responsible person are then described. This responsible person should not be confused with the 'responsible person' to which, in England and Wales, the Regulatory Reform (Fire Safety) Order makes reference. In workplaces, the latter responsible person (or 'RP') is the employer. The responsible person to which BS 5839-1 makes reference is normally simply someone in the premises who is allocated responsibility for looking after the fire alarm system (e.g. a building manager, facilities manager or building services engineer).

48 Log book

This clause provides recommendations regarding the information that should be recorded in a system log book.

Annexes

The code contains seven annexes. Five of these are 'informative', meaning that compliance with the code does not involve compliance with these annexes; they are provided purely for information, and their contents do not form part of the recommendations of the code. The remaining two annexes are 'normative', so that compliance with the code involves compliance with these annexes, as they contain recommendations that form part of the code.

Annex A – Choice of appropriate category of fire detection and alarm system

This informative annex describes the categories of system that are typically installed in various types of premises. Obviously, however, decisions regarding the minimum appropriate category of system for any building rests with the authorities responsible for enforcing fire safety legislation in the building. The purpose of the annex is to assist those who are unfamiliar with custom and practice in this respect.

Annex B – Typical noise levels in buildings

This annex, which is identical to that contained in BS 5839-8,[14] provides noise levels that may be expected in a range of building types. The annex is, therefore, informative. This information is of assistance to the designer in ensuring that the sound pressure level of the fire alarm exceeds background noise levels that can reasonably be anticipated in the building.

Annex C – Control and transmission equipment for tactile alarm devices provided for people with impaired hearing

This normative annex is provided in support of clause 18 of the code.

---

[14] BS 5839-8:1998, *Fire detection and alarm systems for buildings — Code of practice for the design, installation and servicing of voice alarm systems.* In 2008, BS 5839-8:1998 will be superseded by BS 5839-8:2008.

Annex D – Method of calculating standby battery capacity

This annex, which is normative, provides a formula that relates the capacity of valve-regulated lead acid batteries to the required standby duration. The normative nature of this annex should ensure that all those designing or specifying battery capacity do so on a common basis.

Annex E – Schematic for design against false alarms

This informative annex contains a simple flowchart that sets out the approach that should be taken by the designer in considering whether the system is likely to be adequately resistant to false alarms.

Annex F – Model format for system log book

This annex contains a suitable format for a system log book. Since the annex is informative, it is not essential to use this format in order to comply with the recommendations of the code. However, as noted above, the code does recommend that a log book be kept and sets out the information that should be contained within it. The provision of a log book can be of value in demonstrating compliance with the requirements of the Regulatory Reform (Fire Safety) Order 2005 in England and Wales* in respect of maintenance of fire precautions.

Annex G – Model certificates

This clause provides model certificates for design, installation, commissioning, acceptance, verification, servicing and modification of the system. Since, again, the annex is informative, the exact format of these certificates need not be adopted in order to comply with the recommendations of the code.

---

* and equivalent legislation in Scotland and Northern Ireland.

6. Defining the terms

The code contains 63 definitions, which apply in conjunction with the relevant terms and definitions in BS EN ISO 13943.[15] Many of these are either well known and used terms within the fire safety field (e.g. detector, manual call point, short circuit isolator, smoke, etc.), or are terms for which the meaning is entirely obvious.

However, a number of the terms within the 2002 code are new or are either defined in a different way from the manner in which the terms were defined or understood in previous versions of the code, or are defined differently from the definitions found in other codes or possibly used in common parlance. In this section of the guide, a number of such terms are highlighted.

alarm receiving centre This is the new term for what, in previous versions of the code, were called 'remote manned centres' and were once described, in common parlance, as central stations. Thus, an alarm receiving centre is defined as continuously manned premises, remote from those in which the fire alarm system is fitted, where the information containing the state of the fire alarm system is displayed and/or recorded, so that the fire service can be summoned. Usually, of course, an alarm receiving centre is operated on a commercial basis, but it could be operated as an in-house facility within a company that has many locations.

---

[15] BS EN ISO 13943, *Fire safety — Vocabulary*.

alarm zone

This new term within the 2002 code is defined as a geographical subdivision of the protected premises, in which the fire alarm warning can be given separately, and independently, of the fire alarm warning in any other zone. Thus, alarm zones do not occur in premises with single stage evacuation, in which all areas of the building always receive an evacuation signal simultaneously.

competent person

The issue of competence commonly arises now in legislation and, sometimes, contracts. There is often heated debate as to what does, or does not, constitute a competent person. Accordingly, this term is specifically defined in the code as a person with the necessary training and experience, and with access to the requisite tools, equipment and information, and capable of carrying out a defined task. While this definition may not be entirely definitive, since it merely shifts the debate to the matter of what constitutes necessary training and experience or capability, it does provide a yardstick against which, in the event of a dispute, competence can be tested.

detection zone

This is the term used in the 2002 code for what, elsewhere and in previous versions of the code, is described simply as a zone. It is, therefore, a subdivision of the protected premises such that the occurrence of a fire within it will be indicated by a fire alarm system separately from an indication of fire in any other subdivision.

false alarm

There has been much debate, in recent years, over what does, or does not, constitute a false alarm, and it has been suggested, for example, that the term false alarm should not be applied to situations in which an automatic fire detector has responded to a fire-like phenomenon; the term unwanted alarm has often been suggested for such an incident.

The code adopts a slightly different approach, which is probably an accurate reflection of the view taken by those who manage buildings or operate industrial processes; the disruption of processes by operation of the fire alarm system when, in fact, there is no fire, is regarded as, quite simply, a false alarm. Thus, the code defines 'false alarm' as a fire signal resulting from a cause(s) other than fire. However, the code recognizes that false alarms may be subdivided into four categories, one of which is, indeed, unwanted alarms. These categories are defined and discussed further in Chapter 25 of this guide.

fire alarm device

Although this may, at first sight, appear to be an imprecise term, it is clearly defined in the code as a component of a fire alarm system, not incorporated in the control and indicating equipment, which is used to give a warning of fire. Thus, in the context of the code, a fire alarm device is, for example, a sounder or visual indicator.

fire engineering solution

There has been considerable focus on the subject of fire engineering solutions in recent years, and there has been much agonizing over the definition that should apply in other codes and, indeed, within the profession generally. BS 5839-1 provides a definition for the term within the context of the code, which is the application of science and engineering to the achievement of one or more fire safety objectives in such a way that the objectives are achieved without following, in full, prescriptive recommendations of a recognized code of practice.

fire hazard level

This slightly unusual term has been adopted to describe the likelihood of fire occurring. In other codes, this might (arguably, incorrectly) be described as 'fire risk'. However, 'fire risk' is defined in a different manner within BS 5839-1 (see below).

fire risk

The term 'fire risk' has numerous different definitions within codes of practice and guidance documents in the field of fire safety. It is, arguably, one of the most loosely used terms within the profession. As discussed above, many years ago the term was defined, in quite authoritative documents, as the probability of fire occurring. However, this does not adequately address the concept of fire risk as the term is used in fire risk assessments and fire risk management. Accordingly, the code adopts a more modern definition, which is more commensurate with the definition used for 'risk' itself in the field of health and safety. Thus, fire risk is defined in the code as the combination of the probability of fire occurring and the magnitude of the consequences of fire. This coincides with the definition of fire risk given in guidance now produced by the Scottish Government in support of the Fire

(Scotland) Act, although a different (and arguably less appropriate) definition is given in guidance produced by Communities and Local Government in England and Wales in support of the Regulatory Reform (Fire Safety) Order.

low fire risk area or room

This is an important definition within the code, as, even in a Category L1 or P1 system, in which automatic fire detection is installed throughout all areas of the building, fire detectors need not be provided in toilets, toilet lobbies, lobbies to stairways, small cupboards, shower rooms and bathrooms, *provided that they are of low fire risk*. Similarly, in a Category L3 system, in which detectors are installed in rooms or areas that open onto escape routes, fire detectors can be omitted from *low fire risk lobbies*.

The definition in the code for a low fire risk area or room is an area or room containing little or no combustible material and no ignition sources, in which any foreseeable fire is unlikely to spread such as to present any significant threat to escape by occupants or damage to property. For the purpose of the definition, a note gives furniture, fittings, storage or linings as examples of combustible materials.

maintenance

The terms 'maintenance' and 'servicing' are often used interchangeably, and there is often debate as to whether routine preventative attention should be described as maintenance or servicing. In order to promote uniformity of language, the code defines maintenance as the work of inspection, servicing and repair necessary in order to maintain the efficient operation of the installed system. Thus, in the context of the code, maintenance includes routine testing by the user as well as 'servicing' (see below) and repair.

maximum alarm load

This term is important since it is the load that will be used in calculation of battery capacity (see Chapter 21). For this purpose, the definition of maximum alarm load is quite onerous, since it is defined as the maximum load imposed on a fire alarm system power supply under fire conditions, comprising the power required for simultaneous operation of all fire alarm devices, fire signals from all automatic fire detectors and manual call points in the building, any power drawn by other systems and equipment in the alarm condition and any power required for transmission of fire signals to an alarm receiving centre (if a facility for this is provided). The need to take into account the situation in which literally all manual call points and automatic fire detectors are in the alarm condition (and hence all zone indicators are illuminated) has an implication for the capacity of the standby batteries.

responsible person

This term, which is used in Section 7 of the code, in which the responsibilities of users are described, is defined as a person having control of the building and/or premises, whether as occupier or otherwise, or any person delegated by the person having control of the building and/or premises to be responsible for the fire alarm system and fire procedures. A note makes it clear that the responsible person, in this context might, or might not, be the person responsible under fire safety legislation for compliance with legislation. In practice, this latter 'person' is generally, in a workplace, the employer (i.e. the body corporate who employs people to work in the premises).

servicing

As discussed above, the term 'servicing' is often loosely defined, but, within the context of the code, is defined as the routine process of work on the system (including cleaning, realignment, adjustment and replacement) carried out at predetermined intervals.

soak period

This term is important, as it introduces a new concept within the 2002 code in order to assist in the limitation of false alarms. The soak period is defined as the period after a fire alarm system has been commissioned, but prior to handover, during which the system's performance in relation to false alarms and faults is monitored. Thus, this is a period in which, for example, false alarms can be addressed before the system becomes the working fire alarm system for the building.

staff alarm

This is yet another concept within the code that is intended to assist in limitation of false alarms. A staff alarm is defined as a restricted alarm, following the operation of a manual call point or automatic fire detector, given to certain staff in the premises to permit investigation prior to evacuation.

time-related system

This is yet another concept that may assist in the reduction of false alarms. A time-related system is defined as a system in which the response or sensitivity of automatic fire detectors is changed with the time of day. Thus, for example, in a time-related system, smoke detectors might be isolated during the day, when people are present to detect fire, and processes might give rise to false alarms, but are brought into operation when the premises are unmanned.

7. Selecting a suitable fire alarm system

In this chapter of the guide, it is assumed that, for one reason or another, a fire alarm system of some sort is required. It should, however, be noted that, in the case of small premises, particularly those single-storey premises of a predominantly open plan nature, adequate means of warning occupants of fire might comprise word of mouth (i.e. the fire procedure might be that anyone discovering a fire should shout 'Fire') or a mechanically operated device (e.g. a hand-operated rotary gong). Indeed, such an arrangement could satisfy the requirements of the Regulatory Reform (Fire Safety) Order 2005* for 'adequate fire detectors and alarms'.

In the case of electrically operated fire alarm systems of the type addressed by BS 5839-1, the code defines eight 'categories' of system, according to whether the system is purely manual or incorporates automatic fire detection, and, in the latter case, the purpose and extent of the automatic fire detection. The eight categories of system are defined in the code as follows.

Category M systems: These are manual systems and, therefore, incorporate no automatic fire detectors.

Category L systems: These are automatic fire detection systems intended for the protection of life. They are further subdivided into the following subcategories of system as follows.

Category L1:   Systems installed throughout all areas of the building.

---

* and equivalent legislation in Scotland and Northern Ireland.

Category L2: Systems installed only in defined parts of the building, including all parts necessary to satisfy the recommendations of the code for a Category L3 system.

Category L3: Systems designed to give warning of fire at an early enough stage to enable all occupants, other than, possibly, those in the room of fire origin, to escape safely, before the escape routes are impassable owing to the presence of fire, smoke or toxic gases.

Category L4: Systems installed within those parts of the escape routes comprising circulation areas and circulation spaces, such as corridors and stairways.

Category L5: Systems in which the protected area(s) and/or the location of detectors is designed to satisfy a specific fire safety objective (other than that of a Category L1, L2, L3, or L4 system).

Category P systems: These are automatic fire detection systems intended for the protection of property. There are then two subcategories, namely:

Category P1: Systems installed throughout all areas of the building.

Category P2: Systems installed only in defined parts of the building.

In practice, the category of system that is specified for any particular premises depends primarily on three factors.

1) The requirements of legislation, as imposed, or enforced, by the relevant authorities.
2) The requirements for protection of property, which are often 'driven' by the property insurers. The requirements may, equally, arise from a desire on the part of the property owner or occupier to protect the property against fire.
3) Requirements for protection of the business against interruption to its operations. These requirements often arise from the risk management policies of the business, but may, sometimes, be 'driven' by the business interruption insurer.

The sole purpose of fire safety legislation is to protect life; protection of property and business continuity are, therefore, outside the scope of legislation.

Other than in Scotland, building regulations require an adequate means of giving early warning of fire in all new buildings and within new building work (e.g. extensions to existing premises and material alterations to existing premises). The requirements of building regulations are enforced by the building control department of the local authority (or, in England and Wales, by a private approved inspector).

Guidance on the nature of the fire alarm system that will be required to satisfy building regulations is, in the case of England and Wales, given in Approved Document B, which is the responsibility of Communities and Local Government. In Northern Ireland, the relevant guidance is contained in Technical Booklet E, which is the responsibility of the Department of Finance and Personnel in Northern Ireland. The latter document gives no specific advice, but merely refers to an appropriate system complying with BS 5839-1.

Since 2006, virtually all non-domestic premises in England and Wales have been subject to control of fire precautions via the Regulatory Reform (Fire Safety) Order 2005. (In Scotland, the equivalent legislation is the Fire (Scotland) Act 2005 in conjunction with the Fire Safety (Scotland) Regulations 2006. Equivalent legislation will ultimately apply in Northern Ireland.) The above legislation requires that, where necessary in order to safeguard the safety of people who are lawfully on, or in the immediate vicinity of, the premises in case of fire, premises shall, to the extent that is appropriate, be equipped with fire detectors and alarms.

This should not, however, be taken to imply that all premises require an electrical fire alarm system or that they require automatic fire detection. Determination of the appropriate form of fire warning arises from a risk assessment carried out by the person responsible for the premises, although enforcement action can be taken by the enforcing authority if legislation is not satisfied.

The authority that is responsible for enforcing fire safety legislation will depend on the use to which the premises are put. In most occupied premises in England and Wales (other than single-family dwellings), the enforcing authority for the Regulatory Reform (Fire Safety) Order is the fire and rescue authority. However, for some premises, other bodies enforce the Order. For example, in the case of non-defence Crown premises, the enforcing authority under the Order is Communities and Local Government. For Defence premises, the enforcing authority is the Defence Fire and Rescue Service.

It will be noted from the above that, in fact, there may be more than one authority with whom there should be consultation, albeit that, ideally, to meet the spirit of Government policy, there should be a 'one-stop shop' whereby a single authority provides the appropriate information. Thus, for example, in the case of a new building, the building control body should consult the enforcing authority for the Regulatory Reform (Fire Safety) Order* to ensure that requirements in respect of fire alarm systems will satisfy the needs of both authorities. Fire safety legislation was, nevertheless, in 2006, rationalized and consolidated. Once a building is occupied, generally only one legislative instrument, enforced by an enforcing authority applies. The most notable exception is a house in multiple occupation (HMO). For many HMOs, as well as the 2006 fire safety legislation, housing legislation (or similar legislation) imposes fire safety requirements, enforced by the local authority.

It is important to note, however, that the code does not expect the designer of the system to carry out these consultations. Instead, the code advocates that, where there is uncertainty regarding the need for a fire alarm system, or the category of system that should be used, the *developer, potential purchaser*, or *user* should make reference to relevant guidance documents, the relevant authorities responsible for enforcing fire safety legislation and/or the property insurer. The code then recommends that it is the responsibility of the purchaser or user to ensure that the designer of the fire detection and alarm system is adequately apprised of the objectives of the system and any relevant requirements of enforcing authorities and insurers.

Notwithstanding the complexity of fire safety legislation, some simple rules of thumb apply, almost regardless of the specific legislation in question. Thus, for example, a Category M (manual) fire alarm system

---

* and equivalent legislation in Scotland and Northern Ireland.

is generally sufficient to satisfy the requirements of legislation in work-places in which no one sleeps. In the case of premises in which people sleep, quite extensive automatic fire detection is normally required. Generally, this will be a Category L2 or L1 system. (In practice, in premises with cellular accommodation (such as hotels), there is, in fact, very little difference between a Category L2 and a Category L1 system.) In a hotel, the bedroom floors are generally protected by a system that is effectively equivalent to a Category L3 system, but additional detection is provided throughout the premises, thereby making the system a Category L2 or Category L1 system.

As stressed elsewhere in this guide, BS 5839-1 is not a code of practice that addresses the subject of fire safety in buildings; it is merely an engineering code of practice for the design, installation, maintenance, commissioning and use of the system that is determined appropriate by others. Thus, the system 'categories' are simply a menu of systems from which these others may select the one that is appropriate in the circumstances.

Possibly, the least likely life safety system to be specified would be a Category L4 system, in which automatic fire detection is provided only in escape routes. To ensure adequate warning of occupants before escape routes are made impassable by the presence of smoke (as would normally be required in a sleeping risk), at least a Category L3 system would normally be required.

However, there may be circumstances in which a Category L4 system would be appropriate. For example, although traditionally, workplaces in which no one sleeps need only have a manual fire alarm system in order to satisfy legislation, some employers do provide limited automatic fire detection in an effort to enhance the safety of occupants beyond the minimum required by legislation; this may occur, for example, because some employees may work alone in a large building after normal office hours. If the offices are cellular in nature, a Category L3 system rapidly becomes a Category L1 system, at very significant expense. It is sometimes argued that the installation of detectors only within escape routes provides significant enhancement of the safety of these employees at a much lower cost.

It is becoming increasingly common for automatic fire detection to be provided as one component of a fire engineering solution, in which a 'package' of fire precautions is provided to satisfy the life safety objectives of legislation, without necessarily following, exactly, the 'prescriptive' codes of practice that apply under the legislation. Fire risk assessments carried out to satisfy legislation can also identify the need for some form of fire detection, perhaps within a localized area, that does not always need to comply with the recommendations of the code for a Category L1, L2 or L3 system. Such a system would, therefore, be a Category L5 system.

As noted above, the purpose of a Category L5 system is to support a specified fire safety objective. It should, therefore, be possible to articulate the exact objective that the Category L5 system is designed to achieve. This is likely to be the responsibility of the fire safety specialist, rather than the designer of the fire alarm system.

However, a Category L5 system could be very simple in nature. For example, in the design of means of escape, there is a fundamental principle that occupants of an 'inner room', from which escape is possible only by passing through a further ('access') room, must have adequate means of warning them of a fire in the access room. This is most commonly achieved by the provision of a vision panel between the inner room and the access room. However, it has long been accepted that the provision of smoke detection within the access room is an alternative to the vision panel. Even in a large building, there might, therefore, be just one smoke detector that is installed for this purpose. This system, incorporating just one smoke detector, would be a Category L5 system, and would normally be provided in conjunction with a manual fire alarm system. The resulting system would then be described as a Category M/L5 system.

The fire alarm trade have tended to view the Category L5 system with some suspicion and trepidation. Some companies have even refused to quote for a Category L5 system, fearing that it would then be their responsibility to carry out a fire risk assessment, incurring liability for fire safety advice that they might not be competent to give. In fact, the reverse is true and, in many respects, the Category L5 system, if anything, is one of the least likely to result in liability on the part of the designer or system supplier; it is certainly less likely to do so than, say, tendering for a Category P2 system without further information from the specifier.

The reason for this is that it should never be the case that a specifier simply calls for a Category L5 system, without information as to the areas that are to be protected by automatic fire detection. Thus, it is not so much the case that the specifier will call for a Category L5 system and then leave the designer or supplier to carry out a fire risk assessment. It is much more likely to be the case that a fire risk assessment has determined the need for fire detection in only specific areas, identified in the fire risk assessment. Such a system is then a Category L5 system, and the specifier can, and *should* for compliance with the code, identify the areas to be protected. If he/she omits to do so, all the designer should need to do is ask!

The April 2008 amendment to BS 5839-1 contains an amendment to de-emphasize the risk assessment, which is only one possible reason for specification of a Category L5 system, in an endeavour to dispel the notion that it is the responsibility of a fire alarm contractor to carry out such a risk assessment before becoming involved with a Category L5 system. Rather than suggesting, as originally, that the design of a Category L5 system is often based on a fire risk assessment, or forms part of a fire engineering solution, the code now states that the design is often based on a *'localized need for fire detection in only part of the building'*, which better expresses the intent of the Committee in introducing the Category L5 system.

While Category P systems may well greatly enhance life safety within a building, that is not their objective, which is purely protection of property or protection against interruption to the normal operations of the company as a result of fire. (The code points out that, if the objective were protection of the environment against the effects of a fire, a Category P system would also be appropriate.)

From the point of view of a fire insurer, and for the highest level of protection for the purposes described above, ideally a Category P1 system would be provided. Equally, many companies install such systems in buildings that are critical to their operations. However, the code recognizes a Category P2 system, in which automatic fire detection is installed simply to provide an early warning of fire in areas of high fire hazard or in areas to which the risk to property or business continuity from fire is high.

Clearly, in the case of a Category P system, consultation with fire insurers and the in-house risk managers within a company is important. Again, however, the code acknowledges that this is the role of the user or purchaser of the system (or an appointed representative of these parties, such as a consultant), rather than the designer of the system.

It follows from the above considerations that, since eight categories of system are defined in the code, a reference to BS 5839-1, without reference to system category, will be virtually meaningless. The category of system to be installed should always be included within a specification, within statutory requirements imposed by enforcing authorities, and as part of any requirements imposed by insurers. Moreover, other than in the case of a Category L1 or P1 system, information needs to be included regarding the areas of the building that are to be protected by automatic fire detection, since all other systems involve a form of partial protection.

Although the purchaser of the system or their agent should inform the designer of the system as to the category of system that is required (sometimes via a tender specification), if this does not occur the code recommends that the designer should make clear to the purchaser or the agent, the category of system that is proposed, prior to an order for the system being placed. This is to avoid disputes during the course of a contract regarding the form of system that is required and the areas that should be protected. It would be wise of designers (e.g. the fire alarm contractor) in such cases to protect their liability by recommending to purchasers that, before placing an order for the system, they should seek further advice from the building control body, fire and rescue authority and insurer to confirm that the system proposed satisfies the requirements of these parties.

It then follows that, when a system design certificate is issued (see Chapter 30), the certificate should clearly state the category of system that has been designed. Also, except in the case of a Category M, L1 or P1 system, there should be a brief description of the areas of the building that are protected by automatic fire detection.

8. The fire alarm contract and definition of responsibilities

The code attempts, in the manner in which it is subdivided, to reflect the way fire alarm contracts operate. In the most complex cases, a single main contractor is often responsible for the construction of a new building. The main contractor will subcontract the electrical installation to an electrical contractor. The electrical contractor will often take on responsibility for the installation of the fire alarm system. The design of the fire alarm installation (and the electrical installation in the building) will often be the responsibility of a consulting engineer. A specialist fire alarm manufacturer, or a fire alarm contractor (who may, or may not, be the manufacturer of the system), may then be contracted by the electrical subcontractor to supply and commission the system. Ultimately, maintenance may be undertaken by the company that supplies and commissions the system, or by a yet further party.

In the experience of the author, it is 'supply and commission' contracts of the type described above that have the most potential for inadvertent non-compliances with BS 5839-1 and for contractual disputes. Often, in the past, the 'designer' has merely included a page or two of description of the fire alarm system within a much longer and more general electrical specification. This description will largely rely on a requirement for compliance with BS 5839-1, although drawings are often prepared showing the locations of devices.

Problems can then arise if the specification contains requirements or design detail that do not, in fact, comply with the code. For example, a non-fire resisting cable might be specified, contrary to the recommendations of the code, detector siting and spacing, as shown on the drawings, might not comply with the code, and sounder layout may be insufficient to achieve the required sound pressure levels. The question then arises as to whether the 'designer' can rely on the reference to BS 5839-1, making all errors the responsibility of the installer, or whether the installer is correct to adopt the non-compliances with the code explicitly contained within the specification. Further complications can arise from the fact that the specialist company responsible for supply and commission of the system may have given advice on the design, and, in previous versions of the code, their commissioning engineer was expected to issue a certificate of compliance with the code as part of the commissioning process.

For these reasons, the 2002 version of the code endeavours to create 'fire walls' between the responsibilities of the various parties. However, clause 6 of the code contains recommendations regarding the consultations that should then take place between the various interested parties. The code recommends that, before any order is placed for the system, the responsibility for system design, installation and commissioning should each be clearly defined and documented.

Even before design begins, the code recommends that the user or purchaser of the system, or someone on acting on behalf of these parties (such as a consultant) should ensure that, to the extent appropriate, there is consultation with the authorities responsible for enforcing fire safety legislation and the property insurer. It is important that, in these consultations, account is taken of the fire safety strategy proposed for the building.

A fire alarm system is not an end in itself; it is merely there to support the fire safety strategy for the building. Yet, a common error in approach is to permit a designer to specify the system with attention mainly focused on matters of engineering, rather than the principles of fire safety. It is not unknown for a user to endeavour to formulate fire procedures around a system that has been provided, rather than determining the fire procedures and arranging for a system that can suitably support them – a clear case of the tail wagging the dog!

The code then advocates that the designer should, to the extent appropriate, consult, during the design stage, with the user or purchaser (to ensure that the system will meet the objectives of the end user) and with relevant consultants. The latter may include architects, mechanical and electrical consultants and, in the case of a complex building, fire engineering consultants. At the end of the design stage, the designer then certificates that the design complies with the recommendations of Section 2 of the code, which is, by far, the largest section and deals with all aspects pertaining to design.

Of course, as BS 5839-1 is a code of practice, rather than a product standard, 'variations' may be incorporated within the design. Variations may arise simply because the recommendations of the code are unsuitable for a particular installation. Strict compliance with the code might then result in unnecessary expense, installation difficulties or even (albeit rarely) an inadequate level of fire protection. In the previous version of the code, variations were described as 'deviations'. However, this term implied shortcomings or errors in design, whereas what are now termed as 'variations' are, in reality, aspects of design that are appropriate and intentional departures from the recommendations of the code.

This does not imply that the designer has carte blanche to ignore good practice or design a system that compromises the intended fire safety objective, simply to result in a cheaper system that is easier to install. The code stresses that variations need to be the subject of specific agreement amongst all interested parties and need to be clearly identified in all relevant system documentation, including the design certificate.

The code takes particular note of the fact that, where values are quoted for certain design parameters, including detection zone size, travel distance to the nearest manual call point, maximum area of coverage of an automatic fire detector, minimum sound pressure levels, etc., the figures quoted in the code are often entirely arbitrary. This does not imply that they are meaningless or 'founded on sand', but simply that there is little or no engineering or scientific basis for the values given, which are merely the best judgement of experts in the field as to the figure that is reasonable.

Thus, the 2,000 m^2 maximum zone size was originally based on an (electrical engineering) limitation on the number of detectors that could be connected on a single circuit in a conventional system. The maximum area of protection that may be disabled in the event of a specified fault condition, as defined in the code, is then based on the fact that, in a conventional system, a single fault on field wiring will not normally disable protection throughout an area greater than a single zone of the system. The maximum travel distance to the nearest manual call point is based on the maximum distance of travel to a storey exit permitted in the design of means of escape; this figure, itself, is somewhat arbitrary.

The code is filled with numerous such arbitrary limitations or recommended performance levels. The implications of this are that minor departures from such arbitrary figures may have little effect on the overall protection afforded by the system. Variations, are, therefore, not necessarily significant and, as the term is used in the code, they are not 'errors' in the design.

When the design is completed, and is handed over to an installer, the code advocates that the installer consult, to the extent appropriate, with the designer, the user or purchaser, the supplier of the system, and the relevant consultants with whom the code also recommends that the designer should consult. In a simple project, there may be very little, if any, need for such consultation. However, as a large project progresses, points of detail often arise where simple consultations with the parties described above may be appropriate.

In order to avoid other disputes during the contract, the code recommends that responsibilities for certain other matters are properly defined and documented. For example, where a fire detection and fire alarm system is to be integrated with a voice alarm system, the code recommends that one organization should take responsibility for the interface connections and all necessary communications between the two systems. This recommendation has arisen out of experience in which, for example, monitoring of wiring between the two systems has been inadequate or non-existent, simply because the interface between the two systems 'falls between two stools'; the fire alarm contractor often considers this as an input to the voice alarm system and therefore the responsibility of the voice alarm supplier, while the voice alarm supplier considers that the interface is an output from the fire alarm system that should be monitored by that system. The manner in which this should be dealt with is addressed in BS 5839-8.[16]

Often a fire detection and fire alarm system is interfaced with other systems associated with life safety (see Chapter 9). For example, the system may be required to operate a fire extinguishing system or charge a pre-action sprinkler system. If a smoke control system is provided, it will normally be triggered by automatic fire detection. It is also common to arrange for lifts to ground automatically on operation of the fire alarm system. Since, in each of these cases, the other system with which there is an interface is often the responsibility of another party, the code recommends that the responsibility of each organization (the installer of the fire alarm system and the organization responsible for the other system) should be clearly defined and documented.

---

[16] BS 5839-8, *Fire detection and alarm systems for buildings — Code of practice for the design, installation and servicing of voice alarm systems*. In 2008, BS 5839-8:1998 will be superseded by BS 5839-8:2008.

9. The interface between the fire alarm system and other systems

It is now quite common to use a signal from a fire alarm system to initiate the operation of other systems or equipment, or to cause other systems to change state when a fire alarm signal occurs. These other systems may be other forms of fire protection system; examples are fixed fire extinguishing systems, such as gaseous systems, deluge systems, drencher systems, etc., or, with increasing frequency in fire engineering solutions, smoke control systems. Other systems that are not, strictly, fire protection systems, but may be required to change state in the event of fire, include lifts, which are often grounded automatically when a fire alarm signal occurs, HVAC systems, which may stop recirculation of air to prevent the spread of smoke in the event of fire, etc.

Some fire protection equipment may also be required to 'change state' on receipt of a signal from the fire alarm system. Examples include fire resisting doors and shutters – these may close automatically on receipt of a signal from the fire alarm system. Also, electronic locking devices on fire exit doors, except in the case of certain high security premises, are normally required to release automatically when the fire alarm system is operated. In addition, powered sliding doors on means of escape (as sometimes occur at the main entrance/exit of retail premises), are usually required to open automatically when the fire alarm system operates.

In some of the above cases, the fire alarm system is merely a convenient and common-sense means of triggering the action, but the fact that the fire alarm system is interfaced with the other system does not necessitate any modification of the design of the fire alarm system. An example is electronic locks on fire exits; it is not normally necessary to take this interface into account in the design of the fire alarm system.

In other cases, the category of fire alarm system specified may be determined by the need for an interface with another system. An obvious example of this arises in the case of a smoke control system. To satisfy the needs of legislation for giving warning in the event of fire, it is quite possible that a Category M system may be all that is necessary. However, a Category L system may be required so that the smoke control system is triggered by automatic smoke detection.

Some cases fall between the two extremes described in the above two paragraphs. For example, if a Category L1, L2 or L3 system is already proposed, there will, for compliance with BS 7273-4,[17] be no need for additional smoke detectors, or new requirements in relation to siting of smoke detectors, if the system is used to trigger the closing of fire resisting doorsets. If, however, a Category M system were all that was necessary to satisfy legislation, additional detection would be required if, for example, magnetic door holders were to be fitted. The resulting system would then become a Category M/L5 system. Also, if a Category L4 or L5 system were originally proposed, the extent of automatic fire detection, and the siting or spacing of detectors, might or might not be sufficient to be used to trigger closing of fire doors.

Philosophically, in some of the above cases, the automatic fire detection is not provided primarily to give a warning of fire, but to trigger the other system. Thus, in a smoke control system, the smoke detection may be regarded as part of the smoke control system. However, in terms of system engineering, the automatic fire detection in such cases is invariably incorporated within the fire alarm system, and the system is required by the interested parties to comply with the recommendations of the code.

If any additional considerations, over and above those applicable to any fire alarm system covered by the code, apply as a result of the need for the system to actuate other fire protection systems or safety facilities, these considerations are outside the scope of the code. Accordingly, in these circumstances, the recommendations of the code might, or might not, be necessary or sufficient. Thus, the code points out that, in these circumstances, the system might have special requirements in respect of the number, zoning and siting of fire detectors, provision of power supplies, control, indication or other facilities, or monitoring and fire resistance of interconnecting wiring.

---

[17] BS 7273-4:2007, *Code of practice for the operation of fire protection measures – Actuation of release mechanisms for doors.*

The sole purpose of clause 9 of the code, which deals with actuation of other fire protection systems or safety facilities, is to ensure that, by interconnecting the fire alarm system with some other system or equipment, the reliability of the fire alarm system is not prejudiced. Clause 9 of the code recommends that, in the case of systems intended to actuate other fire protection systems or safety facilities, the system should comply with the recommendations of any applicable part of BS 7273. At the time of writing, possible relevant parts of BS 7273 are Parts 1, 3, 4 and 5. BS 7273-1 provides recommendations for the interfacing of the fire alarm system with a gaseous fire extinguishing system; in practice, these recommendations could also apply if the fire alarm system is intended to trigger other forms of fire extinguishing system (e.g. a deluge system). BS 7273-3 provides recommendations for interfacing fire alarm systems with pre-action sprinkler and water mist systems, in which the pipework is 'dry' until a signal from a fire alarm system results in charging with water. BS 7273-5 deals with the interface with water mist systems.

BS 7273-4 deals with the interface between fire alarm systems and release mechanisms for doors. Thus, for example, it deals with the interface between fire alarm systems and electronic locking systems for doors on means of escape, the interface with magnetic door holders and similar devices that allow fire doors and shutters to close, and the interface with powered sliding doors on means of escape, which are required to open automatically in the event of a fire alarm signal.

The code recommends that, if no part of BS 7273 is applicable, any special requirements for system design should be identified in the purchase specification or design proposals. One possible special requirement might relate to systems in which coincidence operation is used to trigger some other facility. With this arrangement, the other facility does not respond unless two independent fire detectors operate.

In modern addressable systems, the 'coincidence' can usually be between any two detectors in the system or the part of the system in question. However, in conventional systems, coincidence can only be arranged on a zonal basis. On operation of the first detection zone, no other detectors within that zone can then initiate the second signal required for the coincidence operation. Accordingly, the designer might wish to specify an increased density of detectors in the case of conventional systems. This is recognized in BS 6266,[18] in which, for example, it is recommended that the density of fire detectors be

---

[18] BS 6266:2002, *Code of practice for fire protection for electronic equipment installations.*

increased from one per 25 m^2 to one per 15 m^2 if coincidence operation is used but cannot be achieved from any two addresses (i.e. can only be achieved from any two zones, for example).

Where the fire alarm system interfaces with some other system, the two systems might be regarded as a form of integrated system, to which the recommendations of BS 7807[19] would apply. In practice, BS 7807 gives very little practical guidance in respect of the arrangements to which this chapter of the guide applies. However, one, relatively little-known recommendation may be relevant, namely that, if a signal from a fire alarm system is intended to trigger the operation of some other system for the purposes of life safety, it is unlikely that facilitating this via a building management system (BMS) will be sufficiently reliable. This is because a BMS is unlikely to be designed to have the same level of integrity and reliability as a fire alarm system. BMS outstations may also be disabled at certain times (e.g. during maintenance) without full realization of the impact on the provisions for fire safety in the building. This is recognized by some enforcing authorities, who require 'hard-wired' connections between, for example, a fire alarm system and the control units of other systems with which it is interfaced, rather than using a BMS as a form of interface. BS 7807 will be withdrawn during 2008, in favour of a European standard that largely covers the same material. However, the above philosophy remains sound. In the meantime, BS 5839-1 now refers to DD CLC/TS 50398,[20] rather than BS 7807. (A new part of BS 7273 will eventually deal with the interface between fire alarm systems and other measures for which use of a BMS may be possible, but for which use of the BMS may remain inappropriate.)

It is recognized in the code that, where the fire alarm system is interfaced with other systems, weekly testing of the fire alarm system might cause undesirable disruption. Thus, the code recommends that, if operation of the fire alarm system during routine testing would have an undesirable effect on other systems or equipment, means should be provided for disabling the automatic actuation of the system or equipment (i.e. a facility should be provided to isolate the output to the other system or equipment). However, there should be suitable

---

[19] BS 7807:1995, *Code of practice for design, installation and servicing of integrated systems incorporating fire detection and alarm systems and/or other security systems for buildings other than dwellings.*

[20] DD CLD/TS 50398, *Alarm systems – Combined and integrated alarm systems – General requirements.*

indication of disablement, and the code recommends that the facility and the indication should comply with BS EN 54-2.[21]

While outside the scope of the code, it should, of course, be borne in mind that there will be a need for periodic testing of the automatic actuation of the other system or equipment. In the case of measures such as grounding of lifts, it should be checked periodically that the lifts do ground automatically on operation of the fire alarm system. This is particularly important in the case of a fire-fighting lift intended for use by the fire and rescue service. However, this may be undertaken at a more convenient time than that of the normal fire alarm test (e.g. at times when the lifts are not in great demand). If the fire alarm system is interfaced with an automatic extinguishing system, it is not, of course, feasible to discharge the extinguishing agent during periodic testing, but it should still be confirmed periodically that the output operates correctly and that a signal is received at the actuating mechanism.

In order to ensure that other systems do not prejudice the reliability of the fire alarm system, the code recommends that no other equipment or systems should draw power from the fire alarm system in the non-fire state, other than for indicators and interface devices, such as relays; thus, a normally energized relay would still be acceptable. However, it is important that the power consumption of any such indicators and interface devices is taken into account in the calculation of battery capacity (see Chapter 21).

---

[21] BS EN 54-2:1998, *Fire detection and fire alarm systems — Control and indicating equipment.*

10. The components of the system

The primary objective of BS 5839-1 is to ensure that automatic fire detection and fire alarm systems are reliable and that, when faults occur, system down time is minimized. Reliability, in this context, involves not just relative immunity to faults, but capability of performing the objective of giving early warning of fire to all occupants of the building.

In order to ensure that the components of the system are fit for this purpose, the code recommends the use of components, such as manual call points, detectors, control and indicating equipment, fire alarm devices and power supply equipment, that comply with the relevant product standards for these devices. Generally, the relevant product standards are European standards that it has been necessary, under the agreement within the European standards Forum, CEN, for the UK to adopt as national standards. These standards are published as various parts of BS EN 54.[22]

European standards for point heat and smoke detectors have existed since the 1970s; the latest versions are published as BS EN 54-5 and BS EN 54-7 respectively. In the case of BS EN 54-5, the standard defines eight classes of detector. For normal ambient temperatures, class A1 or A2 are appropriate, the former being more sensitive than the latter. The code recommends that, if the maximum ambient temperature in the protected area is 40 °C or above, class B–G detectors should be used as appropriate. These are detectors with a high temperature of operation, extending from the 69 °C–85 °C range in the case of class B detectors to a range of 144 °C–160 °C in the case of class G detectors.

Some of the European standards are much more recent and have either replaced an existing British Standard or are the first recognized standard for the product in question. For example, BS EN 54-3 is the first British Standard for audible fire alarm devices, BS EN 54-10 is

---

[22] BS EN 54, *Fire detection and fire alarm systems*.

the first British Standard for flame detectors, while BS EN 54-20 is the first British Standard for aspirating smoke detectors. In contrast, BS EN 54-2 and BS EN 54-4 have replaced BS 5839-4, which was the British Standard for control and indicating equipment. BS EN 54-2 relates to the control and indicating equipment, while BS EN 54-4 deals with the power supply equipment.

One of the most recent of the significant European standards has been published in the UK as BS EN 54-11, the product standard for manual call points, which replaced BS 5839-2. BS EN 54-11 recognizes two different types of manual call point, reflecting the different practices in manual call point design between the UK and a number of other European countries. In the UK, a fundamental principle of manual call point design has always been that it should require only a single action (e.g. breaking a glass element) to operate the call point. Elsewhere in Europe, it has commonly been the practice that two actions are required (e.g. breaking a glass element and, thereafter, pushing a button). BS EN 54-11 refers to these 'single action' and 'double action' call points as type A and type B manual call points, respectively.

However, although the European product standard recognizes both types of manual call point, BS 5839-1 recommends that only the type A ('single action') manual call points should be used in the UK, continuing existing practice. Nevertheless, as discussed in Chapter 16, a variation, whereby a hinged cover is fitted to the manual call point, may be acceptable in certain circumstances in order to avoid malicious false alarms.

At the time the code was written, there was no British, European or international standard for carbon monoxide fire detectors, although work was being carried out to draft suitable standards. However, such devices are manufactured, and their use is increasing. The code recognized this and, until such time as a suitable British or European standard is published, a sensitivity level is recommended, namely that the detector should be capable of detection within 60 seconds if the carbon monoxide concentration exceeds 60 parts per million. In addition, the code recommends that the detector should be capable of responding to two smouldering fire tests from BS EN 54-7 if the manufacturer declares that the detector is only suitable for detecting smouldering fires. If the manufacturer claims that the detector is suitable for installation instead of a smoke detector, the code recommends that the detector should be capable of responding to a fast burning fire test defined in BS EN 54-7. This latter test is particularly difficult for carbon monoxide detectors to sense, and the more restricted application is likely to apply unless the carbon monoxide sensor is used simply as one sensor within a multi-sensor detector.

An international standard (ISO) for carbon monoxide detectors has been published as ISO 7240-6, but has not been adopted as a British Standard (BS ISO). Work on such a standard is in progress within the European standards forum (CEN). In the meantime, BS 5839-1 recommends that multi-sensor carbon monoxide and heat detectors should conform to BS ISO 7240-8.

In large networked systems, it is now quite common to use a PC as the user interface (e.g. in a security control room). PCs are often used to provide text information, which can include various instructions to operators, and sophisticated graphic displays to enable the location of the fire to be easily identified. However, the code points out that it is unlikely that a PC would meet the requirements of BS EN 54-2. Accordingly, the code recommends that a PC should be considered purely as a supplementary form of indicating equipment and that there should be control and indicating equipment complying with BS EN 54-2 adjacent to it. The term *adjacent* is not defined (e.g. in terms of distance), but it is likely that, in the case of a security control room, conventional BS EN 54-2 equipment anywhere within the room would be acceptable for the purposes of satisfying this recommendation.

Since the code specifically recommends compliance with the standards referred to above, a failure to use equipment that complies with these relevant standards and/or the recommendations of this clause (clause 11) of the code would constitute a variation from the code, which would need agreement by all interested parties if the recommendations of the code are to be satisfied.

However, compliance with the code does not necessitate third-party certification of any of the products. Nevertheless, the commentary (against which, of course, systems should not be audited) does advocate the use of components having certification under a recognized product certification scheme. Such a scheme should comprise third-party certification of product conformity against a relevant standard, based on testing and continuous surveillance, together with assessment of the manufacturer's quality assurance systems against BS EN ISO 9000.

The code also points out that, where there is no British, European or international standard, it is advisable that care is taken to ensure, as far as possible, that the components are fit for purpose. The code points out that third-party approval against an appropriate test standard may provide assurance of this. In this connection, BRE Certification are already able to 'approve' carbon monoxide fire detectors against their own approval procedures for these devices, which are based on the requirements of BS EN 54-7 and published as Loss Prevention Standard LPS 1265 for carbon monoxide detectors, and as LPS 1274 for combined carbon monoxide and heat multi-sensor detectors. (As noted above, a BS ISO standard does, however, exist for the latter detectors.)

In the case of multi-sensor optical and heat detectors, BS 5839-1 offers a choice of standard, with which it is recommended these detectors conform. Firstly, they may simply meet the relevant European standards for heat and smoke detectors (BS EN 54-5 and BS EN 54-7 respectively). Alternatively, they may conform to an international standard, published in the UK as BS ISO 7240-15. As a final alternative, they may conform to a European fire insurers' standard, CEA 4021.

11. Design of fire alarm circuits

In the context of the code, the circuits regarding which advice on design is given are purely those external to control equipment; the code is not concerned with the internal circuitry of control equipment or devices, as this is a matter for the relevant product standards. The relevant clause of the code is clause 12, which is entitled 'Monitoring, integrity and reliability of circuits external to control equipment'.

Before examining the 'meat' of this clause, which is quite considerable in that there are 20 specific recommendations, we should examine the title of the clause quite closely. The terms 'monitoring', 'integrity' and 'reliability' have been chosen quite carefully. Monitoring of critical signal paths ensures that, when a fault occurs, a suitable warning is given. The purpose of this warning is, of course, to ensure that the fault is rectified as quickly as possible. This reduces the system 'down time', during which the fire protection afforded by the system may be impaired or have greater exposure to impairment.

Monitoring does not, however, affect the likelihood of impairment. Nevertheless, if we regard 'reliability' as the probability that the system will perform correctly on demand (i.e. when a fire occurs), monitoring obviously does increase reliability, since the shorter the period of down time the lesser the probability that a fire will occur during the down time. Reliability, in the narrower sense of immunity to faults in the operation of devices, is a matter for product standards, rather than the code; it is for this reason that the code recommends the use of products conforming to the relevant product standards (see Chapter 10).

The integrity of the installation may be considered to comprise three aspects. First, the installation should have a certain immunity to damage; it may be considered that recommendations to further this aim percolate throughout the code (e.g. in the clause on cables, recommendations for protection of cables against mechanical damage). Secondly, integrity must surely include the ability of the system to operate, for at least a limited period, during the course of a fire; again, recommendations to this effect extend beyond merely those contained in clause 12 (e.g. recommendations for fire resistance of cables, contained within clause 26).

However, given that, notwithstanding all the measures described so far, faults may occur (either in the non-fire state or the fire state), integrity also involves a limitation of the effect of such faults, so that, for example, the entire system is not compromised. As we shall see below, clause 12 of the code contains a number of recommendations that have this specific aim.

The code recognizes the distinction between fault monitoring and system integrity. Accordingly, subclauses of clause 12 deal with these two design aspects quite independently.

With regard to the recommendations on fault monitoring, some of these overlap with the product requirements of BS EN 54-2[23] and BS EN 54-4.[24] Thus, the code recommends that a fault indication be given at the control and indicating equipment within 100 seconds of various specified faults occurring (or specified longer periods in the case of specified faults associated with power supplies). In each case, the specified faults are merely those for which BS EN 54-2 would require that a fault warning be given within the same specified periods.

It may be argued that this overlap with BS EN 54-2 is unnecessary. However, users of the code (including installation designers, installers and those charged with auditing installations) may be much less familiar with BS EN 54-2 than with BS 5839-1. Inclusion of these recommendations, many of which are easily verifiable in the field, within the code provides an opportunity for 'double checking' that the products used will satisfy the requirements of BS EN 54-2 when assembled into an actual installation; it is just possible that, in some installations, this might not be the case, although such a situation would probably result from a failure of the installer to comply with the recommendations of the equipment manufacturer. Moreover, the language used within the code is arguably clearer than that of BS EN 54-2 and BS EN 54-4. This can obviate any ambiguity.

A particular point to note within these recommendations is that concerning monitoring of wiring between main and repeat control and/or indicating equipment. Consider, for example, a repeater mimic,

---

[23] BS EN 54-2:1998, *Fire detection and fire alarm systems — Control and indicating equipment*.

[24] BS EN 54-4:1998, *Fire detection and fire alarm systems — Power supply equipment*.

perhaps located at a secondary entrance to a building and provided for the information of the fire and rescue service.

It is not unknown, particularly in the case of conventional systems, for this mimic to comprise, in effect, a box of LEDs connected to the main control panel by unmonitored wiring. In order to consider how this should be viewed under the code, we need to return to an assertion within an earlier chapter that the purpose of a fire alarm system is to support a fire safety strategy. If the mimic is provided in furtherance of that strategy, it clearly forms part of the BS 5839-1 system. In such a case, the wiring between the mimic and the main control panel must be monitored if the installation is to comply with the code.

This is somewhat implicit in the requirements of BS EN 54-2, which requires that a fault warning be given in the event of short circuit or interruption in transmission paths between parts of the control and indicating equipment contained in more than one mechanical cabinet, if the fault is capable of affecting 'a mandatory function'. This requirement of BS EN 54-2 is translated in the code into a recommendation that a fault warning be given in the event of a short circuit or open circuit in the wiring between separate control and/or indicating equipment that is provided in order to satisfy the recommendations of the code. However, to avoid any ambiguity, a further recommendation in the code is more specific; it is recommended that a fault warning be given in the event of a short circuit or open circuit in the wiring between main and any repeat control and/or indicating equipment (such as a mimic diagram) that is provided in order to satisfy the recommendations of the code.

A further requirement of BS EN 54-2 that has become a recommendation in clause 12 of the code concerns the connection between the control and indicating equipment and any facility for transmission of alarm signals to an alarm receiving centre (i.e. for automatic transmission of fire alarm signals to the fire and rescue service). The code recommends that a short circuit or open circuit in the wiring between control equipment and *any separate enclosure of equipment* used for transmission of alarm signals to an alarm receiving centre should result in a fault indication *at the fire alarm control and indicating equipment*.

This recommendation raises a number of issues. First, it would not be acceptable for the interconnection to 'fail safe', such that a fire alarm signal resulted from either a short circuit or an open circuit fault; a fault warning must be given for compliance with the code. Secondly, the fault warning should be given at the fire alarm control and indicating equipment; compliance could not be achieved by either the provision of an indication at the transmitting equipment or an indication at the alarm receiving centre.

It can be very difficult, in practice, to comply in full with this recommendation. It has, traditionally, been common practice to use the common fire relay within the control and indicating equipment as the 'trigger' for the transmitting equipment used to transmit signals to an alarm receiving centre. Without additional sophistication in the monitoring of the interconnection (involving facilities not normally provided within the transmitting equipment), this arrangement clearly cannot comply with the code. The use of, for example, a switched, unmonitored 24 V output from the fire alarm panel to the transmission equipment would clearly be an equal non-compliance. The non-compliance is often exacerbated by use of transmission equipment that is also used to transmit intruder alarm signals and so is located within, or adjacent to, intruder alarm control equipment; this may be sited some considerable distance from the fire alarm control equipment, resulting in a significant length of unmonitored cable.

Obviously, one solution is to incorporate the transmission equipment within the fire alarm control equipment (or in sufficient mechanical contact with it for the two to be regarded as one mechanical enclosure). The need for monitoring does not then arise, as the recommendation only applies to situations in which the two enclosures are separate. Another possibility is to use a monitored output from the fire alarm control and indicating equipment (e.g. a monitored 24 V auxiliary circuit) as the trigger circuit for the transmission equipment. Note that a sounder circuit cannot be used for this purpose, as, in clause 15, the code recommends that automatic transmission of alarm signals should not be prevented by the act of silencing fire alarm sounders.

A further recommendation of clause 12 goes beyond the European standard. The code recommends that, if a standby power supply comprises a number of batteries connected in parallel, a fault indication should be given in the event of disconnection of any one battery. Parallel connection of batteries tends to occur only in larger installations, or those in which a standby duration of greater than 24 hours is necessary (see also Chapter 21). Under these circumstances, installers do sometimes parallel batteries in order to increase the available capacity. Some control equipment is specifically designed to cater for this situation, and each of the parallel batteries are separately charged and monitored. However, possibly more commonly, no such special arrangements exist, and the effect is that it is possible to disconnect totally one of the parallel batteries without the system detecting this and giving a fault warning. As this clearly affects system integrity, in that the standby duration is halved, the code recommends that a fault warning be given.

Two further 'Achilles heels' in monitoring are highlighted by the code. These are the interconnections that occur between the fire alarm system and either a voice alarm system or another fire protection system (e.g. a gaseous extinguishing system). In the former case, as the voice alarm system forms a crucial part of the fire warning system within the premises, it is appropriate for the code to deal with the monitoring of the interconnections between the fire detection and fire alarm system and the voice alarm system. Interconnections between a fire alarm system and any transmission equipment used to transmit signals to vibrating pagers that give fire warning to deaf people are also covered.

Thus, the code recommends that, if the fire alarm system and the voice alarm system (or fire warning system for deaf people) are separate, any short circuit or disconnection of the communicating link between the two should be indicated *at the fire detection and alarm system control and indicating equipment* within 100 seconds. In effect, therefore, the code treats the interconnecting wiring between the two systems in the same way as it treats the wiring to a normal fire alarm sounder. Equally, in the case of voice alarm systems, the code refers the reader to BS 5839-8,[25] which merely supports, and slightly amplifies, this recommendation.

It should be noted that, with regard to this recommendation, the code refers to a *separate* voice alarm system. This would seem to imply that, for example, if the fire detection and alarm system control equipment and the voice alarm system rack were virtually integrated (e.g. were installed side-by-side and in contact with each other), so that the interconnecting wiring effectively becomes internal wiring within a single mechanical enclosure, the recommendation might not apply. The same situation would arise in the case of paging transmission equipment provided to warn deaf people in the event of fire.

With regard to the interconnecting wiring between the fire detection and fire alarm system and any other fire protection system or safety facility, as discussed in Chapter 9 the interface is not strictly within the scope of the code. However, clause 12 recommends that, for recommendations regarding monitoring of the interconnections, reference should be made to BS 7273 or other applicable codes of practice.

As discussed in Chapter 14, the code gives considerable advice on fire alarm warnings for deaf people. Most of the recommendations of the code in this respect are concerned with systems that use tactile devices, including vibrating pagers. The code recommends that 'circuits' serving

---

[25] BS 5839-8, *Fire detection and alarm systems for buildings — Code of practice for the design, installation and servicing of voice alarm systems*. In 2008, BS 5839-8:1998 will be superseded by BS 5839-8:2008.

these devices should be monitored. This includes wiring of circuits to vibrating pads, although, in practice, these are not always monitored up to the pad itself.

The recommendations in respect of system integrity are somewhat more subtle, and certainly more complex, than those relating to monitoring. Indeed, within these recommendations is one that, since it was introduced into the code in 1980, has become the most misunderstood aspect of engineering design within the entire code. Accordingly, it is this recommendation that we will consider first.

At the time of drafting BS 5839-1:1980, concern arose that, if fire damaged a fire alarm sounder circuit, causing the circuit protection to trip, fire alarm sounders would stop operating throughout the building, unless there were more than one circuit. In practice, it was considered that the potential for this to occur is not generally significant enough to have a major impact on the safety of those occupying a building at the time of a fire. After all, it has long been recommended within the code that fire alarm sounder circuits be protected against fire, normally by the use of a fire resisting cable. Moreover, the code has long recommended that joints in cables (which are potential points of weakness in the fire resistance of the overall cable system) be avoided. Accordingly, the probability that fire disables a sounder circuit before it is detected and occupants have evacuated the building, is very low; there is certainly no evidence that, in practice, systems designed in accordance with the code have failed to protect occupants adequately as a result of fire damage to a sounder circuit.

However, what of those who have evacuated the building and are awaiting instructions as to whether it is safe to re-enter the building? The technical committee were concerned that, if all fire alarm sounders stopped operating, these people might reasonably assume that the fire alarm signal had been a false alarm (given that most fire alarm signals are, indeed, false alarms), or that the incident was merely a fire drill. Again, it could be argued that this is an unlikely event, given that the fire and rescue service should have been summoned and that staff training should be such that occupants do not re-enter a building after evacuation, until they are instructed by someone in responsible charge to do so (after agreement by the fire and rescue service).

Even so, given that even fire resisting cable systems may fail after a prolonged period of time (often at the terminations within devices), it was considered appropriate to address this scenario within the recommendations of the 1980 version of the code. The issue was addressed, in the 1980 version of the code, by a recommendation that, in the event of the scenario described, the audible alarm signal should continue to be given at, at least, a single point in the building. The intention of this recommendation was that, for example, a single fire alarm sounder, located somewhere in the vicinity of the control equipment, would continue to operate. As a result of the recommendation, it became necessary for fire alarm control panels to incorporate at least two sounder circuits; previously, this would not have been necessary.

The control equipment is normally located close to the entrance to the building in a relatively sterile area. This has two benefits. First, the short length of cable between the control equipment and the single bell envisaged in the code is unlikely to be affected by fire. Secondly, the location at which the signal would be given would be appropriate to warn those who might otherwise re-enter the building.

Unfortunately, this recommendation was widely misunderstood. It was interpreted by many as a recommendation that there be 'dual' circuits throughout the building, so that, if any one circuit failed, the fire alarm signal would be audible throughout all areas of the building. While this may, or may not, be a laudable design principle, it was never the intent of the recommendations in the code to achieve this level of integrity.

Moreover, it is not uncommon for those who strive to achieve this level of integrity to 'interleave' two fire alarm sounder circuits in each area, so that adjacent sounders are each on the alternate circuit. While such an arrangement would not actually contravene the recommendations of the code, it could be argued that this arrangement less satisfactorily addresses the scenario that the code attempts to address than the single sounder on the second circuit; if fire is severe enough to cause failure of one circuit, it is very likely that it could also damage a second circuit within the same area.

The above considerations only address, of course, a failure of a sounder circuit as a result of fire damage. What of mechanical damage to the circuit or disconnection of the circuit during maintenance? With regard to mechanical damage, the code already recommends that, where cables are exposed to mechanical damage, there should be suitable mechanical protection. Also, this is where monitoring becomes of importance. An indication of cable fault will be given, and the code recommends that, where maintenance is carried out by a third party, such as a fire alarm maintenance organization, there should be an agreement for emergency call-out to deal with any fault or damage that occurs to the system. Thus, mechanical damage to cables should be a rare event of short duration.

Fire, itself, is also, happily, a rare event. The probability of fire occurring during the short period between occurrence of a cable fault and repair of the fault is therefore extremely low, to the extent that it has not been considered necessary to further address this scenario within the code. Similarly, durations for which circuits are disabled during maintenance should be short and, in the event of fire, it is likely to be possible to reinstate the circuit.

In view of the above considerations, the recommendation of the code is that, in the event of a single open circuit or short circuit fault on any circuit that serves fire alarm sounders, at least one single fire alarm sounder, normally located in the vicinity of the control and indicating equipment, should still sound correctly if a fire alarm condition occurs anywhere within the building. This fire alarm sounder should have an identical sound to the general fire alarm sounders in the building (i.e. the recommendation is not satisfied by, for example, an internal sounder within the control and indicating equipment).

In order to obviate the confusion that has arisen, a note within the code points out that the recommendation can be satisfied by two different methods. The first is to wire all fire alarm sounders within the building on a single sounder circuit, with the additional provision of a second independent sounder circuit, to which only a single sounder is connected. In the case of systems with addressable sounders, however, the same level of integrity can be achieved by wiring all fire alarm sounders on a single addressable loop, provided the first (or last) three devices on the loop comprise a short circuit isolator, a sounder and a further short circuit isolator. In the latter case, regardless of the location within the building at which a single cable fault occurs, at least one sounder, in the vicinity of the control equipment, will continue to operate. The note is amplified by two drawings, which are reproduced in this guide as Figures 1 and 2.

Notwithstanding the above considerations, the code regards duplication of sounder circuits as justifiable in a building, or part of a building, designed to accommodate a large number of the public in a single, open, un-compartmented space. Examples include transport termini, shopping centres, places of public entertainment, department stores and leisure centres. In this case, the lack of compartmentation of the space exposes a large number of people to a single fire. Moreover, shepherding the public from such a space, without the assistance of a fire alarm system, would create great difficulties. Also, it is possible that, during maintenance, a sounder circuit could be disabled when the public are on the premises.

As a result of these further considerations, the 2002 version of the code, for the first time, contains an additional recommendation that, within the un-compartmented public space, there should be at least two sounder circuits if the space is either greater than 4,000 m² in area or is designed to accommodate more than 500 members of the public. These two sounder circuits should be evenly distributed and interleaved, such that adjacent sounders are on different circuits, or such that no more than 50% of the sounders in the area are lost in the event of a single open or short circuit fault.

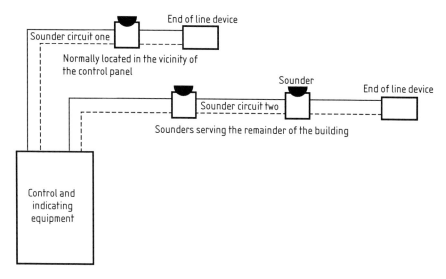

Figure 1 — Radial sounder circuits

Several aspects of this new recommendation warrant further consideration. First, the figure of 4,000 m² and the figure of 500 members of the public are entirely arbitrary. They have been adopted from BS 5839-8, primarily for consistency between the two codes. However, it can be asserted quite definitively, that these figures were entirely arbitrary when they were incorporated within BS 5839-8. The implications of this are that minor departures from these figures (e.g. use of a single circuit within an area designed to accommodate 505 members of the public) are of no real significance.

It should also be noted that, where two independent circuits are used, it is quite clear that these should be interleaved throughout the area. The alternative given in the code is to use a (presumably single) loop circuit, arranged such that no more than 50% of the sounders in the area are lost in the event of a single cable fault. Although, in the opinion of the author, the wording that relates to this arrangement is not entirely clear, it would presumably not be adequate to have an arrangement whereby the 50% of the sounders that continue to operate were all in one half of the un-compartmented space. If the principle of 'interleaving' is to be followed in this case, so that only each alternate sounder fails to operate in the event of a single fault on the loop, in practice this is only likely to be achieved by the use of a system in which there is a short circuit isolator within each sounder.

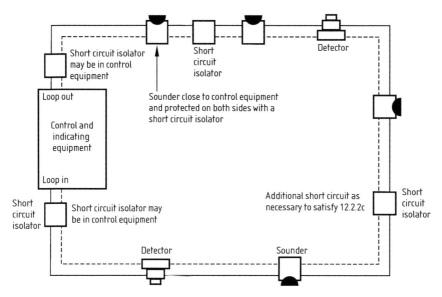

Figure 2 — Ring sounder circuits

On the one hand, this results in a higher level of integrity (and more onerous recommendation) than applies to the conventional two circuits, as, in the event of a cable fault, in practice, it will, at most, be two sounders that are disabled, rather than 50% of the sounders in the area (assuming that there are more than four sounders within the space). On the other hand, the arrangement might be regarded as of lower integrity than the two circuit solution, as failure of a loop driver or disablement of the single loop circuit during maintenance will result in total failure of alarm sounders within the area. In any case, the two different arrangements are acceptable for compliance with the code, perhaps on the basis that the lower level of integrity that results from the use of, in effect, a single circuit, is balanced by the higher level of integrity, in terms of the number of sounders disabled by a single cable fault.

It should be noted that the duplicate sounder circuits (or equivalent) need only be provided within the open, un-compartmented space described above. Thus, for example, in an airport terminal, the duplicate circuits are likely to be required within the main concourse, but this is not intended to imply that, in other areas of the building, duplication of sounder circuits is necessary. Moreover, even if there are many thousands of occupants in a building, duplication is not necessary unless, within the building, one or more open, un-compartmented spaces exceed the limits specified.

In practice, of course, electrical engineering considerations (e.g. circuit load and voltage drop) alone necessitate the provision of more than one sounder circuit, other than in small buildings. Accordingly, in general, the number and configuration of sounder circuits may be designed, in most buildings, purely on the basis of the most economic design commensurate with electrical engineering requirements. For example, circuits may be routed via different electrical risers, such that each circuit serves a different part of each floor; alternatively, each circuit may serve a different floor(s). Under these circumstances, compliance with the code would not seem to necessitate yet a further single circuit with its single sounder in the vicinity of the control equipment; this would only be the strict minimum in circumstances in which the remainder of the building is served by just one sounder circuit.

Even the recommendation for duplication in respect of large, un-compartmented public spaces is not particularly onerous, since such a large space might well warrant a second sounder circuit on the basis of electrical installation design; the only 'penalty' then is the need for the two circuits to be 'interleaved'. Where the recommendation is satisfied by the provision of two completely independent sounder circuits (as opposed to a single addressable loop), obviously the two circuits cannot be served by, say, a single four core cable, as it cannot be assumed that a fault disables only two cores of such a cable. On the other hand, if multiple sounder circuits are provided purely to satisfy electrical engineering considerations, as opposed to the recommendations of the code for sounder circuit integrity, several sounder circuits could be run in a single multi-core cable.

The code also addresses the integrity of circuits containing automatic fire detectors, by limiting the maximum area throughout which automatic detection may be disabled in the event of a single short circuit or open circuit fault. In this case, the recommendation is based on the traditional circuit design encountered in conventional (i.e. non-addressable systems).

In a conventional system, each detection zone is served by an independent circuit; it is only by this means that a separate indication can result from each zone. Thus, in a conventional system, a single open or short circuit on the wiring of a detector circuit can, at most, disable protection throughout one zone of the system. Traditionally, the maximum area of a zone has always been limited to 2,000 m². Moreover, except in very small buildings, a detection zone should not serve more than a single floor of the building (see also Chapter 12).

Since it would be inappropriate to have different recommendations for the integrity of conventional systems and addressable systems, the code takes the above considerations into account and applies them to all systems, regardless of whether they are conventional or addressable.

In the case of an addressable loop, an open circuit fault does not normally disable any fire detectors (unless a number of detectors have been connected on a single 'spur' derived from the loop). However, unless short circuit isolators are incorporated within the loop, a short circuit has the potential to disable the entire loop, which may serve a very large area that exceeds the normal limits for a single zone of the system. It has, therefore, become recognized practice for short circuit isolators to be installed at zone boundaries, so that, in the event of a single short circuit cable fault, the area disabled does not exceed that of a single zone of the system.

Strict adoption of this policy may, however, be unnecessarily onerous in some installations, and it is not always necessary for compliance with the code. For example, if a designer decides to adopt very small detection zone sizes, below the zone limits recommended within the code, he/she should not be penalized for providing a system that is, in terms of zoning, better than the minimum recommended within the code. In a conventional system, each of these small zones will, of course, constitute a separate circuit, but, in an addressable system, many zones may be served by a single loop. It should not then matter too much if, in the event of a single short circuit fault, several of these small zones are disabled simultaneously, as the designer could have provided a conventional system and amalgamated these small zones into one larger zone served by a single conventional circuit.

Furthermore, for convenience of wiring, an addressable loop that predominantly serves only a single floor of the building may 'stray' into the floor above or below, simply to pick up a few detectors that can be conveniently wired by this method. In the past, strictly, this would have necessitated two short circuit isolators, located at the points of exit and entry of the cable from/to the main floor served by the loop. If the number of devices on the floor above or below is small, it is questionable as to whether the addition of these short circuit isolators is really necessary. Indeed, it could be argued that inclusion of too many short circuit isolators actually reduces the circuit reliability, since each short circuit isolator involves a further junction (i.e. potential point of weakness) within the cable, and, of course, a short circuit isolator itself is a fallible device.

If the considerations within the above paragraphs are combined, the recommendations of the code in terms of integrity of automatic fire detector circuits becomes clear and logical. The code recommends that a single short circuit or open circuit fault on an automatic fire detector circuit should neither disable protection (i.e. the automatic fire detectors) within an area of more than 2,000 m², nor on more than one floor of the building plus a maximum of five devices (automatic detectors, manual call points, sounders or a combination of these) on the floor immediately above and five devices on the floor immediately below that floor.

Several points about this recommendation should be highlighted. First, it would be acceptable for five devices on the floor above *and* five devices on the floor below to be disabled in the event of a short circuit; it is not necessary to limit the disablement to, say, three devices on the floor above and two devices on the floor below, thereby limiting the disablement to five devices in total as well as those on the main floor served by the loop.

Secondly, contrary to popular misconception, there is no numerical limit on the number of detectors that may be disabled by the single fault. The limit is expressed in terms of the area of disablement. In an open plan area, the 2,000 m² will, typically, be served by around 20 smoke detectors. However, in a predominantly cellular area with comprehensive automatic fire detection, a much greater number of detectors may be disabled by the single fault.

Thirdly, it should be noted that this recommendation does not apply to circuits that serve only manual call points. Thus, an addressable loop that serves only manual call points may serve several floors of the building and a large floor area without incorporating any short circuit isolators.

However, an addressable loop cannot, in practice, serve an infinitely large area, regardless of whether it contains manual call points, automatic fire detectors or a combination of the two. A further recommendation of the code limits the maximum area throughout which manual call points and/or automatic fire detectors should be disabled in the event of two simultaneous faults to 10,000 m². This is, in effect, the maximum floor area that can be served by a single addressable loop. Note, however, that, in the case of an addressable loop serving only manual call points, a *single* short circuit fault could actually disable manual call points throughout a floor area of 10,000 m². Even so, in a large open space, such as a warehouse, a single conventional circuit could serve manual call points throughout an area of 10,000 m² (see Chapter 12); accordingly, what appears, at first sight, to be a fairly generous relaxation for the integrity of manual call point circuits is somewhat logical.

More generally, the code endeavours to limit the effect that a fault on any one circuit will have on the entire system. Thus, it is recommended that a fault on any one manual call point, fire detector or sounder circuit should not affect any other circuit. This is simply good design practice in respect of control equipment, and the design principle is, in any case, a requirement of BS EN 54-2.

However, the code also contains a further, related recommendation that is not incorporated within BS EN 54-2 (and will, in the case of a large, complex system, be quite difficult to prove). The recommendation concerns faults arising from a cross-connection between any detector circuit and any sounder circuit. The code recommends that, in the event of such a fault, the fault should not affect any circuits other than the two circuits involved. This recommendation really relates to product design, rather than installation design, but it has been included within the code, thereby supplementing the requirements of BS EN 54-2, because it has been known for control panel design to be such that a cross-connection between a sounder circuit and a detector circuit could, in the event of a fire alarm signal, result in total loss of power to the system from both the mains supply and the standby supply.

BS EN 54-2, itself, does, however, contain requirements for the design of control and indicating equipment, such as to limit loss of integrity during system faults. One such recommendation relates specifically to software control and indicating equipment that the manufacturer declares can be used for connection to more than 512 fire detectors and/or manual call points. In the case of such equipment, BS EN 54-2 requires that, in the event of failure in the execution of the software program, or corruption of memory contents, no more than 512 fire detectors and/or manual call points, and the associated cause and effect required by BS EN 54-2, can be affected. Alternatively, in the event of such a fault, the system must still be capable of giving a fire alarm indication by means of the general fire alarm indicator and an audible warning, the operation of an output and the transmission of a signal to a transmitter unit by which fire alarm signals are relayed to the fire and rescue service (if such a facility is provided).

In order to ensure that this requirement is satisfied, the manufacturer may need to provide relevant information to the installation designer and installer. Accordingly, the code recommends that, if software control and indicating equipment has more than 512 detectors and/or manual call points connected, reference should be made to the manufacturer's instructions regarding means by which compliance with BS EN 54-2 can be achieved. It should be noted that, in the case of the 'default' option, whereby minimum system performance is maintained in the event of the relevant faults, a common evacuation signal throughout a building might not always be a desirable arrangement. For example, in the case of a phased evacuation building, a single phase evacuation of the building might be quite undesirable (see also Chapter 19).

In order to maintain system integrity, the code also considers the possibility of deliberate disablement of the system, or parts of the system, whether maliciously or during routine maintenance. In the case of fire alarm devices (e.g. sounders), the code recommends that they should only be capable of being removed by the use of a special tool. Within that particular recommendation, the term 'special tool' is not defined, but, in an earlier recommendation, relating to malicious removal of detectors, a 'special tool' is deemed to be a tool not likely to be carried by members of the general public; this precludes the use of slot-headed screws, since the code recognizes that various articles can be used as screwdrivers to remove these.

With regard to removal of detectors that are designed to be detachable for maintenance (i.e. virtually all modern detectors), the code recommends that removal of any detector(s) from the circuit should not affect the operation of any manual call point, even if locking devices are used to secure the detectors within their bases. In the case of an addressable system, isolation of other devices when a detector is removed from its base does not arise. However, in a simple conventional system, it used to be the case that, in order to obtain a head removal indication, removal of a head isolated devices downstream (including the end of line monitoring device). Although most modern conventional systems are more sophisticated than this, such an arrangement would still be acceptable under the code, provided the devices downstream that were isolated comprised only automatic fire detectors and not manual call points.

Compliance with the above recommendation can be achieved by at least three means, namely connecting manual call points and automatic fire detectors on separate conventional circuits, connecting all manual call points as the first devices on the circuit or the use of more sophistication in detector removal monitoring, so that removal does not isolate any other devices on the same circuit. It should be noted that, for compliance with this recommendation, it should be possible to remove *all* fire detectors on a circuit without resulting in the disablement of *any* manual call point.

When a design is carried out, the code recommends that consideration be given to the possibility of malicious removal of detectors. If the designer considers that malicious removal is likely, detectors of a type that can be removed only by the use of a special tool (as defined above) or special technique should be used. It is for the designer to determine whether such malicious removal is likely and the types of premises to which this might apply. However, it could be the case that the recommendation might apply to certain student residences, detention facilities and similar premises.

In general, the code also recommends that removal of any manual call point or detector from its circuit should not affect the ability of any fire alarm device to respond to an alarm signal. However, it is recognized that some manufacturers produce combined detector/sounder units. Obviously, in the case of such a unit, removal of the detector (e.g. because it is faulty) could well result in disablement (indeed removal) of the associated sounder unit. Accordingly, a relaxation applies, so that this situation would not contravene the recommendations of the code.

BS EN 54-2 permits facilities to be provided for the deliberate disablement of manual call points and detectors (and indeed sounders), subject to suitable access control in respect of the facilities. Obviously, it is necessary to use such facilities from time to time, such as during maintenance, when faults in the equipment occur or when circumstances that will give rise to false alarms exist. However, in order to minimize the extent of the disablement that will occur, the code recommends that the facilities for disablement of manual call points or detectors should be such that it is possible to disable protection throughout (at most) one detection zone of the system without disabling protection in other zones. This is merely conventional equipment design practice, in that, in a conventional system, isolation is possible on a zonal basis. In the case of an addressable system, the facilities provided for disablement often go beyond the minimum recommended in the code, in that disablement of specific devices is usually possible.

Regardless of the exact facilities or disablement that are provided, the code recommends that the use of such facilities should not prevent evacuation of the building by use of an evacuate control on, or close to, the control and indicating equipment. Thus, for example, even if the user has isolated all manual call points and fire detectors on the system, if a fire occurs, the building can be evacuated without reinstatement of the disabled devices simply by operating the evacuation control.

The last of the recommendations that need be considered within clause 12 relates to connections between control and indicating equipment and any power supply equipment contained within a separate enclosure. If such a separate power supply unit is used, the connections between the power supply unit and the control and indicating equipment should be duplicated, such that a single open or short circuit in the connections does not completely remove power from the control and indicating equipment. Use of power supply equipment complying with BS EN 54-4, and use of control and indicating equipment complying with BS EN 54-2, will, in any case, ensure that facilities are provided at the equipment for connection of the duplicate circuits. The code also recommends that, where practical, there be 300 mm separation between the duplicate circuits, so minimizing the likelihood of simultaneous physical damage to both circuits, other than, possibly, at the points of entry to the equipment.

12. Detection zones and alarm zones

Traditionally, the term 'zone' has been used to describe an area of the premises in which the occurrence of fire will be indicated separately, at the control and indicating equipment, from the indication of fire in any other area (zone). In BS 5839-1:2002, this 'zone' is described as a 'detection zone', regardless of whether the zone is one that contains purely automatic fire detectors, manual call points or a combination of the two. This is to distinguish this type of 'zone' from an 'alarm' zone. The latter is a subdivision of the premises in which the fire alarm warning can be given separately, and independently, of the fire alarm warning in any other area ('alarm zone'). Although these terms have not been used in previous versions of the code, they are not entirely new, in that they were introduced in HTM 82[26] some years prior to their introduction into BS 5839-1.

The purpose of dividing a system into detection zones is to provide a relatively accurate indication to those responding to a fire, particularly the fire and rescue service, of the location of the fire. It has long been the tradition that a detection zone should not exceed 2,000 m² in area. Although this limitation was originally based on the electrical engineering design of conventional detector circuits, it has been found to be a reasonable limitation for the purposes of providing a sufficiently accurate indication of the location of a fire. Accordingly, with the exception of one situation, the code continues to recommend that detection zone size should not exceed 2,000 m².

The exception relates to a detection zone that comprises mainly a single, open plan area and contains only manual call points (i.e. no automatic fire detectors). In this situation (e.g. a large, un-compartmented

---

[26] HTM 82, *Alarm and detection systems*. Published by NHS Estates. Now superseded by HTM 05-03 Part B, *Alarm and detection systems*. Published by the Department of Health in England and Wales. (In Scotland, SHTM 82, published by NHS Scotland applies.)

warehouse), there might be no real benefit in zoning the manual call points. If someone at one end of the warehouse can see a fire at the other end, they are unlikely to run towards the fire to operate a manual call point in the zone of fire origin, simply to ensure that the correct zone indication is given, nor indeed should they attempt to do so.

If anything, the zone indication that is given is, under these circumstances, likely to represent the zone furthest from the fire, rather than the zone in which the fire is located. If we then take the example of a 100 m × 100 m warehouse, there is no point in providing five manual call point zones (which would be quite expensive in installation costs if a conventional system is used) to provide information that is, at best, of no major benefit, and at worst, grossly misleading. Accordingly, a relaxation in the code applies to a single, open plan area that contains only manual call points. In this case, the maximum floor area of a detection zone is increased from 2,000 m^2 to 10,000 m^2.

The code also maintains the traditional approach that no detection zone should cover more than a single storey of the building, but, again, there is a relaxation; if the total floor area of the building is less than 300 m^2, the entire building may be treated as one detection zone. This recommendation, which has appeared in previous versions of the code, has been known to cause a little confusion. The 300 m^2 is not the 'footprint' of the building, but is intended to mean the aggregate floor area of all floors. The effect is that, for example, a small shop with a basement or upper floor might be treated as a single zone, particularly as, very often, a manual fire alarm system is all that is required.

The zoning of stairwells is treated differently, according to whether the detection zone comprises automatic fire detectors or only manual call points. In the previous version of the code, there was no such distinction; enclosed stairwells, liftwells and similar flue-like structures were treated as separate zones.

The thinking behind this is that smoke within a stairwell or liftwell is likely to have been generated within one of the storeys served by the shaft, as, for example, a stairwell should be a sterile area, free from fire hazards. As smoke enters the stairwell, or similar vertical shaft, it will tend to rise, possibly operating automatic fire detectors on several levels. If the detectors on each level were incorporated within the detection zone serving the accommodation on that level, the indications given at the control and indicating equipment would imply that fire had spread through several floors of the building. A more accurate indication would be that there was a fire on one floor and that smoke had entered the staircase. This more accurate picture is imparted if the stairwell constitutes a separate, vertical zone. Accordingly, the code recommends that automatic fire detectors within any enclosed stairwell, liftwell, or other enclosed flue-like structure should be considered as a separate zone.

If, however, the same principle is applied to manual call points located on the landings of a stairwell, the operation of a manual call point gives no indication whatsoever as to the location of the fire. All that is known is that someone escaping from a fire somewhere in the building has operated a manual call point within the stairwell. Accordingly, the code recommends that, if manual call points are located on the landings of an enclosed stairway (which they may be, but need not necessarily be), the manual call points on each level should be incorporated within the zone that serves the adjacent accommodation on that level.

If someone discovers a fire, the most likely manual call point within the stairwell for them to operate will be that on the same level as the fire. Thus, the above arrangement gives the optimum accuracy regarding the location of the fire. It is, of course, possible that someone will operate a manual call point on a lower floor, but at the very least, it can be reasonably certain that the fire is not located on any floor below that on which the first manual call point is operated. The code makes an exception for the manual call point at the final exit from the stairway to open air; this call point may be connected to the detection zone serving accommodation on the exit level or the detection zone serving the stairwell.

In an addressable system, the separate zoning of manual call points and automatic fire detectors within a stairwell has no associated penalty; the total number of zones for which an indication must be given remains the same. In a conventional system, the only minor inconvenience is that the zone serving each floor will need to be extended into the stairwell to serve any manual call point within the stairwell on that level, while a further circuit will need to be installed to serve the automatic fire detectors within the stairwell. However, as discussed in Chapter 16, it is not essential that manual call points be installed within stairwells in any case; this is merely one option for manual call point siting.

In many situations, the limitation of detection zone size to, at most, a single floor of the building, with a further limitation of 2,000 m^2 in area, is sufficiently accurate to enable the fire and rescue service to locate a fire reasonably quickly. Certainly, in a floor of a building with simple geometry, and in predominantly open areas, this limitation is sufficient. However, if floor layout is complex and predominantly cellular with, for example, a number of side corridors located off main corridors, it may be necessary for the fire and rescue service to carry out a prolonged search, perhaps in smoke-filled conditions, to identify the location of the fire.

To minimize the extent of the search that the fire and rescue service must carry out, the code introduces a limitation on 'search distance', which can further limit the size of a detection zone in certain circumstances. The 'search distance' is the distance that has to be travelled within a detection zone by someone searching for the fire, in order to determine visually the position of a fire. Thus, the search distance is not the distance that has to be travelled within the zone to reach the fire, but simply the distance that must be travelled before someone can first become aware of the location of a fire.

In a predominantly open area, the search distance may be very small, as it might be possible for someone to become aware of the location of a fire as soon as they enter the zone (see Figure 3). However, the code recommends that the area of a detection zone be limited, such that the search distance does not exceed 60 m. Since the worse case scenario must be considered, in which, say, firefighters must search up and down corridors before they can identify the location of a fire that is at the furthermost point from where they enter the zone, in order to comply with the search distance criterion it may be necessary to make detection zones smaller than would otherwise be the case.

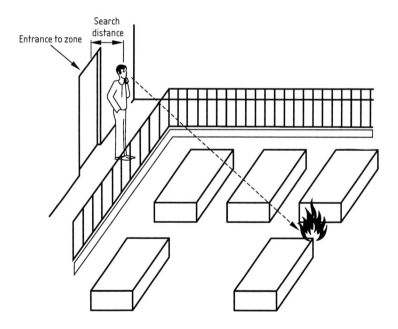

Figure 3 — Examples of search distances in an open area

It may, however, be questioned as to why, in the case of an addressable system, firefighters would have to carry out such a prolonged search, since the location of a fire is usually pinpointed exactly in the form of a text display. In the past, the search distance criterion was applied to addressable systems. This is because early text displays were not always of good visibility, and the text message might not be sufficient for those unfamiliar with the building to identify the location displayed.

However, the quality of visual displays provided on control panels has improved. Accordingly, the code permits the search distance criterion to be waived in the case of addressable systems in which a clear text display of the location of, at least, the first detector to respond to a fire is available at the control and indicating equipment without manual intervention. There is, however, a proviso to this waiver, namely that the display must be such that it would enable firefighters, unfamiliar with the building, to proceed to the location of the fire.

As always, the wording of the recommendation has various implications. First, the display must be available without any manual intervention; firefighters should not be expected to know the method of operation of individual control equipment. Secondly, it would be sufficient for only the location of the first detector that gives an alarm signal to be indicated, as it is this detector that is likely to be nearest to the fire; the location of further detectors that respond to the fire is not as important.

Finally, the 'acid test' is whether those unfamiliar with the building would be able to translate the text information displayed into a location, to which they could proceed directly. The code accepts that this may rely on further information displayed on, or adjacent to, the control and indicating equipment. Thus, the text display might, for example, show floor number and room number, while a correctly orientated plan adjacent to the control equipment might show the location of the room within the floor in question. Note that a description that would require familiarity with the building for it to be of use (e.g. Mr Jones' office) would not satisfy this recommendation, and, if such messages were used, the search distance criterion would have to apply.

While text messages can, therefore, be very useful, the view taken in the code is that these supplement, rather than replace, conventional zonal indicators. Thus, regardless of whether the system is conventional or addressable, and regardless of whether a text display pinpoints the exact location of a fire, the code recommends that, in all systems, the primary indication of the area from which a fire signal has originated should consist of a light-emitting zone indicator. The form of zone indication provided should comprise a separate light-emitting indication for each zone on the system, such that the indicating equipment is capable of simultaneous display of fire signals on every zone.

Given the prevalence of modern addressable systems, with sophisticated text displays, the above recommendation for the traditional light-emitting zonal indicators to indicate detection zone might be regarded by some as rather old-fashioned. Certainly, these indicators are not required by BS EN 54-2, as, in other European countries, the indicators are regarded as unnecessary. However, in the UK, it is considered that the 'at a glance' display of detection zones, and the ability of such a display to give a clear indication of fire spread from one detection zone to another, remains of value to the fire and rescue service, who might fail to notice indications of further alarm signals, from detectors in further zones, on a text display. Unless, therefore, the control and indicating equipment has zonal indicators (which equipment complying with BS EN 54-2 will not necessarily have), an additional form of zonal indication (e.g. a matrix of LEDs or an illuminated mimic) will be necessary for compliance with the code.

Where detectors are installed within floor or ceiling voids, these detectors can normally be incorporated within the zone that serves the accommodation above or below the void respectively. This is accepted by the code, provided the void and the associated room constitute a single fire compartment. Although not explicitly stated in the code, the implications of this are that, if the void is separated from the room by substantial fire resisting construction, such as to form a separate fire compartment for the void, the void should constitute a separate detection zone.

The code does not specifically recommend remote indicator lamps for such concealed detectors, but, of course, if the search distance criterion is applied, remote indicator lamps might be used to limit search distance. Where remote indicators are provided, the code recommends that they should be clearly labelled to indicate their function and that they are sited and/or labelled in such a way as to assist in determining the location of the detectors that they serve.

The recommendations concerning alarm zones are much simpler than those relating to detection zones. Indeed, in a building with a single stage alarm system, supporting single phase (i.e. simultaneous) evacuation of the entire building, the building will not be subdivided into alarm zones.

Alarm zones only occur in situations in which fire alarm sounders in the building are grouped, so that certain areas of the building receive an 'Evacuate' signal, while other areas of the building receive an 'Alert' signal. This will always occur in buildings with phased evacuation and in any building in which, to minimize disruption from false alarms, only a limited area of the building is evacuated immediately, with the remainder of the building evacuated simultaneously only after it has been confirmed that there is a genuine fire.

An alarm zone will often incorporate more than one detection zone, but, clearly, there cannot be more than one alarm zone within a single detection zone. Moreover, the boundaries of alarm zones should coincide with the boundaries of the relevant detection zones. The boundaries of every alarm zone (other than external walls) should comprise fire resisting construction, since this boundary will separate an area in which it is deemed necessary to evacuate people, from an area in which it is deemed acceptable to leave occupants in place, at least until a later stage.

Also, it is important that the overlap of signals between alarm zones cannot result in confusion as a result of occupants hearing both an 'Alert' signal and an 'Evacuation' signal with the same clarity. The use of fire resisting construction at alarm zone boundaries will assist in the attenuation of signals between one alarm zone and the next. These recommendations preclude an arrangement whereby, say, in an open concourse, such as an airport terminal, one area of the concourse is evacuated, while other areas, unseparated from the area in which evacuation takes place, remain occupied. In order to avoid confusion, a common signal should be used throughout the building to indicate 'Evacuation' and a completely different, but common, signal should be used throughout the building to indicate 'Alert'.

It is important that the configuration of alarm zones is approved by all relevant authorities responsible for enforcement of fire safety legislation in the building. The code allocates responsibility for ensuring that such approval is obtained by the user or purchaser, who must then ensure that the designer is apprised of the relevant authority's requirements.

13. Communication with the fire and rescue service

When a fire occurs in an occupied building, the most important initial action is to provide a warning to all occupants. However, the immediate summoning of the fire and rescue service is also important. Accordingly, clause 15 of the code is concerned purely with communication with the fire and rescue service.

In theory at least, the arrival of the fire and rescue service should not be necessary in order to ensure the safety of occupants of a building. All buildings should 'stand-alone', such that there are adequate means of escape and means of giving warning to ensure that occupants can escape safely in the event of fire, without the intervention of the fire and rescue service. In most situations, the building should be evacuated by the time the fire and rescue service arrives. Were this not the case, buildings in rural areas, with long fire and rescue service attendance times, would be less safe than those in urban conurbations, and this is not the case. (The obligation to evacuate the building, without reliance on the fire and rescue service, also extends to disabled people, which often makes the provision of communication systems in disabled refuges, to which BS 5839-9[27] applies, very important.)

The code recommends that, in occupied buildings, the primary means of summoning the fire and rescue service should always involve a call to the fire and rescue service by occupants using the public emergency call system. (The numbers 999 or 112 can both be used for this purpose.) This manually dialled call will usually be sufficient in the case of a Category M system, since, by definition, there must be occupants in the

---

[27] BS 5839-9:2003, *Fire detection and fire alarm systems for buildings — Code of practice for the design, installation, commissioning and maintenance of emergency voice communication systems.*

building in order for the alarm to be raised; these occupants can usually ensure that the fire and rescue service are summoned.

Equally, even if there is a means for transmitting alarm signals automatically to an alarm receiving centre (ARC), from where the fire and rescue service are then summoned, such a system can fail, and accordingly, if the building is occupied, a manually dialled emergency call to the fire and rescue service should still be made even if there is a facility to transmit signals to an ARC. In some areas of the country, this manually dialled call has an additional benefit, as some fire and rescue services dispatch more fire appliances to a confirmed fire than to a call from an ARC, or will 'call challenge' calls via an ARC, requiring an investigation by occupants prior to dispatching appliances. Also, in the event of frequent false alarms, some fire and rescue services may withdraw attendance to calls from the ARC, but not to calls from the premises.

The code recommends that the emergency call be made by a person, rather than by automatic systems that transmit a pre-recorded message direct to the fire and rescue service by the public emergency call system. In practice, the use of the now very old-fashioned 'tape 999 diallers', and even more modern equipment with digitally recorded messages, is uncommon. In any case, use of such equipment would not now comply with the code.

The code recommends that consideration be given to the safety of any person to whom the responsibility for summoning the fire and rescue service is allocated. For example, it should not be expected that the person proceed to a more hazardous location to make the call. Often, it is predetermined that a switchboard operator or receptionist will summon the fire and rescue service in the event of operation of the fire alarm system. If it is the case that an area, such as a telephone switchboard or reception desk, is specifically designated as that from which the fire and rescue service will be summoned, the code recommends that the fire alarm signal in this area should not be so loud as to interfere with telephone speech. Thus, in this area, the normal recommendations in respect of sound pressure level (see Chapter 14) do not apply.

Having made suitable arrangements for immediate summoning of the fire and rescue service in the event of fire when the building is occupied, consideration should always be given to whether there is then a need for additional automatic means of transmission of alarm signals to an ARC. Accordingly, the code recommends that the designer should determine from the purchaser or user whether such a facility is required. It should be noted that the designer has not complied with the recommendations of the code unless a specific enquiry regarding the requirement for this facility is made of the purchaser or user.

It has already been asserted that such a facility will not normally be necessary in the case of a Category M system. In theory, the same should be true of a Category L system, since the purpose of this system is purely to facilitate evacuation in the event of fire. However, there may be circumstances in which the safety of occupants does indeed depend on the early arrival of the fire and rescue service.

A classic case of this is a hospital. Hospitals are normally designed on the basis of 'progressive horizontal evacuation', in which, during the early stages of a fire, patients are moved only horizontally into an adjacent 'sub-compartment'. If fire then threatens the occupants of that sub-compartment, in a large hospital patients will then be moved yet further horizontally into a further sub-compartment. Ideally, there will not be a need to move patients vertically down the stairways, as this is a much more difficult process. Clearly, progressive horizontal evacuation is only a viable concept if the original fire is controlled and extinguished quite quickly. To ensure a high probability that this is the case, the early arrival of the fire and rescue service is vital. The fire and rescue service may also be required to assist in evacuation of patients if the fire cannot be controlled. Similar considerations may sometimes apply in the case of residential care premises, although, in such premises, there should normally be a suitable strategy for evacuation of patients by staff. (In Scotland, therefore, the guidance that supports the Building (Scotland) Regulations 2004 recommends that, for compliance with the Regulations, fire alarm systems in hospitals and residential care premises should have a facility for automatic transmission of fire alarm signals to the fire and rescue service, e.g. via an ARC.)

In view of the above, the code recommends that, if the early summoning of the fire and rescue service is considered critical to the safety of occupants, facilities should be provided for automatic transmission of alarm signals to an ARC, unless there are reliable arrangements for summoning the fire and rescue service by persons in the building. Not surprisingly, a similar recommendation appears in HTM 05-03 Part B.[28] The decision as to whether the early summoning of the fire and rescue service is critical to occupants' safety will often arise from a fire risk assessment.

The above recommendation is intended to apply to all categories of system, but is probably most relevant to Category L systems. Also, in

---

[28] HTM 05-03 Part B, *Alarm and detection systems*. Published by the Department of Health in England and Wales. (In Scotland, the relevant code of practice is SHTM 82 published by NHS Scotland.)

the case of Category L systems, the commentary of clause 15 points out that, if premises that are protected by a Category L system are unoccupied at certain times and the system incorporates automatic fire detection throughout a significant proportion of the premises, it can represent a missed opportunity, in respect of property protection, if no means for automatic transmission of alarm signals is provided. Certainly, under these circumstances, the cost of the facility in relation to the additional protection provided will often clearly point towards the value of the automatic transmission facility.

A further consideration, in respect of Category L systems, relates to commercial premises in multiple occupation (e.g. an office building occupied by various tenants, or a small retail park with a common internal service corridor). In some cases, there is no continuously manned reception or similar facility, occupied by someone who can be made responsible for summoning the fire and rescue service. The reliability of the arrangements for summoning the fire and rescue service might then be less than perfect. While any tenant should appreciate their responsibility to summon the fire and rescue service in the event of operation of the fire alarm system in their premises, it might not be immediately obvious to them that the alarm signal that is given throughout the building has arisen from an automatic fire detector in their premises. Moreover, if the alarm signal arises from operation of a detector in a tenant's premises that is, at the time, unoccupied, there may be no clearly defined responsibility amongst the other tenants for summoning the fire and rescue service.

While the uncertainties described above should be avoided as far as practicable, and the primary responsibility for summoning the fire and rescue service should still be that of persons on the premises, the reliability of this may be, at least, suspect. Accordingly, the code recommends that, in non-domestic premises in multiple occupation, Category L systems should incorporate an automatic means for transmission of alarm signals to an ARC, unless there are arrangements in place for summoning the fire and rescue service by occupants of the building at all times that the premises are occupied (or partly occupied).

Since the purpose of a Category P system is to protect property, one of the primary purposes of the system is to summon the fire and rescue service. Accordingly, the code recommends that, except in the case of continuously occupied premises, all Category P systems should incorporate a means for automatic transmission of fire signals to an ARC. It should be stressed, therefore, that failure of a Category P system to incorporate such a facility constitutes a non-compliance with the code (or, if agreed with all parties, a 'variation'), unless the premises are continuously occupied.

The commentary of clause 15 provides some information on the methods for automatic transmission of fire signals to an ARC. The code expresses a preference for systems in which the transmission path is continuously monitored, so that failures can be identified and the 'down time' is minimized. This implies a preference for systems such as 'carrier' systems (e.g. British Telecom RedCARE) over systems that use the public switched telephone network (e.g. digital communicators). However, since this preference is only expressed within the commentary, and there is not a corresponding recommendation, compliance with the code does not necessitate the use of monitored systems.

The code recommends that any ARC to which fire alarm signals are relayed should comply with the recommendations of BS 5979.[29] Schemes exist for third-party certification of ARCs to BS 5979. For example, BRE certification approve and list ARCs complying with their certification scheme, LPS 1020.[30]

One benefit of the above scheme is that the listing of ARCs indicates the areas of the country for which each ARC is approved to monitor fire alarm signals. This is an important aspect of the scheme, since approval in respect of any area of the country constitutes a verification that the ARC complies with the recommendations of BS 5979 in respect of duplicate means of communication between the ARC and the relevant fire and rescue authority control room. In the past, it has not been unknown for an ARC to monitor a fire alarm system in an area of the country for which there is no suitable means of communication between the ARC and the relevant fire and rescue service control room. This can result in serious delays in transmission of fire signals, while the ARC endeavours to use totally unacceptable methods of communication, such as informing another fire and rescue service with whom they do have communication, or endeavouring to contact the fire and rescue service by means of their normal administrative number (which may not be answered outside normal working hours).

In the above considerations, it has been assumed that the ARC in question is commercially operated. While this will normally be the case, other forms of ARC are possible. An example includes an in-house ARC, serving only the premises of the parent company. Also, some ambulance control rooms monitor fire alarm systems within their NHS Trust area.

---

[29] BS 5979, *Remote centres receiving signals from security systems – Code of practice.*

[30] LPS 1020, *Requirements for alarm receiving centres.*

A fire and rescue service control room, itself, could constitute an ARC, to which alarm signals are relayed. Although monitoring of fire alarm systems at fire and rescue service control rooms is now, sadly, very rare, it is not completely unknown; such an arrangement does, of course, have the advantage that it eliminates the 'middle man', ensuring that signals are transmitted to the fire and rescue service with the minimum of delay.

Normally, other than in the case of systems that use public or private cellular radio communication to transmit fire alarm signals to an ARC, the lines on which communication depends pass through a telephone switch room or frame room. In this case, the code recommends that, if the building is provided with a Category L or Category P system, the telephone switch room or frame room on which automatic transmission depends should be protected by an automatic fire detection system or an automatic fire extinguishing system.

Any connection between the fire alarm control and indicating equipment and the transmission equipment should be fire resisting. In practice, this is not possible in the case of telephone lines. Accordingly, the code recommends that any cables within the building (including telephone lines) on which communication depends should be routed through areas of low fire risk, or routed through areas protected by automatic fire detection or an automatic fire extinguishing system, or comprise cables of standard or enhanced fire resistance. While the last mentioned of these last three alternatives is, in any case, arguably necessary in the case of the cables between the control equipment and the transmission equipment, it is likely that one of the first two alternatives will be selected in the case of any relevant telephone lines that need to run through the building.

The code recommends that power supplies for any facility used for transmission of the fire alarm signals to an ARC should comply with the relevant recommendations of the code in respect of fire alarm power supplies (see Chapter 21). In practice, this will mean that batteries capable of operating the transmission equipment for, at least, 24 h in the event of mains power failure will need to be provided (except in the case of categories M and L systems in buildings with automatically started standby generators). However, in the case of Category P systems, a longer duration (up to 72 h) may be required unless the building is continuously occupied or there are facilities for transmission of fault signals, as well as fire signals, to the ARC.

The above recommendation has major significance in the case of installations in which the fire signal is transmitted to the ARC via a separate channel on transmission equipment provided for transmission of intruder alarm signals to an ARC. Normally, the standby battery capacity for such transmission equipment need only be sufficient to operate the equipment for eight hours in the event of mains failure. If a common power supply is used to operate the transmission equipment and the intruder alarm panel, the sharing of power supplies (both mains-derived and battery) would not strictly comply with the code, and a variation would need to be agreed. Moreover, in these circumstances, removal of the standby battery will not necessarily result in any fault indication, and, even if it did, the fault indication would not normally be given at the fire alarm control and indicating equipment, thereby constituting a further area of non-compliance (or agreed variation).

In practice, these matters are often addressed, in the case of intruder alarm transmission equipment with its own dedicated power supply, simply by increasing the size of the standby battery within the transmission equipment. Although this does not fully eliminate all the non-compliances cited above, it addresses the major issue of standby power supply duration. However, for full compliance with the code, it may be necessary to provide transmission equipment that is primarily dedicated to the fire alarm system and is powered by a monitored power supply unit complying with BS EN 54-4.[31] There would, of course, then be no real objection in using this transmission facility to transmit intruder (and other) alarm signals on separate channels of the transmitter unit, so that they are separately identifiable at the ARC.

---

[31] BS EN 54-4:1998, *Fire detection and fire alarm systems — Power supply equipment.*

14. Audible, visual and tactile fire alarm signals

This chapter of the guide discusses the contents of clauses 16–18 of the code. These are entitled 'Audible alarm signals', 'Visual alarm signals' and 'Fire alarm warnings for people with impaired hearing', respectively. These are clearly important clauses of the code, since they deal with the 'output' of the system and the means by which the system achieves its objective of giving people a warning in the event of fire.

The recommendations regarding audible alarm signals are primarily directed towards Category M and Category L systems, since the primary purpose of these systems is to give occupants an audible warning in the event of fire. In theory, the recommendations need not apply in the case of a Category P system, since its purpose is purely to ensure that fire-fighting action is taken, and this might not necessitate an audible warning to all occupants of the building. In practice, a Category P system is usually combined with a Category M system, in which case the recommendations for audible alarm signals applicable to a Category M system will take precedence and be more onerous. Strictly, nevertheless, the code only recommends that, in the case of a Category P system, the recommendations regarding audible alarm signals need only be applied in areas where such audible alarm signals are required.

The significance of this recommendation is probably most relevant in terms of certification of a Category P system. Consider, for example, a building in which a Category M system is provided to satisfy legislation. At some later time, a separate Category P system might be installed for property protection in, say, a critical electronic equipment room, such as a computer room. Often, in these circumstances, the Category P system would be interfaced with the general building Category M system, such that, when fire is detected by the Category P system, an alarm signal is given at the control equipment of the Category M system so that the fire and rescue service are summoned (perhaps automatically). Note that, in the circumstances described, no fire alarm sounders are connected directly to the Category P system. However, presumably, the designer could certificate the design as fully complying with the recommendations of BS 5839-1 for a Category P system, since the system is not required by the designer to provide directly any audible alarm signal.

The recommendations of the code in respect of the sound pressure level of audible alarm signals are summarized very well in a single diagram within the code, which is reproduced below.

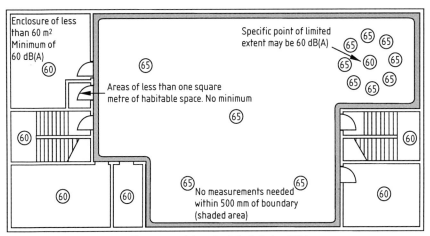

Figures are minimum levels in decibels - dB(A)

Figure 4 — Sound pressure levels

As shown in Figure 4, generally, the minimum acceptable sound pressure level is 65 dB(A). However, no specified minimum sound pressure level applies to enclosures of less than 1 m^2 and areas that are specifically designated as those from which the fire and rescue service will be summoned in the event of fire (see Chapter 13). Where the sound pressure level of background noise is greater than 60 dB(A), the sound pressure level of the fire alarm signal should be 5 dB above the sound pressure level of the background noise. Annex B of the code provides useful information on typical background noise levels in different types of building.

The minimum sound pressure level is, however, reduced to 60 dB(A) in three situations, namely:

1) stairways;
2) enclosures of no more than approximately 60 m² in area, e.g. cellular offices;
3) specific points of limited extent.

The rationale for the relaxation described above is, in the case of stairways, simply that, once occupants are already making their escape from the upper floors of a building via the stairways, there is no need for the fire alarm signal to be maintained at the same intrusive level. The relaxation for small enclosures is merely related to economy in design. To achieve 65 dB(A) in every cellular office within an office building often necessitates the installation of a fire alarm sounder in each office. The relaxation in the minimum sound pressure level makes the need for this less likely.

It might be considered that the relaxation for 'specific points of limited extent' is somewhat vague, particularly in a code that is now intended to be suitable for definitive audit. The purpose of this relaxation is to highlight the fact that, as the figure of 65 dB(A) is somewhat arbitrary and based only on the judgement of the technical committee, minor departures of as much as 5 dB within a limited area are not significant. The intention is to avoid requirements for additional fire alarm sounders merely because, at some point within a storey, the figure of 65 dB(A) is not quite achieved, provided the figure is generally achieved across most of the floor area. The message that the code is endeavouring to impart is that pragmatic common sense should be adopted, rather than rigid application of a rather arbitrary figure.

If the fire alarm signal is intended to rouse people from sleep, the code recommends a minimum sound pressure level of 75 dB(A) at the bedhead within the rooms in which people sleep. At first sight, the qualification that this recommendation only applies if the system is intended to rouse people from sleep may seem strange; in most premises, of course, it is essential that those sleeping in a building are woken by the fire alarm system in the event of fire. However, this is not true in the case of patients in hospitals. The code recommends that, for hospitals, audible alarms should comply with the recommendations of HTM 05-03 Part B.[32] HTM 05-03 Part B recommends that, in patient care areas, where patients require assistance to evacuate, the sound pressure level of fire alarm signals should fall within the range 45 dB(A) to 55 dB(A).

---

[28] HTM 05-03 Part B, *Alarm and detection systems.* Published by the Department of Health in England and Wales. (In Scotland, the relevant code of practice is SHTM 82 published by NHS Scotland.)

The lower figure is intended to ensure that staff are alerted in the event of fire, while the upper limit is intended to ensure that disruption to patients is minimized. In the case of operating theatres, HTM 05-03 Part B recommends that only visual alarm signals be provided.

Similar considerations apply to certain residential care premises. In some cases, it is expected that, in the event of operation of the fire alarm system, occupants of the premises should be capable of evacuating themselves. However, in some residential care premises, it is expected that occupants will require the assistance of staff to evacuate. In the latter case, it may be considered that the alarm signal is not intended to rouse some, or all, of the occupants from sleep. If this is the case, the recommendations of the code are such that the minimum sound pressure level within the occupants' bedrooms should be 65 dB(A), rather than 75 dB(A). However, the code recommends that any such relaxation should be subject to agreement by the authorities responsible for enforcing fire safety legislation in the premises.

The code gives considerable practical guidance regarding the measurement of sound pressure levels. In particular, the following points should be noted.

- A sound pressure level meter complying with BS EN 60651,[33] set to slow response and A weighting, is suitable for measuring the sound pressure level of the alarm signal. (Since publication of the code, BS EN 60651 has been replaced by BS EN 61672-1.[34])
- Measurements should be made with all doors shut.
- Background noise that is unlikely to persist for longer than 30 seconds may be ignored.
- It is not necessary for the sound pressure level to exceed the noise level created by running water in bathrooms and shower rooms by 5 dB; thus the installation of alarm sounders in bathrooms and shower rooms can normally be avoided.
- Other than in rooms in which people sleep, account need not be taken of sound pressure levels within 500 mm of any walls or partitions.

It is often impossible to stop all background noise in order to measure the sound pressure level of the fire alarm system in isolation. However,

---

[33] BS EN 60651:1994, *Specification for sound pressure meters.*

[34] BS EN 61672-1:2003, *Electroacoustics. Sound level meters. Specifications.*

if, say, the background noise level is 65 dB(A), the fire alarm system, when operated in the absence of background noise, should, in order to comply with the code, produce a minimum sound pressure level of 70 dB(A) throughout the area. The decibel scale is logarithmic. Accordingly, if two forms of noise that differ by 5 dB in sound pressure level occur simultaneously, the resulting sound pressure level is likely to be around 6 dB more than the lower of these sound pressure levels. The code advises, therefore, that the sound pressure level of the fire alarm signal can be deemed to be 5 dB greater than background noise if, when the background noise is present, a sound pressure level increase of 6 dB occurs on operation of the fire alarm system. Therefore, in the example in question, the system would be deemed to comply with the recommendations of the code if the reading on the meter increased from 65 dB(A) to 71 dB(A) when the fire alarm system was operated.

In premises in which the sound pressure level of music is likely to be greater than 80 dB(A) (e.g. nightclubs, similar entertainment premises and some boutiques or similar retail premises), the code recommends that the music should be muted automatically when the fire alarm system operates; in buildings with two-stage alarm systems, consideration should be given as to whether this should occur at the 'Alert' or 'Evacuate' stage. Of course, if the sound pressure level of the music is likely to be between 60 dB(A) and 80 dB(A), the music should be treated in the same way as any other background noise, and the sound pressure level of the fire alarm system should exceed the sound pressure level of the music by 5 dB.

In noisy industrial premises, it can be quite difficult to ensure that the sound pressure level from normal 24 V fire alarm sounders exceeds background noise by 5 dB throughout the plant. In this case, the code permits an arrangement whereby additional mains voltage sounders (without a standby supply) are provided to supplement the 24 V sounders, provided the mains supply to the supplementary sounders is derived from the same final circuit(s) as the noise-generating equipment. With this arrangement, although, in the event of mains failure, there is no standby supply for the supplementary sounders, equally, the supply to the noise-generating equipment will also have failed. The 24 V sounders would then produce a minimum sound pressure level of 65 dB(A) (or 5 dB above any remaining background noise). Such an arrangement could comprise a relay operated by the fire alarm system to switch a mains supply to the supplementary sounders, but, presumably, any wiring to this relay, external to the control and indicating equipment, would need to be monitored at the fire alarm control and indicating equipment.

If the ambient noise level exceeds 90 dB(A), the code recommends that visual alarm signals (e.g. flashing beacons) be used to supplement the audible alarm signals. This recommendation also applies in any areas where hearing protection is worn, and this may apply to areas in which background noise level is less than 90 dB(A). It should be noted that these visual alarm signals are purely supplementary to the audible alarm signals, which should still satisfy the recommendations of the code. However, the sound pressure level generated by the fire alarm sounders should not exceed 120 dB(A) at any normally accessible point in the building, so that they are unlikely to cause any damage to hearing.

The code recommends that all fire alarm sounders within a building should have similar sound characteristics, but recognizes that, in certain circumstances, such as an area of high background noise, this could be impracticable. A single, common sound for fire alarm signals is generally regarded as important by enforcing authorities, and, any relaxation for circumstances in which this is impracticable, is unlikely to be easily forthcoming. Nevertheless, on, for example, a large industrial site, it is not unknown for, say, alarm sounders within office buildings on site to comprise bells, whereas high-powered electronic sounders are used within noisy factory buildings on the site.

Whatever device is used to give fire alarm warnings, the warning sound should be distinctive from any other sounders used in the buildings (e.g. plant alarms, intruder alarms, etc.). In addition, fire alarm sounders should not be used for purposes other than warning of fire, unless the response required is identical to that required in the event of fire. However, it has long been custom and practice to use fire alarm signals in schools to indicate class change. The code accepts this arrangement, provided the class change signal does not exceed five seconds in duration.

It is unlikely that, in a situation other than fire, a response identical to that required in the event of fire (i.e. immediate evacuation by use of all escape routes) would be appropriate. In the event of a bomb warning, immediate evacuation of the building may not be appropriate, and it may be that, if evacuation is considered appropriate, only certain escape routes (i.e. those in which it is considered unlikely for an explosive device to exist) will be used. Similarly, in the event of a gas leak, it might be considered inappropriate to operate the fire alarm system in case operation of devices results in ignition of the gas. Thus, while use of the fire alarm system for emergencies other than fire is not precluded by the code, the restricted circumstances in which this is acceptable are likely to preclude such an arrangement in practice.

The code recommends that the frequency(ies) produced by fire alarm sounders should lie in the range of 500 Hz to 1,000 Hz. This recommendation takes into account the sensitivity of the human ear to sound and the fact that lower frequencies are less attenuated by construction than higher frequencies. However, the use of sounder frequencies outside this range is considered acceptable by the code if the frequency of background noise is such as to mask the frequencies in the recommended range. The effect of 'masking' is such that, where background noise is similar in frequency to the sound produced by the fire alarm system, the operation of the system has little impact on occupants, even if the sound pressure level of the fire alarm signal is 5 dB above background noise. Separation of the two frequencies by just one octave (e.g. use of fire alarm sounders that produce a frequency of around 2 kHz) is often sufficient to make the fire alarm signal clearly perceptible. Since the code deems that, in this situation, sounders producing a different frequency would be acceptable, it is probably unnecessary to treat this as a variation.

Many years ago, it was common practice to install at least one fire alarm sounder externally to the building. The purpose of this sounder was to attract attention to a fire when the premises were unoccupied, and to direct firefighters to the appropriate entrance at which the control and indicating equipment would be located. This arrangement used to be necessary to satisfy the requirements of fire insurers, and it was, therefore, recommended in BS 5839-1:1988 for type (now Category) P systems. However, many users regard an external sounder as undesirable, and, in any case, the public now tend to associate external alarms with intruder alarm systems. In the case of intruder alarm systems, the external sounder is often regarded by neighbours as something of a nuisance, and noise abatement considerations now require that the external sounder on an intruder alarm system should silence automatically after 20 minutes.

As a result of the above considerations, the provision of an external fire alarm sounder is no longer necessary for compliance with the code. However, the code acknowledges that, in large sites comprising many buildings in single ownership (and, therefore, with a single address to which the fire and rescue service respond) an external fire alarm device (which could be a sounder or, for example, a flashing beacon) can be of value in directing firefighters to the correct building. An external fire alarm device can also be useful in directing firefighters to the correct entrance of a large building with many entrances. Accordingly, the designer is not precluded by the code from providing these additional devices. However, in order to prevent the unnecessary installation of sounders and/or visual alarm devices, the code recommends that, where the designer considers their provision, there should be consultation with the fire and rescue service to confirm whether there is any need, or even benefit, from their provision. Thus, provision of the devices without consultation with the fire and rescue service would constitute a non-compliance with the code.

If, however, after due consultation with the fire and rescue service, external fire alarm devices are provided, the code recommends that they should be clearly marked with the words 'FIRE ALARM', so that they can be distinguished from intruder alarm devices. In addition, the code does specifically recommend that external fire alarm sounders in Category L and P systems (i.e. any systems including automatic fire detectors) should silence automatically after 30 minutes, unless the premises are continuously occupied so enabling manual silencing by occupants. This recommendation does not apply to a manual fire alarm system, since these systems are unlikely to result in false alarms (and a noise nuisance from external sounders) when premises are unoccupied. Once silenced, the external sounders may, or may not, restart if, before the system is reset, a further alarm condition occurs.

Sounders within the building should not, however, silence automatically, other than in two particular circumstances. The first of these is one in which a radio-linked Category L or P system incorporates battery-powered fire alarm sounders. In this case, if a false alarm occurs outside normal working hours, and no one attends to reset the system for a prolonged period, the batteries may become exhausted. On re-occupation, there then may not be a means of giving warning to occupants in the event of fire. Accordingly, in this case, the code recommends that, subject to the agreement of the relevant enforcing authority, the sounders should silence automatically after 30 minutes, unless the premises are continuously occupied so enabling manual silencing by occupants. These internal sounders should restart if, before the system is reset, a further alarm condition occurs. It is also accepted in the code that, if the fire strategy requires fire alarm sounders to operate for more than 30 minutes (e.g. because of phased evacuation), a period of longer than 30 minutes can apply before fire alarm sounders are automatically silenced.

The second situation in which automatic silencing may be used is one in which there is a two (or more) stage alarm system (see Chapter 15). In this case, the code does not specifically recommend automatic silencing, but permits the 'Alert' signal to be silenced automatically after a predetermined period, since this signal is, in any case, only a 'reminder' to people that a fire situation may exist. This arrangement is discussed further in Chapter 15.

Other than in the above special cases, once operated, the fire alarm system should continue to give an alarm signal until silenced manually. The use of the manual silence control should not cancel any visual signal at the control equipment. Operation of the silence control should not prevent the subsequent starting or restarting of alarm sounders by the manual control that will be provided for this purpose, nor should it prevent the transmission of an alarm signal to an alarm receiving centre. In the event of an alarm condition in a new 'zone', the appropriate fire alarm sounders should operate; normally this will include the fire alarm sounders that were operating prior to use of the silence control. The use of the term 'zone' within the code is rather imprecise, since the code recognizes 'detection zones' and 'alarm zones'. However, traditional design practice has dictated that, after silencing, alarm sounders should restart in the event of a new alarm signal within what is now described as a 'detection zone', as this would imply spread of fire that might need re-establishment of the evacuation signal. Accordingly, it would seem appropriate to interpret the 'zone', to which the code refers, as a 'detection zone'.

If, instead of fire alarm sounders, a voice alarm system is used, BS 5839-8[35] provides suitable recommendations for sound pressure levels, speech intelligibility and message content. Something halfway between normal fire alarm sounders and a full voice alarm system is a system that incorporates 'voice sounders'. These are, in effect, fire alarm sounders that produce a speech message, which is stored digitally within the individual sounders. Where these are used, they should comply with the recommendations of the code in respect of audible sounders, but the code also recommends that reference be made to Annex E of BS 5839-8:1988 as this provides further recommendations regarding the use of these devices.

The code does not provide a great deal of guidance on visual alarm signals. For example, the common-sense recommendation that the number and distribution of devices should be such that they are readily visible under normal ambient lighting levels, from all normally accessible locations throughout the area in which they are provided, does not provide any practical advice to the designer. There is, however, guidance on mounting height, namely that the visual alarm devices

---

[35] BS 5839-8, *Fire detection and alarm systems for buildings — Code of practice for the design, installation and servicing of voice alarm systems.* In 2008, BS 5839-8:1998 will be superseded by BS 5839-8:2008.

should be mounted at a minimum height of 2.1 m. Care needs to be taken that the devices provide sufficient output to attract attention, without causing glare, and that the visual signal is distinguishable from other visual signals used in the premises. (One means of compliance would be to label the visual alarm device with the word 'Fire'.) In connection with the latter point, it should be noted that amber flashing lights are often used in industry to indicate plant alarms or as warning signals on forklift trucks. The Code recommends that the visual signals should be white or red in colour, unless use of another colour is necessary to distinguish the signals from other visual signals in the premises.

The code recommends that visual alarm signals should flash at a rate of 30 to 130 flashes per minute. As flashing lights can, in the case of photosensitive epileptics, trigger epileptic attacks, the code provides a warning that consideration may need to be given to this potential problem. The April 2008 amendment gives further advice on this problem within a note in clause 17. In practice, photosensitive epileptic attacks are only normally triggered by flash rates exceeding 3 Hz (i.e. 180 flashes per minute). Accordingly, compliance with the code is most unlikely to result in such attacks, particularly if the colour red is avoided. However, in a large open area, it might be possible to view several beacons from a single location. If these visual alarm devices are unsynchronized, the effective flash rate might be high enough to trigger a photosensitive epilecptic attack; this can be avoided by synchronization of all devices.

Obviously, the fire safety strategy for any building, and the means for giving warning to persons in the event of fire, must cater for all persons who, at any time, may occupy the building. Happily, there is increasing recognition that this clearly must include those with disabilities. The increasing attention focused on measures to ensure the safety of disabled people in the event of fire has largely arisen as a result of the Disability Discrimination Act, which contains requirements to ensure that there is suitable access to buildings for disabled people.

There is a tendency to associate disability with mobility impairment, simply because wheelchair users are the group with the greatest difficulty in evacuation during a fire. Thus, for example, most of the contents of BS 5588-8[36] are concerned with ensuring the safety of mobility impaired people in the event of fire. However, severe impairment of hearing is also a disability that needs to be taken into account, and this is also recognized in BS 5588-8.

---

[36] BS 5588-8:1999, *Fire precautions in the design, construction and use of buildings — Code of practice for means of escape for disabled people.*

In practice, strategies for warning profoundly deaf people in the event of fire usually need to be 'tailor-made' for each building and any hearing impaired people within it. Both BS 5588-8 and BS 5839-1 stress that impairment of hearing does not mean that the person is completely insensitive to sound. Many people with severe impairment have sufficiently clear perception of some types of conventional audible fire alarm signals to require no special provisions to warn them of the fire. Where this is not the case, BS 5588-8 advises that, in most situations, there will be people about who can alert those with impaired hearing to the need for evacuation, and BS 5588-8 asserts that it will be reasonable to rely upon these others to provide the necessary warning. This is often described as a 'buddy scheme'.

A buddy scheme can work particularly well when a profoundly deaf person spends virtually all of their working time in close proximity to a 'buddy' (with suitable nominated alternative 'buddies') who remain mindful of the need to warn the deaf person when the fire alarm system operates. This arrangement is often sufficiently reliable by itself to secure the safety of deaf people from fire, particularly in situations such as a factory production line and certain other working situations, in which employees remain within a defined area of the premises for most of the working day.

In these circumstances, the 'buddy' arrangement can be supplemented, or perhaps even replaced, by visual alarm signals, provided these are treated as fire alarm devices and are, for example, connected on monitored circuits (usually fire alarm sounder circuits). In any case, there may be a need for visual alarm devices within sleeping accommodation and toilets. In England and Wales, Approved Document M[37] advises that Regulation M1 of the Building Regulations 2000, which requires that reasonable provisions be made for people to use buildings and their facilities, will be satisfied if there is, in non-domestic buildings, facilities that include visual warning of fire in bedrooms and sanitary facilities. (The equivalent guidance under building regulations in Northern Ireland makes a similar recommendation regarding guest bedrooms, wheelchair accessible changing facilities, and sanitary accommodation.)

There has been much confusion regarding the purpose of the visual warnings in bedrooms. There was common misconception that their purpose was to rouse deaf people from sleep. In fact, such an objective has been shown to need extremely high light output from the visual warning devices, to the extent that the flashing beacons would virtually

---

[37] Building Regulations 2000. *Approved Document M. Access to and use of buildings. 2004 Edition*. The Stationery Office.

cause disorientation. Moreover, the current required would present engineering difficulties (and hence significant cost, particularly in the case of loop-powered visual devices on addressable systems). Even then, research in North America has shown that visual alarms are not reliable in rousing deaf people from sleep. In fact, the visual warning devices that Approved Document M advocates be installed in bedrooms are only intended to give warning to deaf people who are alone and awake; it is not intended that they be used to rouse deaf people who are asleep. Even so, at the time of writing, no guidance is available as to the minimum light output required to achieve the objective intended by Approved Document M, and a pragmatic approach must be adopted. (Guidance is, at the time of writing, under preparation by the Loss Prevention Certification Board.)

Within BS 5588-8, it is pointed out that, in certain situations, alternative types of alarm signal may be necessary. One example of an alternative alarm device, given in BS 5588-8, is the vibrating pager. In BS 5588-8, the example of a situation in which such an alternative form of alarm warning might be necessary is a noisy area, where audible alarms may not be heard. In fact, this is not a particularly good example, as, except in the case of hearing impaired people who have a sensitivity to the sound of the fire alarm signal, the whole reason for an alternative fire alarm signal is the difficulty experienced in hearing the normal audible fire alarm signal, regardless of background noise!

In practice, the use of vibrating devices to warn deaf people in the event of fire is increasing, and proprietary systems, designed to meet, at least, the spirit of the 1988 version of BS 5839-1 have been available for some time. Thus, BS 5839-1 goes further than BS 5588-8, at least in the commentary to clause 18 'Fire alarm warnings for people with impaired hearing' by suggesting that, in circumstances such as buildings with a significant number of people with impaired hearing, buildings in which one or more persons with impaired hearing work in relative isolation, and buildings in which one or more persons with impaired hearing tend to move around the building to a significant extent, additional means of giving warning to people with impaired hearing might be appropriate.

It is recognized in the code that the additional means could include 'tactile devices', with or without associated visual alarm devices, particularly if people sleep in the building; in the latter case, the 'tactile devices' can comprise vibrating pads placed under pillows or mattresses, and either wired into monitored fire alarm device circuits or triggered by radio signals; if radio is used, the tactile device is simply analogous to a radio-linked fire alarm sounder. Performance requirements for vibrating devices that are intended to wake deaf people in dwellings are now given in BS 5446-3.[38] It must be reasonable to assume that the same performance requirements can be applied to vibrating devices in bedrooms within non-domestic premises, such as hotels, hostels and student halls of residence. Most of the recommendations of clause 18 are, however, directed towards 'portable alarm devices', such as radio pagers.

Radio operated vibrating pagers can provide a major benefit to deaf people, by giving them total freedom to use a building without the need for the presence of a 'buddy' at all times. The intent of the recommendations in the code for such 'portable alarm devices' is to provide reliability and integrity that is closely equivalent to, or at least based on the same principles as, the reliability and integrity of audible warning signals. Such equivalence can never be absolute. For example, if a deaf person leaves their pager behind when they move from one part of a building to another, there might be no alternative arrangements for warning them of fire. There may, therefore, be a need for some caution on relying totally on vibrating pagers.

Equally, in the experience of the author, most disabled people acknowledge that their safety from fire can never be quite equivalent to those without disability. For example, no matter how reliable the arrangements for evacuation of a wheelchair user, it would be difficult to claim that the wheelchair user was, at all times, exactly as safe from fire as an able-bodied person.

In the experience of the author, disabled people rightly expect merely that a robust arrangement exists that, as far as practicable, ensures a level of safety from fire that is based on the same principles that apply to able-bodied persons. There is often an acceptance that a marginal increase in risk (e.g. associated with scenarios for which it is difficult to cater, such as the mislaid radio pager) is more than balanced by the personal freedom that disabled people reasonably demand to enjoy the use of a building in a manner equivalent to those without disability.

Radio paging systems need to be licensed with OFCOM. Three different types of licence are available, and the security against interference is different for each licence. Accordingly, the code advises that advice should be sought from OFCOM regarding the compliance requirements for any tactile alarm system that uses radio signals.

A further 10 recommendations are analogous to those applicable to hard-wired audible fire alarm circuits. Thus, the code recommends

---

[38] BS 5446-3:2004, *Fire detection and fire alarm devices for dwellings — Specification for smoke alarm kits for deaf and hard of hearing people.*

that the alarm should be given at the portable alarm device within five seconds of the generation of the alarm signal at the fire detection and alarm control and indicating equipment, thereby minimizing any delay in the tactile warning signal. Once received at the device, the alarm signal that it emits should continue for at least 60 seconds or until it is acknowledged. However, the code recommends that the paging transmitter should continue transmitting the alarm signal, either continuously or at periods not exceeding 10 seconds, until the alarm is 'cancelled' by a signal from the fire alarm control equipment. This implies that the paging transmitter should 'latch' until a specific cancellation signal is received from the fire alarm control equipment. (This is similar to the arrangement that applies to separate voice alarm control equipment.) Notwithstanding this recommendation, Annex C appears to accept the provision of a control at the transmission equipment that would cause repeat transmissions to cease.

The implication of the recommendation for 'latching' is supported by a recommendation in Annex C (see below) that the control and transmission equipment for tactile alarm devices should be designed in accordance with the principles of BS EN 54-2.[39] The nature of the 'cancellation' is not further amplified in the recommendations of the code, but, presumably, the cancellation should occur when either the audible alarms are silenced or the fire alarm control and indicating equipment is reset. In any case, the effect of these recommendations is that, if the deaf person acknowledges the alarm signal, it will restart, as a result of a new signal from the transmitter, within a maximum of 10 seconds, and this process will continue to occur until manual action is taken at control equipment.

In much the same way as a voice alarm system can be used for broadcasting messages other than fire warnings, portable alarm devices for deaf people may be used for other purposes, including general paging, provided the fire signal is distinctive, by means of the cadence pattern, and has priority over any other alarm signal, unless, in rare cases, another alarm signal warrants higher priority than a fire warning signal.

There is no applicable product standards, with which the paging and similar equipment should conform. Accordingly, within clause 18 of the code, a number of product-type recommendations are included. Moreover, Annex C, which is normative, contains further recommendations for the

---

[39] BS EN 54-2:1998, *Fire detection and fire alarm systems — Control and indicating equipment.*

control and transmission equipment for tactile alarm devices. It should be stressed that the fact that Annex C is normative effectively makes it part of the code.

Recommendations for the portable alarm devices are such that they may be operated from a single power source, without any standby. However, low voltage of the power source (in practice, a battery) should be identified at the portable alarm device by a visual and tactile signal. If the portable alarm device is fitted with an off-switch, or a switch that disables the alarm signal, the design of the switch should be such as to avoid inadvertent operation.

As noted above, the control and transmission equipment should be designed in accordance with the principles of BS EN 54-2 (other than in respect of the colours used for visual indicators). Annex C specifies the particular recommendations of BS EN 54-2 that should be applied. Any fault conditions that Annex C necessitates be identified at the paging transmission equipment need to be relayed to the fire alarm control and indicating equipment, where they should be displayed as, at least, a simple common fault warning. For compliance with Annex C, the equipment should be marked to indicate compliances.

Finally, there is one very important recommendation that applies to the system design as a whole. This is that any failure in transmission between the paging transmitter and the portable alarm device should be identified at the portable alarm device by a visual and tactile signal within five minutes of the failure. In effect, this recommendation necessitates the transmission of a 'monitoring' signal to pagers every five minutes, so that users are warned within a very short time if the transmitter fails or the user is in an area in which there is inadequate radio signal strength. This recommendation is much more onerous than the recommendations that apply to radio-linked fire detectors or sounders, in which a fault indication (at the fire alarm control and indicating equipment) need only be given if radio transmissions are not received from any radio-linked device for two hours. One possible justification for this more demanding recommendation is the mobile nature of the paging devices, compared with the static locations of other radio-linked fire alarm devices.

15. Staged fire alarms

It has been asserted in various chapters of this guide that the design of a fire detection and fire alarm system should be based on a proposed fire evacuation strategy, rather than vice versa. Nowhere is this truer than in the case of a building that necessitates a staged fire alarm system. In complex buildings, a fire alarm system that was not designed to accommodate a fire evacuation strategy that is formulated at a later date may be quite difficult and expensive to modify. In particular, hard-wired sounder circuits might need to be completely reconfigured to accommodate the alarm zones (see Chapter 12) needed to facilitate the staged alarm arrangements that are ultimately required by the building user.

Moreover, in, for example, the case of phased evacuation of a tall building, normally a voice alarm system will be required to support the evacuation strategy. The strategy may also require additional facilities, such as fire telephones, so that fire wardens on each floor can advise those responsible for controlling the evacuation when their particular floors are cleared. (BS 5839-9[40] provides recommendations for the design, installation, commissioning and maintenance of these fire telephones.)

Clause 19 of BS 5839-1 is dedicated to the subject of staged fire alarms. Much of the benefit of this clause lies within the commentary, which provides an excellent discussion of the applications for staged fire alarm arrangements and the forms of staged alarm that are used. However, up to 11 specific recommendations are given, according to whether or not the staged alarm system incorporates a 'staff alarm' arrangement (see below).

---

[40] BS 5839-9:2003, *Fire detection and fire alarm systems for buildings — Code of practice for the design, installation, commissioning and maintenance of emergency voice communication systems.*

As noted in the commentary of clause 19, there are a number of circumstances in which a staged fire alarm arrangement may be appropriate. Those cited in the code comprise the following.

- Buildings with phased evacuation. These are normally high-rise or large buildings, in which those closest to the fire (such as those on the floor of fire origin and the floor immediately above) are evacuated in the 'first phase', with other areas evacuated in a series of further phases, which, in the case of a high-rise building, each traditionally comprise two complete floors of the building. In tall buildings, a phased evacuation arrangement can reduce the number and/or widths of stairways, as the entire population of the building will not need to evacuate at the same time. This is appealing to architects, as it increases the lettable floor space. In the event of false alarms, phased evacuation may avoid disruption of the entire building. It is generally accepted, however, that phased evacuation of tall buildings is suitable only for office buildings, as, in other types of building, a controlled and managed evacuation may be more difficult to achieve, and the rate of fire development may be such as to preclude prolonged delay in the evacuation of certain floors. However, phased evacuation is also sometimes used in other types of building in which staircase capacities are not reduced. Examples are leisure complexes, shopping centres and transportation termini. In these latter cases, usually the first stage of evacuation is horizontal, rather than vertical. Caution should be exercised in the use of phased evacuation in buildings, such as leisure complexes, where family groups might be separated; evacuation of some members of the family group, while others are expected to remain in occupation, could create serious difficulties.
- In hospitals, a system of 'progressive horizontal evacuation' is used. In this arrangement, the intention is never to need to move patients vertically down staircases, but simply to move them through one set of fire resisting doors into an adjacent 'sub-compartment'. In large hospitals, if fire continues to grow, patients may be moved into yet a further sub-compartment, without the need for evacuation to a lower floor.
- In buildings with a 'staff alarm'. A staff alarm is a restricted alarm, following the operation of a manual call point or automatic fire detector, given to certain staff in the premises to permit investigation prior to evacuation. There are two quite different reasons why a staff alarm may be used. The first, and more

common, reason is to avoid disruption by false alarms from automatic fire detectors. The staff alarm permits a time delay, during which staff can investigate, before any general evacuation signal is given or the fire and rescue service are summoned. In this example, it is usually only permissible for the staff alarm arrangement to apply to signals from automatic fire detectors; signals initiated by manual call points should, with very few exceptions, always result in an audible alarm signal in, at least, the alarm zone of origin. The second reason for a staff alarm arises mainly in premises used for public entertainment. In some such premises, particularly those designed to accommodate a substantial number of members of the public, the delay in warning occupants is to permit staff to take up appropriate positions to shepherd members of the public and control the evacuation, often by use of a voice alarm system. In this case, subject to certain safeguards, it is sometimes permissible to apply the staff alarm to signals initiated by manual call points.

- In a widely spread range of low-rise buildings, such as an industrial complex. In this case, the distance between one end of the long range of buildings and the other end is such that there might be no need to evacuate occupants in one area of the complex, even if a confirmed fire of limited size occurs some considerable distance from these occupants.

In all of the above examples, other than simple buildings with a staff alarm, there is a need to subdivide the building into 'alarm zones' (see Chapter 12). In the case of a building with a staff alarm, once it is determined that evacuation is necessary this might involve simultaneous evacuation of the entire building. In this case, there is a two-stage alarm, comprising, first, the staff alarm and, secondly, the evacuation signal. In more complex buildings, following the staff alarm stage, the building may still be evacuated in more than one phase. In the latter case, the fire alarm system will operate on a three-stage system, comprising the staff alarm, an 'Alert signal', and an 'Evacuation signal'. The code recommends that, where any form of staged alarm system is proposed, there should be early consultation with all relevant enforcing authorities. This is to ensure that an arrangement in which, in the event of a fire alarm signal, there is not immediate evacuation of all occupants, is acceptable under legislation.

As noted above, in multi-storey buildings with phased evacuation, it is permissible to reduce the capacity of stairways, such that it would not be entirely safe for simultaneous evacuation of all floors, as this would result in overcrowding in stairways. Thus, the code recommends that in this situation, there should be no single, master 'Evacuate' control that will cause an evacuation signal to be given throughout the building. However, a separate 'Evacuate' control should be provided for each individual alarm zone. If, on the other hand, staircase capacity is sufficient for simultaneous evacuation of all occupants, there is no hazard associated with the provision of a master 'Evacuate' control that initiates simultaneous evacuation of all areas.

The code recommends that the 'Alert' signal should be intermittent, with one second on and one second off. (A tolerance of ±0.5 seconds is permitted.) To avoid confusion with the 'Evacuate' signal, signals from different fire alarm devices should be synchronized, otherwise there is a danger that, at particular points in the building, the different 'on' periods of different sounders will result in an apparently continuous signal that demands immediate evacuation. The code recommends that facilities be provided for manually changing the 'Alert' signal to the 'Evacuate' signal. In some buildings, the change from 'Alert' to 'Evacuate' occurs automatically, and, while this is permitted by the code, it does not preclude the need for the provision of manual controls for this purpose.

Normal practice during the 'Alert' stage is for most normal activities to continue, but occupants should be prepared to evacuate when necessary; this preparation could result in certain normal activities being suspended. Once occupants have been informed of possible impending evacuation by means of the 'Alert' signal, there is no need for this signal to be repeated continuously. Indeed, to do so can be counterproductive to the intention that normal activities may continue in the interim period. Accordingly, the code permits the 'Alert' signal to cease automatically after 30 seconds, provided that, at periods not exceeding three minutes, the signal is restored for a period of at least 10 seconds until the incident is completed and the system is manually silenced. While such an arrangement is permitted by the code, and will prove attractive to many users, it is not a specific recommendation of the code that it be used; continuous sounding of the 'Alert' signal would, therefore, also comply with the code.

A staff alarm arrangement can be very useful for filtering out false alarms in buildings with a large number of automatic fire detectors (see Chapter 25). However, it is always important to ensure that arrangements to limit false alarms do not compromise fire safety. Thus, the code recommends that staff alarms should only be used where staff, including any night staff, are sufficient in number and fully trained in the action they are to take in the event of fire. Since operation of a manual call point needs to be regarded as a report of fire by whoever operates the call point, the code recommends that staff alarms should normally be generated only in response to signals from automatic fire detectors, but not in response to signals from manual call points.

It is, however, acknowledged that subject to special consideration and agreement by enforcing authorities, a high level of training, and a high level of awareness on the part of staff, a staff alarm might be used as the first response to a signal from a manual call point. As discussed above, this normally only arises in the case of large places of public entertainment and special cases, such as London Underground stations. As this arrangement runs contrary to the recommendation that, in the event of operation of a manual call point, the operator should hear the sounding of alarms within three seconds (see Chapter 16), the code recommends that, in special circumstances in which this arrangement is acceptable, the person operating the manual call point should not be left in doubt as to the success of the operation. Thus, normally, it is necessary to provide a visual indication at the call point that the signal has been correctly received at the control equipment, and a warning notice needs to be displayed that operation of the manual call point will not result in an immediate audible fire warning. Note that this visual indication should indicate the correct receipt of the signal at the control equipment; an LED that merely confirms the operation of a microswitch within the call point itself would not satisfy this recommendation.

A further safeguard incorporated within the code is that staff alarm signals should automatically change to audible fire warnings, in at least the relevant alarm zone, after a preset period, unless manual intervention to stop the associated timer occurs at the control equipment. In the past, unrealistically short times (e.g. 90 seconds) for this changeover have been demanded by enforcing authorities. In practice, this can actually be counterproductive to fire safety, as the time in question has often been long enough only for occupants to stop the timer immediately and then investigate at leisure. Accordingly, the code recommends that the period, which should be agreed with the relevant enforcing authorities, should be sufficient to enable staff to investigate the initial alarm signal. Even so, the code recommends that the period should not normally exceed six minutes.

Obviously, if, on investigation, staff determine that there is a fire, the audible fire alarm signal should be given without waiting for expiry of the pre set time delay. Thus, the code recommends that facilities be provided at the control and indicating equipment, and at additional locations as appropriate, to change the stage of alarm from the staff alarm stage to the 'Evacuate' stage. Since operation of a manual call point should not normally result only in a staff alarm, it should normally be possible for those responding to a staff alarm signal to change the stage of the alarm by operation of the nearest manual call point. If this is not possible, it might be reasonable to provide the additional facilities for this purpose at the additional locations throughout the building, to which there is reference in the code.

It is common practice to incorporate yet a further safeguard by use of 'coincidence operation'. In this arrangement, a staff alarm is changed automatically to an audible alarm if a second automatic fire detector operates. This arrangement, which is sometimes described (incorrectly) as 'double knock', is often required by enforcing authorities as a condition of incorporating a staff alarm stage. However, this safeguard is not specifically recommended by the code, although its common use is acknowledged and accepted in the code.

The code does not provide recommendations as to the means by which selected staff should be advised of the staff alarm stage. In practice, this would normally involve the use of radio pagers (but the code makes no recommendations regarding the engineering of these in this situation), or a coded voice alarm message. The code recommends that, if visual fire alarm devices are used to provide a restricted warning to staff, they should comply with the recommendations of clause 17 of the code for visual alarm signals.

16. Manual call points

Matters pertaining to manual call points are covered in clause 20 of the code. Two issues addressed in clause 20 relate to the requirements of European standards (published in the UK as British Standards), which are modified in certain respects by the recommendations of clause 20. The first of these relates to the type of call point used. BS EN 54-11[41] recognizes two different types of call points, described as type A and type B. As discussed in Chapter 10, the difference between the two types of call points concerns the number of actions required in order to operate the call point. In the case of type A manual call points, which are described in BS EN 54-11 as 'Direct operation' call points, the alarm condition is initiated automatically when the frangible element is broken or displaced, without the need for further manual action. They are, in effect, 'single action' manual call points, as opposed to type B manual call points, which require two actions to trigger the alarm system.

Although both types comply with the requirements of BS EN 54-11, the code recommends that only type A manual call points should be used in the UK. However, in areas where manual call points are likely to be subject to casual, malicious operation, the code suggests that it may be acceptable for a transparent, hinged cover to be fitted, subject to the agreement of the relevant enforcing authority. This, in effect, converts a type A manual call point into a type B manual call point, since two actions are required in order to trigger the alarm system. If this is acceptable to the relevant enforcing authorities in order to minimize a genuine potential for false alarms, this should be recorded on the design certificate as a variation. In practice, such a variation might not apply to all manual call points in the building; some enforcing authorities restrict the use of the hinged cover to areas in which its use is warranted by the potential for false alarms.

---

[41] BS EN 54-11:2001, *Fire detection and fire alarm systems — Manual call points.*

The second recommendation that affects the requirements of a European standard concerns the delay between operation of a manual call point and the sounding of the fire alarm signal. In the case of control and indicating equipment complying with the requirements of BS EN 54-2,[42] this delay can be as long as 10 seconds. However, the code recommends that the time delay in any installation should not exceed three seconds. In the case of many control panels complying with BS EN 54-2, this latter recommendation would, in any case, be satisfied, but this will not necessarily be the case and compliance may depend on, for example, the number of devices connected on a loop, rather than purely the design of the control equipment. The code acknowledges that delays of between 3 seconds and 10 seconds are possible if control equipment complying with BS EN 54-2 is used. However, a note in the code points out that this situation would constitute a variation from the recommendations of the code, which would, therefore, need approval by the relevant enforcing authority and the recording of the variation on the relevant certificate.

The basic principle of manual call point siting is that no one should be able to leave a building, or a storey of a building, without passing a manual call point. Thus, the code recommends that manual call points should be located on escape routes and, in particular, at all storey exits and all exits to open air. Note that, in the case of exits to open air, these may, or may not be designated as fire exits. The reason that the code recommends that manual call points be provided adjacent to exits that may not be designated as fire exits is that, in the event of fire, occupants will tend to use the nearest exit, which, in the case of, for example, a loading bay, may not actually be designated as a fire exit.

In the case of manual call points located at storey exits, the code offers a choice of siting. The manual call points may either be located on the staircase landings or within the accommodation, adjacent to the door to the stairway. In practice, it is now the custom for the latter option to be selected. The benefit of the former option is that, as someone fleeing from a fire passes down the staircase, they can operate a manual call point at any floor level. The downside to this is that an inaccurate indication may be given as to the storey on which the fire is located. Accordingly, in a multi-storey building with phased evacuation, the two options for manual call point siting are not given by the code; in this case, manual call points should not be located on stairway landings. Where horizontally adjacent areas may be evacuated separately in a

---

[42] BS EN 54-2:1998, *Fire detection and fire alarm systems — Control and indicating equipment.*

building with phased evacuation, the code recommends that additional manual call points are provided to ensure that one manual call point is located at every designated exit from an alarm zone; unless this recommendation is satisfied, the appropriate areas might not be evacuated in the first phase.

Having, conceptually, begun design of manual call point layout by siting manual call points at the exits described above, the code further recommends that a limit is imposed on the maximum distance that anyone should have to travel to reach the nearest manual call point. Generally, this figure is 45 m, but the figure is reduced to 25 m where processes in the area result in the likelihood of rapid fire development (e.g. as a result of the presence of highly flammable liquids or flammable gases) or where a significant proportion of occupants have limited mobility and it can reasonably be anticipated that one of these occupants will first operate the fire alarm system in the event of fire.

It is not anticipated that the shorter travel distance will apply to many premises. For example, the mere presence of a small number of wheelchair users in a building would not necessitate reduction of the travel distance to the nearest manual call point. The wording of the clause implies that reduction of travel distance to cater for mobility impaired occupants might only arise in the case of premises specifically provided for occupancy by mobility impaired people. Similarly, it would not seem reasonable to apply the shorter distance in the case of, for example, retail premises with high fire loads; the example given in the code of premises using, or processing, highly flammable liquids or flammable gases suggests that, again, in only a limited number of premises will there be a need to reduce the travel distance as a result of the fire hazard. The reduction could, of course, apply to restricted areas of a building, such as in the case of chemical laboratories within a building that is also put to other uses.

At the design stage of the system, it may be difficult to measure, on drawings, the maximum distance that anyone will have to travel to reach a manual call point. For example, the final fit-out or layout of partitions, equipment, etc. may not be known. In this case, the code recommends that sufficient manual call points be provided to ensure that the maximum straight line distance between any point in a storey and the nearest manual call point does not exceed 30 m (or 16 m in situations in which the maximum distance of travel to a manual call point is limited to 25 m). Ultimately, on completion of a system, however, it is the actual distance of travel to a manual call point, measured along the route that a person would follow that matters; at that stage, the straight line distance does not matter.

Once the above criteria are satisfied, for compliance with the code the designer will need to ensure that, where specific equipment or activities result in a high fire hazard, a manual call point is sited in close proximity. Examples of such areas given in the code are kitchens or cellulose paint spray areas. As it happens, in both these cases, further special requirements might apply to the manual call points. For example, the cellulose spraying area might require the use of equipment certified for use in potentially explosive atmospheres. Within kitchens, it is possible that call points with non-glass frangible elements are necessary, although, in practice, such call points are more usually limited to food processing factories and the like.

The code recommends that manual call points are fixed at the traditional height of 1.4 m above finished floor levels, at easily accessible, well-illuminated and conspicuous positions free from potential obstruction. Moreover, they should be sited against a contrasting background to assist in easy recognition.

Measurement of call point height should be made between finished floor level and the centre point of the frangible element. The figure of 1.4 m, although traditional, is purely arbitrary. Accordingly, a 'tolerance' of 200 mm in mounting height is permitted under the code without the need for it to be treated, or recorded, as a variation. Sometimes light switches are mounted at 1.2 m to make them more accessible for disabled people. The tolerance permitted by the code would permit the same arrangement for manual call points. Furthermore, in any case, the code states that a mounting height lower than 1.4 m is acceptable in circumstances where there is a high likelihood that the first person to raise an alarm of fire will be a wheelchair user. Again, the implication here relates to premises with a large number of wheelchair users, possibly in premises designed specifically for them. Since, in these circumstances, the code acknowledges that a lower manual call point mounting height is acceptable, it is presumably not necessary to treat the lower mounting height (regardless of whether it is even lower than the 200 mm tolerance already permitted) as a variation.

Manual call points may be flushed-mounted in locations where they will be seen readily. However, where they will be viewed from the side, they should be surface mounted or only semi-recessed, such that the front face is proud of the mounting surface (e.g. the wall of a corridor) by at least 15 mm.

In public car parks, there is often significant risk of malicious operation of manual call points. Accordingly, the code suggests that the use of an emergency voice communication system that permits speech communication with a permanently manned location (e.g. a security control room) could be used in lieu of manual call points. However, the code recommends that such an arrangement should be subject to approval by the relevant enforcing authority. If such a system is used, it should comply with the recommendations of BS 5839-9.[43] The code recommends that the 'outstations' provided within the public car park should be type B outstations, as defined in BS 5839-9. These take the form of an 'intercom', rather than, for example, a telephone.

---

[43] BS 5839-9:2003, *Fire detection and fire alarm systems for buildings — Code of practice for the design, installation, commissioning and maintenance of emergency voice communication systems.*

17. Which type of detector?

To the extent that the question that forms the title of this chapter is addressed by the code, guidance on the answer may be found in clause 21 of the code 'Types of fire detector and their selection'. Although this clause contains 10 specific recommendations, much of its value is contained within the commentary, which provides a short 'textbook' review of the various forms of fire detection and considerations in their selection. However, ultimately, selection of the correct detector for the application is a critical factor in the design of any automatic fire detection and alarm installation, and it is, therefore, very much a matter for decision by the designer.

Any fire detector is simply a sensor that responds to one or more of the characteristic phenomena of fire. These are:

- heat;
- smoke;
- combustion gases;
- radiation (flame).

Heat detection

Most heat detectors are of the 'point' type. Point detectors respond to the particular characteristic phenomenon that they are designed to detect, simply at a single point in space. Thus, a point-type heat detector relies principally on convection to transport hot gases from the fire to the detector. The relevant standard for point-type heat detectors is BS EN 54-5.[44] In this standard, detectors are classified according to their temperature of operation or, in the case of detectors intended for normal ambient temperatures, their sensitivity.

Fixed temperature heat detectors behave like thermostats, in that they are designed to respond at a specific temperature. In view of the thermal inertia of the device, in a growing fire the fire gases in the vicinity of the detector will significantly exceed this temperature. In a fixed temperature/rate of rise heat detector, the detector will respond if the temperature rises sufficiently rapidly, even though the notional fixed temperature of operation has not yet been reached.

It is possible to manufacture heat detectors that respond only when the rate of rise of temperature is sufficient, and there is then no 'long stop' temperature at which the detector will operate when the temperature is increasing at a very slow rate. While the latter detectors have been used on the continent, they have never been accepted in the United Kingdom, as they might fail to detect a slowly developing fire. These detectors would not now comply with BS EN 54-5, as this standard now contains a test to confirm the ability of a detector to respond correctly to a slow rate of rise of air temperature.

In a line heat detection system, rather than detecting the hot gases at a point in space, the detector is capable of sensing heat along a line in space. Therefore, most line heat detection systems comprise a heat sensitive cable. Either the cable insulation melts catastrophically at a specific temperature, or the impedance of the insulating material is temperature dependent. Line heat detection systems tend to be most suitable where the geometry of the protected area is long and narrow. Classic examples are cable tunnels and the areas below escalators, particularly in, for example, underground railway stations. In the case of underground railway stations, the line heat detection is installed to satisfy legislative requirements and operates an extinguishing system.

Heat detectors are relatively insensitive devices, compared with the most obvious alternative of smoke detectors. BS 5839-1:1988 suggested that, as a simple rule of thumb, flames will reach about one-third of the distance from the floor to the ceiling before heat detectors will operate. For this reason, they are often regarded as somewhat old-fashioned and suitable for use only in situations in which a smoke detector would be unsuitable (e.g. because of the potential for false alarms). This is not exactly the stance adopted by the code, which, instead, specifies

---

[44] BS EN 54-5:2001, *Fire detection and fire alarm systems — Heat detectors — Point detectors*.

merely four areas in which heat detectors should *not* be used. These are discussed below.

The first situation comprises areas of a Category P system in which a small fire has the potential to cause unacceptable damage. The obvious example of this would be a room containing critical electronic equipment, on which, for example, real time data processing or a production process might depend. In the latter situation, general use of heat detectors would also be precluded by the recommendations of BS 6266.[45] In these situations, extensive damage would occur to the equipment before a heat detector operated. Similar considerations might apply in, for example, a stately home that houses fine art that could be destroyed before operation of a heat detector and subsequent fire fighting action.

The second situation comprises escape routes within a Category L system. Again, it is essential that, in such a system, there is early warning of fire or smoke within escape routes. Heat detectors would be unsuitable for this purpose. However, the code accepts that heat detectors may be used in all other areas of any Category L system. The obvious example would be within rooms opening onto escape routes (e.g. bedrooms within sleeping risks, such as hotels and hostels) in a Category L3 system. Equally, the code does not preclude the use of heat detectors in any areas, other than escape routes, even in a Category L1 system.

More generally, the code recommends against the use of heat detection in areas in which the production of smoke could present a threat to occupants' escape before it is likely to be detected by people or heat detection. Again, however, a note within the code implies that this situation is not intended to relate to typically sized bedrooms, but that the recommendation against the use of heat detection could apply in the case of dormitory accommodation or rooms intended for mobility-impaired disabled people, who require additional time to escape from a fire in their bedroom.

Finally, as something of a truism, the code points out that heat detectors should not be used in areas in which they would have a high potential for false alarms. In practice, if the ambient temperature is sufficient to cause false alarms from heat detectors, heat detectors with a higher temperature of operation are used. Therefore, generally, if it is found that heat detectors are causing false alarms as a result of their environment, it is usually because heat detectors responding to rate of

---

[45] BS 6266:2002, *Code of practice for fire protection for electronic equipment installations.*

rise of temperature have been used in an area in which there is rapid fluctuation in temperature; an example would be commercial kitchens, in which the temperature above ovens can rise rapidly when oven doors are opened.

Smoke detection

The sensors in smoke detectors operate either on the ionization chamber principle or the principle of optical scattering. The ionization chamber smoke detector was the earliest form of common smoke detector. The sensor contains a radioactive source (Americium), which ionizes the air in the chamber. When smoke particles enter the chamber, they absorb the charged particles (positive ions and electrons), and the recombination into neutral air molecules results in a reduction in current.

Ionization chamber detectors are sensitive to the large number of very small particles produced in a clean burning fire. They are less sensitive to smoke that has 'aged', in which there is coagulation of particles, so that what began as a large number of small particles becomes a smaller number of larger particles. Ionization chamber detectors are also less sensitive than optical detectors to the products of smouldering plastics (e.g. polyurethane foam), which produce smoke having mainly larger particles.

Most point-type optical smoke detectors operate on the principle of optical scattering. The principle of detection is similar to that in which, when smoking was permitted in cinemas, a projector beam could be seen very clearly from all parts of the cinema, even though light travels in straight lines; the beam was visible because of the light scattered in all directions by the particulate matter within the tobacco smoke in the atmosphere. The same effect can be observed when driving through smoke or fog with headlamps on main beam; light is scattered back towards the eyes of the driver.

In the optical smoke detector, usually a pulsed LED transmits bursts of light, which, as a result of the chamber geometry, do not reach the photosensitive receiver until smoke enters the chamber. It is, however, possible to design a point-type optical detector that operates on the principle of obscuration, whereby the effect of smoke is to reduce the intensity of light received at the receiver.

Optical smoke detectors are not sensitive to the largely invisible particles produced by a clean burning fire, but are more sensitive to the larger particles produced by smouldering fires and smoke that has 'aged', as described above. Dark smoke, on the other hand, by definition, absorbs light rather than scatters it, and optical smoke detectors that operate on the principle of light scatter may be less sensitive to such smoke.

In practice, the code considers that both optical and ionization chamber smoke detectors complying with the BS EN 54-7[46] have a sufficiently wide range of response to be suitable for most applications in which a smoke detector is appropriate. However, in some situations, an understanding of the principle of operation of the detector may suggest that one type is more appropriate than the other. The rationale may be earlier detection of fire or avoidance of false alarms. Considerations in respect of the false alarm potential of different types of detector are discussed in Chapter 25 of this guide and in Section 3 of the code.

A number of specific recommendations contained within clause 21 of the code do, however, emanate directly from the principles of smoke detector operation described above. First, consider the escape routes. The main hazard to occupants in the early stages of a fire is the presence of smoke on escape routes. The resulting reduction in visibility can prevent occupants from using the escape routes (even though, at these early stages, it might actually be safe to do so).

Generally, however, escape routes are relatively sterile areas, in which a rapid burning, flaming fire is not expected. Smoke on the escape routes has probably travelled some distance from its source. Accordingly, the code recommends that, in Category L systems, smoke detectors installed within corridors and stairways that form part of the means of escape should be of the optical type, unless the use of optical detectors would significantly increase the rate of false alarms. The code does not attach the same criticality to the choice of detector type in the case of a Category P system, but the same principles may reasonably be applied.

The second practical consideration emanating from the above considerations is that, where early detection of a smouldering fire is required, the code recommends that optical smoke detectors, optical beam detectors (see below), carbon monoxide fire detectors or suitable multi-sensor fire detectors be used. Some of these types of detector are discussed later in this chapter, but the point to note at this stage is that the list of detectors deemed suitable by the code does not include ionization chamber smoke detectors. On the other hand, where detection

---

[46] BS EN 54-7: 2001, *Fire detection and fire alarm systems — Smoke detectors — Point detectors using scattered light, transmitted light or ionization.*

of a relatively fast and clean burning, flaming fire is required, the code omits optical smoke detectors from the list of suitable detectors.

Optical beam smoke detectors are a form of line-type detection. They comprise a light source and receiver, either separated or housed within a single unit. If the two are housed in the same unit, passive reflectors are used to reflect light from the transmitter back to the associated receiver. Optical beam detectors operate by detecting the obscuration of the light source that occurs in the presence of smoke. Some optical beam detectors can also detect heat by means of the variation in the refractive index of light that occurs at turbulent interfaces between hot and cold air. This 'shimmer' effect can be observed by looking across the bonnet of a car when the engine is very hot.

Optical beam smoke detectors can be very economical for the protection of large, open plan spaces. For example, consider a warehouse that is 100 m × 30 m. Using the normal siting recommendations of the code (see Chapter 18), the warehouse could be protected by two optical beam smoke detectors, with transmitters and receivers mounted at either end of the warehouse. Typically, around 30 point-type smoke detectors would be required to protect the same area. The optical beam detectors would be cheaper to install and easier to maintain. However, it is necessary to ensure that they are mounted on solid construction that does not 'flex' with changes in temperature, wind, or snow load, as this will cause misalignment of the beam and either fault signals or false alarms.

The code also discusses two special forms of smoke detection, namely the aspirating smoke detection system and video smoke detection. In an aspirating smoke detection system, air samples are drawn through sampling points within the protected area to a central detector, which is usually of very high sensitivity. These systems are commonly used for protection of critical electronic equipment rooms, and their use is, therefore, also discussed in BS 6266.

The technology of video smoke detection is still somewhat in its infancy. It involves the use of closed circuit television cameras to monitor a protected space. Detection is therefore based on obscuration of the camera's field of view, but sophisticated analysis enables discrimination between, for example, persons moving around the protected space, steam and other causes of obscuration of the field of view. There may be applications for this form of detection in, for example, high spaces in which detection installed at ceiling or roof level could be slow to operate and be capable of detecting only a large fire. However, clearly, the field of view of the cameras needs to be illuminated (whether by visible or infrared light).

Equally, it is likely to be essential that the system is capable of operating in the absence of normal lighting. Accordingly, the code recommends that video smoke detection systems should be capable of detecting smoke reliably in the absence of the normal lighting in the building. If any special lighting is provided to enable the system to operate, it effectively forms part of the fire detection arrangements. Accordingly, in this case, the code recommends that the system should be capable of operating correctly in the absence of a mains power supply to such lighting; thus a standby supply would be necessary.

As discussed earlier in this chapter, many people now regard smoke detectors as the 'default' form of detection, for which other forms of detection are substituted only when circumstances dictate. Certainly, the code accepts that, like heat detectors, it is necessary only to define those areas in which smoke detectors cannot be used. The only such areas that are defined in the code are those in which the principal fire hazard is the presence of flammable liquids or gases that produce little smoke when involved in a fire and areas in which smoke detectors would have a high potential for false alarms.

Even in the first of the above cases, the code notes that the presence of clean burning flammable liquids and gases does not necessarily preclude the use of smoke detection if the fire is likely to involve normal carbonaceous materials, such as wood, paper, textiles, etc. in its early stages. Moreover, it is not acceptable, under the code, to 'write off' smoke detection purely on the basis of its high potential for false alarms. The code acknowledges that, if the risk from fire warrants the provision of automatic fire detection, and other forms of fire detection will not respond to the fires that can be anticipated quickly enough, smoke detection might still be necessary, but false alarms might be minimized by the correct choice of smoke detector (see above), the use of multi-sensor detection that incorporates smoke sensors (see below), or by filtering techniques, such as the use of a staff alarm (see Chapter 25).

Combustion gas detectors

Although the code recognizes, and discusses, combustion gas detectors, in practice the recommendations made within the code relate to carbon monoxide fire detectors. It should, however, be noted that detectors that respond to other combustion gases, or at least incorporate a sensor that responds to another combustion gas, are likely to become available during the lifetime of the code.

Carbon monoxide is produced when incomplete combustion occurs as a result of restriction of the amount of oxygen available to support the combustion process. Where there is sufficient oxygen, a flaming fire would tend to produce carbon dioxide. Accordingly, carbon monoxide detectors will be most sensitive to smouldering fires and fires in which the rate of burning is controlled by the supply of air. The corollary is that, in a large space with a plentiful supply of oxygen, less carbon monoxide will be produced and that which is produced will become diluted. The future for the carbon monoxide sensor may well, therefore, be as a component of a multi-sensor system (see below), in which, for example, other sensors incorporated within each detector are sensitive to heat and/or smoke.

With regard to carbon monoxide fire detectors themselves, rather than the code defining those areas in which they cannot be used (which is the way the code treats smoke detectors and heat detectors), the code defines the areas in which they *are* acceptable. However, these include any area in which the use of a heat detector would be acceptable, other than areas in which the principal fire hazard comprises flammable liquids that, when ignited, result in a rapid, flaming fire; the assumption is that, generally, a carbon monoxide fire detector will be at least as good as a heat detector.

The code also accepts the use of carbon monoxide fire detectors in rooms opening onto escape routes in a Category L3 system. This is possibly the classic application for carbon monoxide fire detectors. As noted in the code, their use in bedrooms, for example, will provide a higher standard of protection for sleeping occupants than heat detectors, but potential for false alarms (e.g. from steam and tobacco smoke) will be less than in the case of smoke detectors. Since carbon monoxide diffuses readily to fill a space with an even concentration, it may well be the case that, in certain smouldering fires, carbon monoxide fire detectors will operate even earlier than a smoke detector.

The code also accepts carbon monoxide detectors for use in escape routes within Category L3 or L4 systems, but only if they are used in conjunction with smoke detectors. Even then, the code recommends that, in this case, specialist application guidance should be sought from the manufacturer. Some manufacturers would certainly claim that, because of the ability of carbon monoxide to diffuse readily throughout an area of a building, it is possible for a carbon monoxide fire detector in a corridor to detect a fire in a room adjoining the corridor before it is detected by a smoke detector in the corridor.

More generally, the code accepts carbon monoxide fire detectors for any area in which the fire hazard is of such a nature that there is test evidence to demonstrate that the carbon monoxide detectors proposed would offer adequate fire protection. In this respect, the designer would need to take into account the type of fire that could be expected and the amount of ventilation available. There would be a need for good liaison with the manufacturer of the detector to ensure that available test evidence could support the application proposed.

The code also notes, within the commentary to clause 21, that the ability of carbon monoxide to spread by diffusion through certain forms of construction means that, in the event of fire, these detectors could operate at a considerable distance from the fire. Indeed, they could operate on floors other than the floor of fire origin. This could result in misleading information regarding the location of the fire, and manufacturers' guidance should normally warn users that this might occur.

As noted in Chapter 10, there is, at the time of writing, no British or European standard for carbon monoxide fire detectors, although such standards will be produced in the future and a standard for multi-sensor carbon monoxide and heat detection exists. While use of all fire detection products that are certificated or approved by a recognized certification body is always desirable, but not essential for compliance with the code, users might well be advised to express a preference for, or even a restriction to, independently approved carbon monoxide fire detectors, such as those approved in the UK by BRE Certification.

Flame detectors

Flame detectors tend to be used only for special applications. The classic application is for detection of fires involving flammable liquids. However, infrared flame detectors are sometimes used in very high buildings, such as cathedrals, where, in the stages of a fire at which detection is desirable, smoke may not reach detectors mounted on the ceiling or roof. Indeed, the height of the ceiling might exceed the limits specified in the code for, at least, point-type detectors. However, ultraviolet flame detection is not suitable in these circumstances, as ultraviolet radiation is significantly attenuated by smoke.

More generally, the code recommends that flame detectors should only be used in situations in which it is sufficient for the system to respond to flaming fires, but not fires that produce smoke without significant flame. If flame detection is to be effective, it should, of course, have a clear line of sight to the area being protected.

Multi-sensor fire detectors

These detectors contain more than one form of sensor, so that they are able to monitor more than one of the characteristic phenomena of fire. The purpose may simply be to provide a more sensitive form of fire detection. For example, optical smoke detectors and carbon monoxide fire detectors have difficulty in responding to a very clean burning, free flaming fire. The addition of a heat sensor to the detectors can provide a more effective form of detection, and, for example, an increasing signal from a heat sensor may be used to increase the sensitivity of the optical smoke sensor; this level of sensitivity might exceed that at which it would be desirable for the optical sensor to be maintained at all times, since this might result in too many false alarms.

The use of multi-sensor technology might, instead or in addition, be intended to filter out false alarms. In such cases, systems tend to use proprietary software to analyse the signals from each sensor to determine whether the overall 'picture' presented is representative of a fire or merely an environmental phenomenon that affects one of the sensors. Rarely, if ever, will the analysis be as simple as an 'and gate', since this would simply result in the detector having the sensitivity of the least sensitive sensor within it.

Most multi-sensor systems include a smoke sensor within each detector. For example, one proprietary system incorporates an ionization chamber smoke sensor, an optical smoke sensor and a heat sensor in each detector. Another incorporates an optical smoke sensor and a heat sensor, while yet another incorporates an optical smoke sensor, a carbon monoxide sensor and a heat sensor. It is not, however, necessarily the case that a multi-sensor detector will incorporate a smoke sensor; the use of, for example, a detector incorporating a carbon monoxide sensor and a heat sensor has already been discussed.

There appears to be an assumption in the code that any multi-sensor detector will perform at least as well as a heat detector. For example, multi-sensor detectors are accepted without qualification for installation in rooms opening onto escape routes in Category L3 systems. In practice, this assumption will normally be valid, although, strictly, this need not, theoretically, be the case. For early detection of smouldering fires or clean burning flaming fires, the code recommends that, in either case, a suitable multi-sensor detector could be used. Determination of the suitability of a multi-sensor detector will, in either case, necessitate a good understanding of the manner in which the detector operates or, possibly, liaison with the manufacturer.

Perhaps one area of ambiguity within the code's recommendations in respect of multi-sensor detectors concerns detectors used within escape routes. In categories L1–L4 systems, the code recommends that the detectors used within escape routes should comprise smoke detectors, or a mixture of smoke and combustion gas detectors; there is no explicit mention of multi-sensor detectors. The reason for this is, possibly, simply that, as discussed above, it is not necessarily the case that a multi-sensor detector will contain a smoke sensor, or perform in the same manner as a smoke detector. A carte blanche acceptance of just any multi-sensor detector for use in escape routes would, therefore, be inappropriate.

However, it would seem quite reasonable that, if a multi-sensor detector can meet all the requirements of BS EN 54-7, including the relevant fire tests, it can be treated as a smoke detector and used, without restriction, in escape routes. A minor note of caution may, nevertheless, be necessary, as the code recommends that, for reasons described above, smoke detectors within escape routes should be of the optical type. If a multi-sensor detector is used, care would be warranted to ensure that the detector was capable of responding well to smouldering fires and 'aged' smoke.

Which detector?

This is the question with which we began this chapter, but it should be obvious from the consideration of the various types of detector that, in many circumstances, there is no right or wrong answer to the question. The code advises that final choice will depend primarily on:

- the speed of response required;
- the need to minimize false alarms;
- the nature of the fire hazard.

Other factors to consider include:

- the nature and quantity of the combustible materials present, including ease of ignition, heat release rate, likely form of combustion (e.g. smouldering or flaming) and propensity for smoke production;
- probable rate of fire growth and spread;

- the nature of the environment (e.g. humidity, temperature, cleanliness, extent of pollutants and nature of work processes);
- the proposed fire evacuation strategy;
- the height and geometry of the protected area;
- the attendance time of the fire and rescue service (particularly in the case of Category P systems);
- other active and passive fire protection measures present;
- the susceptibility of contents to heat, smoke and water;
- the speed of response to fire, and the probable false alarm rates, of different types of fire detector.

As in the case of all fire protection measures, the overriding consideration is the fire protection objective. If one expects a building owner or occupier to spend money on fire protection, whether in the form of fire detection or a fire resisting wall, it should surely be possible for whoever advocates the specific form of fire protection to articulate, quite clearly, the objective of the measure. In this sense, before we address the question of which form, or forms, of detection should be used, we should ask whether automatic fire detection is required at all. For example, if the objective is merely to satisfy minimum legislative requirements for an ordinary commercial property in which no one sleeps, a Category M system, without any form of automatic fire detection, will normally suffice.

However, let us assume that, for some reason that we can articulate, automatic fire detection is necessary. The objective of this detection, in conjunction with other matters listed above, will normally lead to identification of the appropriate forms of detection.

For example, suppose we consider an art gallery, housing valuable paintings. A fire risk assessment might determine that the level of security, absence of ignition sources and limitation of combustible materials in the areas housing the works of art might be such as to make automatic fire detection unnecessary in these areas. The risk to the paintings may arise from the potential for fire in ancillary areas, such as offices and workshops. This might suggest the need for a Category P2 system, with detection only in these areas.

However, what form of detection would be appropriate? If the protected areas are separated from the works of art by fire resisting construction, the fire and rescue service attendance time is short and, perhaps, there is a 24-hour security presence, heat detection might be perfectly acceptable. Surely, however, smoke detection would be better because of its even earlier response? Many would say that this is the case. Nevertheless, while smoke detection may offer earlier response and is certainly *sufficient* to meet the fire safety objective, is it *necessary*? Smoke detection will have greater potential for false alarms, and the life cycle maintenance cost will be higher. (The code does, in fact, suggest that maintenance costs are a valid factor to consider in selection of the type of detection. For example, one consideration in the use of carbon monoxide detectors is that the electrochemical cells within the detectors have a finite life, after which replacement is necessary.)

Now assume that there is no significant fire resisting construction between the fire hazards and the works of art, and/or assume that the fire and rescue service attendance time is likely to be long. The provision of smoke detection throughout the areas protected in this P2 system would probably be justifiable. If there is potential for false alarms as a result of certain processes, or simply because of the number of detectors necessary, and the management regard these as a serious form of disruption, consideration might be given to a suitable multi-sensor detection system.

What then if there are sources of ignition, including the potential for arson, within the areas housing the works of art? Smoke detection in these areas might be necessary. The detection in the ancillary areas could then be heat or smoke detection, according to the rationale described above.

Now assume that there is concern that a fire in unoccupied parts of the ancillary accommodation could present a threat to occupants of the galleries, but that a fire in the galleries themselves would be detected at an early stage by occupants. This might warrant the installation of a Category M/L5 system, with fire detection throughout the ancillary areas as described above, but this time to protect life instead of, or as well as, property. According to the nature of the fire separating construction, heat or smoke detection within the ancillary areas would be appropriate.

However, if there were concern regarding occupants of the ancillary areas themselves, the detectors within the escape routes in the ancillary accommodation (corridors and staircases) would need to be smoke detectors (or suitable multi-sensor detectors or, possibly, a mixture of smoke detectors and carbon monoxide fire detectors). Note that, if smoke detection had already been used for the purpose of property protection, all the smoke detectors could have been of the ionization chamber type; for protection of life, smoke detectors within the escape routes would need to be of the optical type.

Now imagine that a caretaker and family sleep within the premises. There may be a need for relatively comprehensive fire detection to ensure that the family are given an adequate warning before fire threatens their escape route(s). On the escape routes themselves, there will be a need for smoke detection. Elsewhere, heat detection would probably be sufficient. However, in sleeping risks, such as hotels, it can normally be assumed that the construction that encloses escape routes is fire resisting. What if some of the construction that opens onto the family's escape route is of dubious fire resistance? It could, of course, be upgraded. Alternatively, in the areas adjacent to the escape route, it might, instead, be acceptable to upgrade the heat detection to smoke detection, so that the family were guaranteed a warning well before the construction of dubious fire resistance were threatened by fire.

It should be noted that, in the above scenarios, the automatic fire detection and the passive (structural) fire protection measures formed an integrated system, designed to achieve a specific objective. Thus, the design of the fire detection system and choice of detector type should not be considered in total isolation of consideration of other fire protection measures.

This principle may apply on a very localized basis. An example of this is given in the code. The example considers a transformer chamber in a dirty environment. If detection were installed within the transformer chamber to address the hazard that the transformer creates to adjacent areas, from which it were separated by substantial fire resisting construction, heat detection within the transformer chamber might be appropriate. The most likely fire scenario is one involving the flammable oil, which would be detected quite quickly and well before the integrity of the fire resisting construction was threatened. In the discussion contained in the code, it is pointed out that earlier warning could be given by smoke detection, but the increased potential for false alarms and increased maintenance burden might not be warranted. If, alternatively, the reason for the protection were to protect the transformer, on which a high revenue earning process depended, from a fire in cables within the enclosure, the code points out that smoke detection might then be necessary.

The message that the code is trying to impart is that one should not think 'in a box' when considering the design of an automatic fire detection system, nor should the provision of a system be a knee-jerk reaction to a specific situation. This message is in keeping with the modern concept of fire risk assessment, in which an integrated package of 'risk appropriate' measures is formulated to achieve a specified objective, which may be related to protection of life, protection of property, protection of business against interruption or any permutation of these three.

It is, therefore, important for the designer to understand the objectives of the system before design begins. While this is the moral of a consideration of selection of detectors, it is also merely a more detailed reiteration of the message contained in Chapter 7.

18. Spacing and siting of automatic fire detectors

Spacing and siting of automatic fire detectors is covered in clause 22 of the code. The detailed figures for spacing, etc. are not reproduced in this chapter of the guide, and reference should be made to the code for this information. The purpose of this chapter is to discuss the principles on which the detailed information in clause 22 of the code is based. Much of this information is also discussed within the commentary of clause 22.

The fundamental principles on which the recommendations of clause 22 are based comprise the following.

- Smoke and hot gases from a fire rise in a relatively narrow, conical plume as a result of convection. Heat and smoke detectors rely upon this convection to transport the products of combustion to the detectors. Ultimately, the smoke and hot gases will reach the highest point in the space, which is, therefore, where detectors should be located.
- As the plume rises it entrains cool, clean air. This results in a lowering of the temperature of the gases and dilution of the smoke. When the plume reaches ambient temperature, it will cease to rise. Visually, the effect is as if the rising plume has hit an invisible ceiling, under which the smoke and hot gases then spread out horizontally, failing to reach detectors at a higher level. Sometimes designers have attempted to predict where this 'stratification' will occur, and have then sited detectors at this level. In practice, this is unlikely to be successful, as the level at which stratification occurs will depend on the heat output of the fire and the temperature profile within the protected space, neither of which can be predicted accurately. Because the angle of the rising plume is relatively small, there is then the danger that

the plume will bypass these lower level detectors. Ultimately, as the fire grows, the heat output will increase and the smoke and hot gases will reach ceiling mounted detectors, albeit after a delay.

- It is a simple law of physics that the higher the ceiling, the larger will be the fire at its point of detection by heat or smoke detectors. There must, therefore, be some limit of height, beyond which heat or smoke detectors should not be used, as the fire at the point of detection will be so large that the detectors can hardly be described as giving 'protection'.

- As the hot gases and smoke flow horizontally across the ceiling, there is a stagnant boundary layer at the surface of the ceiling. Thus, the sensitive elements of heat and smoke detectors need to protrude into the moving gas layer.

- At the junction of a wall and ceiling, there is a 'dead space', in which heat and smoke detectors will not be properly exposed to the products of combustion. Thus, detectors should not be sited within the corners of rooms, as is often requested in, for example, historic buildings, in which there is a desire to make detectors as unobtrusive as possible.

- The streamlines of horizontally moving hot gases do not accurately follow the shape of large obstructions; they take a gentle curve around the obstruction, so, again, creating a 'dead space' within the 'shadow' of the obstruction. Thus, for example, detectors should not be sited close to deep structural beams, etc.

- Voids above false ceilings and below false floors create two hazards. First, they are routes for hidden fire travel, albeit that unbroken lengths of ceiling void are normally limited in horizontal extent by cavity barriers. In addition, the voids may contain sources of ignition and, certainly, combustible materials, thereby creating an unprotected area if detectors are not located within the voids.

- Vertical enclosed shafts, such as lift shafts, are also routes for fire spread between floors. It is, therefore, desirable that products of combustion are detected before they enter the shaft and as they leave the shaft. In the case of a lift shaft, there is the possibility of a fire within the shaft itself, often ignited by oil and debris at the bottom of the lift shaft.

Numerous, highly detailed recommendations follow from the above considerations. The areas in which detectors should be sited will be defined by the category of system, which, in turn, should be such as to meet a specified fire safety objective. Having decided the areas that are to be protected, other than in Category L4, L5 and P2 systems, a fire detector should be sited at the top of any shaft or enclosure that penetrates through ceilings. In addition, on each floor, a detector should be sited within approximately 1.5 m of the penetration. Even in the case of Category L5 and P2 systems, the code suggests that the need for detectors in these positions should be considered at the design stage.

The word *approximately* in relation to the figure of 1.5 m should be noted. Often, in large buildings, there is a bank of lifts, each in their own shaft. It might be regarded as unreasonable to provide a row of smoke detectors parallel to the lift doors on each floor level, simply to meet exactly the 1.5 m distance from every shaft. An economic design might involve the use of one detector to protect the penetration created by more than one shaft, provided this detector is *approximately* 1.5 m from each shaft.

The above recommendation also applies to open stairways that penetrate floors. It does not, however, apply to enclosed stairways. However, in enclosed stairways, fire detectors should be sited at the top of the stairway and on each main landing, regardless of the category of system provided.

Traditionally, previous versions of the code have recommended that voids that are greater than 800 mm in depth be protected, but those less than 800 mm in depth need not be protected. Interestingly enough, the same recommendation is made in BS EN 12845[47] in relation to sprinkler protection of concealed spaces. However, BS EN 12845 contains a relaxation from protection if the void is a fully non-combustible construction and it contains no combustible material.

There is nothing 'magic' about the figure of 800 mm, and the code now takes a more pragmatic view, with a strong hint that a relaxation, somewhat akin to that contained in BS EN 12845, might be possible. Thus, a note in the code suggests that, if the fire risk within a void of 800 mm or more is considered to be low, consideration might be given to the omission of fire detection from the void, subject to the agreement of the interested parties. The example given in the note is that of a void in which the probability of ignition and development of fire is very low, or a void that is limited in extent so that spread of fire beyond the room of origin, via the void, is unlikely. However, if such a relaxation is agreed by the interested parties and implemented, this should still be recorded as a variation on the design certificate.

---

[47] BS EN 12845, *Fixed firefighting systems – Automatic sprinkler systems – Design, installation and maintenance.*

The corollary also applies in that, even though the void is less than 800 mm in depth, the code recommends that it be protected if, on the basis of a fire risk assessment, the fire risk in the void is such as to warrant protection. Protection of voids less than 800 mm in depth is also recommended if the void is such that extensive spread of fire or smoke, particularly between rooms and compartments, can take place before detection. In practice, therefore, consideration may need to be given to the extent to which cavity barriers are provided within such a void. The classic case, in which voids less than 800 mm in depth are protected virtually as a matter of course, is the floor void in a computer room, in which the fire load created by cables is virtually always deemed to warrant automatic fire detection within the void.

If detectors are located in unventilated voids, particularly shallow voids, it is important that the sensing element of each detector is located sufficiently high within the void to prevent a thin layer of smoke from spreading through the void above the level of the sensing element. Thus, in this case, the code recommends that, if the void is not greater than 1.5 m in depth, fire detectors should be sited within the top 10% of the void or the top 125 mm, whichever is the greater. This might necessitate mounting the detector on a bracket, but care needs to be taken that the orientation does not permit the ingress of dirt and dust to an extent that would adversely affect the operation of the detector. (Voids greater than 1.5 m in depth should be treated as rooms.)

A lantern light within a protected area is a reservoir for smoke, and so it too should be protected if it is 800 mm or more in depth. Also, it should be protected if it is used for ventilation, as smoke and hot gases will flow out of the lantern light, and they may not then readily reach the nearest ceiling-mounted detectors.

When siting heat and smoke detectors, the basic principle is that no point in the protected area should be further than 5.3 m from the nearest heat detector or more than 7.5 m from the nearest smoke detector. If a multi-sensor detector performs as a smoke detector, the spacings adopted for smoke detectors can be applied. However, in some multi-sensor detectors, it is possible to disable one or more of the sensors at certain times of day, leaving only a heat sensor. In such a case, these detectors should be sited in accordance with the recommendations for heat detectors.

In the past, designers have often applied the above recommendations somewhat religiously within corridors, so that the 7.5 m dimension was deemed to be the maximum distance between any point on the ceiling, adjacent to the wall of the corridor, and the nearest detector. This led to unnecessarily complex tables for spacings between detectors in corridors, according to the corridor width. Since fires do not constitute point sources and the plume of gases spreads as it rises, this approach is now regarded by the code as unnecessarily purist. Accordingly, in corridors of no more than 2 m in width, the code considers only the distance between points close to the centre line of the corridor and the nearest detector. The effect of this is that, in these corridors, smoke detectors can be spaced 15 m apart, while heat detectors (e.g. in a Category P system) can be spaced 10.6 m apart. (It should be noted that, under some circumstances in which the system Category is not L1, L2 or L3, BS 7273-4 recommends closer spacing of detectors that are used to trigger the release of held-open fire doors.)

In an apex roof, the apex itself is the point at which smoke and hot gases will collect. Accordingly, detectors need to be sited at, or near, each apex. However, the horizontal distances of 7.5 m and 5.3 m between any point and the nearest detector can be increased by 1% for each degree of slope, up to a maximum increase of 25%, as a result of the efficiency of the apex in collection of smoke.

In the case of large open areas with flat ceilings, the 7.5 m and 5.3 m 'rule' equates to approximately one smoke detector per 100 m^2 or one heat detector per 50 m^2. These figures are very useful for estimating the number of detectors required for the purpose of preparing a quotation. They are also useful when auditing a system, to determine whether sufficient detectors have been provided within a large open area. However, these figures are only approximations, and, by staggering rows of detectors, it is possible to use slightly lower numbers of detectors than would be calculated by this approach.

In order to protrude adequately into the flow of hot gases, both heat and smoke detectors should be sited such that their sensitive elements are at least 25 mm below ceilings. In the case of heat detectors, the maximum distance of the sensitive element below the ceiling is 150 mm, whereas, because the layer of smoke will be sufficiently deep, the maximum distance of the sensitive element below the ceiling is 600 mm for smoke detectors.

An exception to the guidance contained in the paragraph above applies in the case of Category L3 systems. As discussed in Chapter 7, in a Category L3 system the purpose of the detectors in the rooms that open onto escape routes is primarily to give a warning to those beyond the room of origin before the door of the room suffers serious attack by fire. Accordingly, as a special relaxation that applies only to these detectors within a Category L3 system, the detectors may, alternatively, be sited on a wall close to any door that opens onto an escape route. These wall-mounted detectors should be sited such that the top of the detection element is between 150 mm and 300 mm below the ceiling, while the bottom of the detection element should be above the level of the door opening.

A number of points arise from the above recommendation. First, if a large room contains a number of doors, each opening onto an escape route, there could be a need for a detector to be sited close to each one of these doors. The test of adequacy would be whether a detector would operate sufficiently early before any door suffers serious attack by fire. If the relaxation offered by the code is adopted, it might be quite reasonable to install a detector close to each door if the doors are separated by a significant distance. However, if the room is protected in the normal manner by ceiling mounted detectors complying with the normal recommendations for such detectors in any Category of system, there would be no need for additional detectors, and the number of detectors used might actually be less than that required if the relaxation is adopted.

Another implication of the relaxation would seem to be that the size of the room is relatively insignificant. Accordingly, if a very large room that would need several ceiling-mounted detectors to protect it fully in any other category of system had, say, only one door opening onto an escape route, it would seem sufficient, in the case of a Category L3 system, to install just one detector close to the door, regardless of whether this detector is ceiling- or wall-mounted.

On the other hand, a note to the recommendation advises that care should be taken in rooms with a high ceiling height (for example, exceeding 4 m in height). Thus, consider a very high space, in which the purpose of the fire detection is to provide a warning before fire threatens an adjacent escape route. If the 150 mm to 300 mm below ceiling level recommendation is adopted for a wall-mounted detector, this detector may not be as effective in meeting the intended objective as one sited much lower down, but, say, just above the level of the door. Given that this note advises care in these circumstances, this would, presumably, be a reasonable variation from the recommendation.

The main use of the L3 system, and the particular relaxations described above, is in hotel and similar accommodation. Occasionally, the hotel may be fully equipped with sprinklers, so that each bedroom contains one or more sprinkler heads. Although this is still not very common practice in the UK, it often occurs in the case of the hotels of American-parented chains, as sprinkler protection of hotels in the USA is quite common. It is also sometimes adopted in situations in which the hotel forms part of a complex, high rise multiple occupancy building. A sprinkler head is, of course, a form of heat detector. Although, depending on the type of head used, the sprinkler head may be a little less sensitive than an automatic heat detector, the sprinkler head begins extinguishing action as soon as the head operates.

Accordingly, providing that the sprinkler system transmits a signal to the fire alarm system on flow of water from any single sprinkler head, a sprinkler head within a room may be regarded as a heat detector for the purpose of satisfying the recommendations for a Category L3 system. If the sprinkler head(s) in the room is suitably sited, no automatic fire detector would then be needed. Equally, if, say, a smoke detector were sited in each bedroom in addition to the sprinkler protection, there would, presumably, be no need for this detector to give an immediate warning when it operated, unless to give a warning to the occupant of the room (in which case it might be regarded as a Category L2 detector, rather than purely a Category L3 detector).

The code recommends that carbon monoxide fire detectors should be sited exactly in accordance with all recommendations applicable to smoke detectors. It is sometimes claimed that, in the case of carbon monoxide fire detectors, some of the recommendations set out in the paragraphs that follow are less critical. For example, it is sometimes claimed that, as carbon monoxide is a gas that will rapidly diffuse uniformly throughout the area in which it occurs, the 'dead spaces' in the corners of rooms and close to obstructions do not arise and these detectors may be located in such positions. While there may be some validity in such an assumption, no such relaxation exists within the code. Accordingly, any variation from the recommendations applicable to smoke detectors would need to be justified and agreed by the interested parties.

Perhaps the most significant recommendation in relation to obstructions to the flow of smoke and hot gases is that relating to the proximity of detectors to walls and partitions. Heat, smoke and carbon monoxide detectors should not be mounted within 500 mm of walls and partitions. The same recommendation applies to obstructions, such as structural beams and ductwork, if the obstructions are greater than 250 mm in depth. Obviously, this recommendation does not, however, apply to detectors within rooms opening onto escape routes in a Category L3 system, as these detectors may be wall-mounted. Clearly, it is also impossible to comply with the recommendation in an enclosed area that has no horizontal dimension of more than 1 m. In this case, the impossibility of complying with the recommendation does not constitute a variation, but the detector should be sited as close as possible to the centre of the space.

If structural beams or ductwork are less than 250 mm in depth, detectors should not be mounted closer to the obstruction than twice the depth of the obstruction. This recommendation also applies to 'isolated ceiling attachments', including light fittings.

Certain obstructions have such an effect on the ability of smoke and combustion gases to reach the nearest detector that not only need the above recommendations be applied, but, in addition, the obstructions need to be treated as walls, with the consequent need for the provision of additional detectors. This recommendation applies to ceiling obstructions, such as structural beams, that are deeper than 10% of the overall height from floor to ceiling.

Within voids, particularly ceiling voids, structural beams, ductwork and similar obstructions take up a significant part of the height of the space between a false ceiling and the structural slab above. The recommendations in the above paragraph apply to such situations, so that, if such obstructions are deeper than 10% of the overall depth of a floor or ceiling void, they should be treated as walls that subdivide the void. This can mean that, in a void that contains frequently spaced structural beams, the number of detectors required for compliance with the code can appear somewhat inordinate. For example, strict compliance with the recommendation in question could result in many times more detectors within the ceiling void than required to protect the area below the false ceiling. There are, however, at least, three approaches that the designer can adopt in order to avoid a design that is unnecessarily expensive.

One approach would be to base the design on a pragmatic risk assessment that considers the hazards present in the void and the risk that is created by the presence of the void. This may lead to adoption of a variation, perhaps based on nothing more than a judgement made by the designer in conjunction with the interested parties. A second, more scientific approach, would be to use the principles of fire engineering to calculate the rate at which the smoke reservoirs created by the structural beams would fill with smoke that would then spill over into the adjacent reservoirs. By this technique, it might be possible to show that adequately early detection of fire could still be achieved without installing a detector within each of the long smoke reservoirs created. This would then be the basis for a variation.

However, the code itself offers a third approach. This approach is set out in recommendation 22.3k) of the code, which applies to any situation in which, at ceiling level, there is a number of closely spaced structural beams or floor joists. In this situation, the code provides special recommendations for the maximum spacing between any two detectors, measured across the beams (presumably, regardless of whether these beams are within a void or not). The recommendation that applies in this situation is quite complicated and, accordingly, the relevant table and associated diagram within the code are reproduced below.

Table 1 — Spacing and siting of detectors on ceilings with closely spaced structural beams or joists

Overall ceiling height from floor to structural slab (to nearest whole metre) H	Beam depth D	Maximum spacing between any two smoke (heat) detectors measured across the beams M
6 m or less	less than 10 % H	5 m (3.8 m)
more than 6 m	less than 10 % H and 600 mm or less	5 m (3.8 m)
more than 6 m	less than 10 % H and more than 600 mm	5 m (3.8 m)
3m or less	more than 10 % H	2.3 m (1.5 m)
4 m	more than 10 % H	2.8 m (2 m)
5 m	more than 10 % H	3 m (2.3 m)
≥6 m	more than 10 % H	3.3 m (2.5 m)

Table 1 only applies if the longer dimension of the cells, L, is no more than 10.6 m in the case of smoke detectors and 7.5 m in the case of heat detectors. The code recommends that, if the longer dimension of the 'cells' exceeds these figures, the cell should be stopped to the depth of the beam, such that the reservoir created is no longer than these figures. If this is impractical, the code recommends that detection should be installed in every 'cell'.

It should be noted that, depending on the spacing between the beams or joists, in many cases this recommendation constitutes a relaxation from the '10% rule' described above, obviating the need for detectors to be installed in the space between each beam or joist.

However, in some cases, this recommendation is more onerous than the '10% rule' in isolation. Consider, for example, the case of a single isolated structural beam. If the depth of the beam is greater than 10% of the height between floor and ceiling, it needs to be treated as a wall, and detectors will need to be installed within the space on either side of it. Equally, the corollary presumably applies, so that, if the depth is less than 10% of the ceiling height, the beam can be ignored and detectors would be sited as they would be on an uninterrupted flat ceiling, subject to their installation at a suitable distance from the beam.

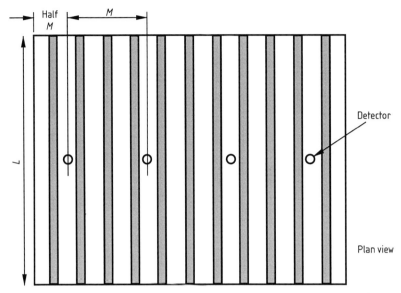

In this example beam downstands are greater than 10 % of ceiling height, *H. H* = 3 m
Smoke detectors are used in this example.
Using Table 2, the spacing, *M* should be no more than 2.3 m

Figure 5 — Cells formed from joists

However, if there is now a 'number of closely spaced structural beams' of the same depth, the beams cannot be ignored in this way. Moreover, if the unstopped length of each 'cell' is greater than 10.6 m in an area protected by smoke detectors, detectors will need to be installed in every 'cell'. Since the code is, effectively, then treating these quite shallow beams as walls, presumably the spacing between detectors in a long cell can follow those specified for spacing of detectors in corridors, if the distance between beams is no more than 2 m. The justification for this recommendation is presumably the cumulative effect of the reservoirs created by a number of relatively shallow beams, but the recommendation may prove somewhat onerous in a case of very shallow beams that are almost insignificant in relation to the depth of the smoke layer.

While the above recommendation at least gives definitive guidance on a matter that has often perplexed designers, only time will tell whether it always works well for every possible permutation of ceiling height, beam depth, protected space dimensions and spacing between beams.

A further traditional perplexity that is now addressed in the code is the honeycomb ceiling, which is divided into a large number of small cells. The two issues that have always tended to cause contention are the number/spacings of detectors required and the location of each detector, i.e. on the structural slab at the highest point within the cell, or on the underside of the structure that forms the cell. The code resolves these issues for the designer by means of Table 1 and Figure 10b) within the code, which are reproduced as Table 2 and Figure 6 respectively.

Table 2 — Spacing and siting of detectors on honeycomb and similar ceilings

Overall ceiling height from floor into cell H (to nearest whole metre)	Beam depth, D	Maximum distance between any point and the nearest smoke (heat) detector	Detector location if W is 4D or less	Detector location if W is more than 4D
6 m or less	less than 10 % H	As per flat ceilings	Underside of beams	On structural slab in the cell
more than 6 m	less than 10 % H and 600 mm or less	As per flat ceilings	Underside of beams	On structural slab in the cell
more than 6 m	less than 10 % H and more than 600 mm	As per flat ceilings	Underside of beams[a]	On structural slab in the cell
3m or less	more than 10 % H	4.5 m (3 m)	Underside of beams	On structural slab in the cell
4 m	more than 10 % H	5.5 m (4 m)	Underside of beams	On structural slab in the cell
5 m	more than 10 % H	6 m (4.5 m)	Underside of beams	On structural slab in the cell
≥6 m	more than 10 % H	6.5 m (5 m)	Underside of beams	On structural slab in the cell

Key
W = Width of cell;
D = Depth of beams that form each cell.

[a] Since mounting detectors at a depth of more than 600 mm below the highest point in the protected spaces does not comply with **22.3**d), protection in these circumstances might need careful consideration to determine the most suitable location and spacing of detectors.

The principles that underlie Table 2 are quite simple. First, the '10% rule' is applied. Thus, if the depth of the cells is less than 10% of the height between the floor and the true ceiling slab, the effect of the cells can be ignored; detectors can be spaced as they would under a flat ceiling. If, however, the width of the cells is narrow compared to the depth of the cells, the hot gases flowing across the ceiling will not 'zigzag' to reach a detector mounted on the slab, at the highest point in the cell. Under these circumstances, it should be noted that Table 2 recommends that the detectors be installed on the underside of the 'beams' that form the cell.

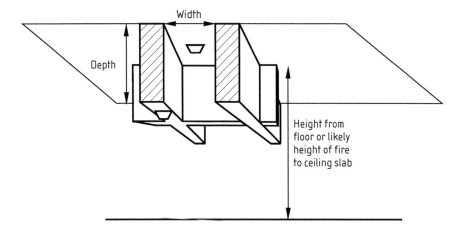

Figure 6 — Horizontal ceiling comprising a series of small cells

As the somewhat conical plume of smoke and hot gases rises, it does, of course, spread out. Accordingly, as ceiling height increases, the rising plume will simultaneously fill more and more cells. At greater ceiling heights, detectors can then be spaced further apart without the need for too many cells to fill and spill over into adjacent cells before smoke reaches the nearest detector. This is clearly reflected in Table 2. (The same principle could be used to argue that, even under a flat ceiling, detector spacing should depend on ceiling height, but, for simplicity, the code only uses this principle in determining detector spacing on honeycomb ceilings.)

Storage racks and partitions that do not extend to ceiling height may also form obstructions to the flow of smoke and hot gases towards detectors. Thus, the code recommends that these be treated as walls if they reach within 300 mm of the ceiling. Care is needed, therefore, in the case of warehouses with rack storage or even stockrooms and similar storage areas in, for example, retail premises. Although the code refers to racks that encroach within 300 mm of the ceiling, strictly, it would seem reasonable to apply the recommendation to the storage itself. Therefore, if the top of a rack extends to just over 300 mm from the ceiling, it will not be possible to site storage on the top of the rack.

More generally, the code recommends that a clear space is maintained within 500 mm radius of every detector. Thus, care will be needed in, for example, the case of free standing storage to ensure that the top of the storage does not encroach within the 500 mm radius of any detector.

Ventilation systems can also affect the flow of smoke, so preventing it from reaching detectors. Accordingly, the code recommends that detectors should not be mounted within 1 m of any air inlet of a forced ventilation system. If air is forced through a perforated ceiling (e.g. from a plenum above), the ceiling should be imperforate for a radius of at least 600 mm around each detector.

Perforated ceilings, particularly those of the open grid type, have also created yet a further perplexity for the designer. Should the detectors be mounted on the open grid or should they be mounted on the true ceiling slab above? The code now provides the answer. Detectors on the slab above the perforated false ceiling provide protection of the area below the ceiling if the perforations are uniformly distributed across the ceiling, are substantially uniform in size and, in aggregate, the free space created by perforations makes up more than 40% of the area of the ceiling.

However, to ensure that there is not undue resistance to flow, the minimum dimension of each perforation in any direction would need to be 10 mm, and the thickness of the ceiling should not be greater than three times the minimum dimension of each perforation. If any of these conditions cannot be satisfied, the detectors should be mounted below the false ceiling. Then, if protection of the void above the false ceiling is necessary, further detectors should be installed on the true structural slab above the false ceiling.

As noted at the beginning of this chapter, the size of fire at the point of detection by ceiling mounted detectors, particularly point-type detectors, increases as ceiling height increases. There must then exist a ceiling height above which the size of fire at the point of detection would be so large that the detection cannot sensibly be regarded as a valid form of fire protection. Tables 3 and 4 of the code specify the heights in question for point heat, smoke and carbon monoxide detectors, optical beam detectors and aspirating smoke detection systems. These tables are reproduced below. Note that a minor relaxation in the maximum ceiling height at which these detectors can be used is permitted for small sections of ceiling not exceeding in total 10% of the ceiling area within the protected area.

Table 3 — Limits of ceiling height (general)

Detector type	Column 1 Generally applicable maximum ceiling height	Column 2 10 % of ceiling height no greater than

Heat detectors conforming to
BS EN 54-5
  Class A1
  Other Classes
	
	9.0
	7.5
		
		10.5
		10.5

Point smoke detectors	10.5	12.5
Carbon monoxide detectors	10.5	12.5
Optical beam smoke detectors	25.0	25.0

Aspirating smoke detection
systems complying with BFPSA
code of practice for:
Category 1 aspirating detection
systems
  Normal sensitivity
  Enhanced sensitivity
  Very high sensitivity
	
	10.5
	12.0
	15.0
		
		12.5
		14.0
		18.0

Other fire detectors	As specified by the manufacturer	

Table 4 — Limits of ceiling height (Category P systems and
five minute fire service attendance)

Detector type	Column 1 Generally applicable maximum ceiling height	Column 2 10 % of ceiling height no greater than

Heat detectors conforming to
BS EN 54-5
  Class A1
  Other Classes
	
	13.5
	12.0
		
		15.0
		15.0

Point smoke detectors	15.0	18.0
Carbon monoxide detectors	15.0	18.0
Optical beam smoke detectors	40.0	40.0

Aspirating smoke detection
systems complying with BFPSA
code of practice for:
Category 1 aspirating detection
systems
  Normal sensitivity
  Enhanced sensitivity
  Very high sensitivity
	
	15.0
	17.0
	21.0
		
		18.0
		21.0
		26.0

Other fire detectors	As specified by the manufacturer	

In the case of property protection, the time that matters is the time between ignition of fire and the arrival of the fire and rescue service (or more strictly, the time at which the fire and rescue service begins extinguishing action). Thus, if very prompt arrival of the fire and rescue service can be expected, this may act as a form of compensation for greater fire size at the point of detection. Accordingly, in the case of Category P systems, the higher maximum ceiling heights contained in Table 4 may be applied provided the fire and rescue service attendance time is no more than five minutes.

How is the designer to determine whether the fire and rescue service attendance time will be no more than five minutes? A note in the code recommends that the fire and rescue service response time ought to be the subject of consultation, but the code gives no further practical guidance on determination of attendance time. In the past, determination of attendance time was not too difficult, as there were Government-imposed 'standards of fire cover'. These set maximum attendance times for all areas of the country, according to the nature of the population density; thus congested urban conurbations had much shorter attendance times than rural areas. This has largely changed with the introduction of 'integrated risk management plans' within fire and rescue services. Attendance times are now less easily predicted, and may vary with the time of day. Moreover, if the fortuitous close proximity of the nearest fire station were to be accepted as justification for the use of higher ceiling heights, there would be a need to ensure that the station was manned by whole time firefighters on a 24-hour basis. The proximity of a fire station manned by retained personnel, or manned by whole time firefighters only during the day, would not be acceptable, as an extra five minutes would need to be added to the attendance time during times when the fire station was not normally manned.

It should also be noted that, if Table 4 is to be used, it would be a reasonable prerequisite that the designer complies with the recommendations of clause 15 in respect of communication with the fire and rescue service. Thus, unless the premises were continuously occupied, the system would need to incorporate a means for automatic transmission of fire signals to an alarm receiving centre. If, on the other hand, a variation from this latter recommendation had been accepted, it would not be reasonable to apply Table 4; the ceiling heights specified in Table 3 would then be more applicable.

Clause 22 also contains recommendations specific to optical beam smoke detectors, line heat detectors, aspirating smoke detection systems and flame detectors. These primarily apply the principles that are applicable in the case of point detectors to these special forms of fire detection.

In the case of optical beam smoke detectors and line heat detectors, the devices may be thought of as an infinite number of point detectors arranged along the line of the line heat detector or the beam of the optical beam detector. Thus, each detector may be considered to protect a rectangle that is 15 m in width in the case of the optical beam smoke detector or 10.6 m in width in the case of the line heat detector. Care must also be taken, in the case of optical beam detectors, to ensure that the beam cannot be obstructed by the passage of people, forklift trucks, etc. It is also important that the transmitters, receivers and reflectors are mounted on solid construction that will not be subject to movement.

Sometimes, in buildings with very high spaces, such as an atrium, optical beam smoke detectors are mounted much lower than the highest point within the space. The reason for this is that, stratification of smoke may occur before the smoke reaches a beam detector at the highest point in the space. However, as discussed at the beginning of this chapter, it is never possible to predict exactly where stratification will occur. If the beam runs at a much lower level than that at which stratification does occur, the relatively narrow rising plume may bypass the beam. Thus, the low level beam detectors should only be regarded as supplementary to the high level detection recommended by the code.

Nevertheless, the code does give guidance on the siting of these supplementary beam detectors, taking into account that the plume does spread out as it rises. Accordingly, the code recommends that the width of the area protected on each side of a supplementary optical beam should be regarded as 12.5% of the height of the beam above the highest likely seat of fire. For example, if the supplementary beam detectors were mounted 10 m above the base of an atrium, optical beam detectors would need to be sited every 2.5 m across the width of the atrium.

Sometimes line heat detectors are installed to protect a particular item of plant or to protect a cable tray (e.g. in a cable tunnel). Under these circumstances, since the detection is not intended to provide general fire protection of the area, the line heat detector need not be installed in accordance with the principles applicable to the installation of point heat detectors. Instead, the detector should be mounted as close as possible to the place where fire or overheating might occur, and either be mounted above the risk or in thermal contact with it. For example, in the case of a cable tray, the line heat detector could be installed on the tray itself.

In the case of an aspirating smoke detection system, if the system is intended to provide general fire protection for an area of the building, the principles of design should be such that each sampling point (hole through which air is drawn) is regarded as a point smoke detector. However, as the detector actively draws samples of air through the sampling points, the code advises that it might be possible to mount the sampling points flush with a ceiling, provided the manufacturer confirms that this will not be detrimental to the effectiveness of the system to detect fire.

Thus, a relaxation in the guidance that the sensitive element need be 25 mm below ceiling level might be possible. This is attractive to designers in cases in which the purpose of using the aspirating system is to make the detection as unobtrusive as possible. For example, the main aspirating pipework may be concealed above the ceiling, and small bore sampling tubes might be dropped through a small hole drilled in the ceiling, but it might not be necessary for this tube to descend below the ceiling by the full 25 mm.

Often, high sensitivity aspirating smoke detection systems are used for protection of critical electronic equipment rooms. The use of these systems for this purpose is discussed in BS 6266.[48] Commonly, in this situation, the aspirating system is not used to provide the general fire detection throughout the space (which often takes the form of normal point smoke detectors), but the system is used to monitor the return air to air conditioning units in the protected space. The intention is to detect very small amounts of combustion products transported within the conditioned air in the room.

In this case, the code recommends that the system should be installed in accordance with the guidance of the manufacturer. However, a code of practice for aspirating detection systems[49] has been published by the British Fire Protection Systems Association (BFPSA)*, and, in the case of any aspirating fire detection system, it would be advisable for the designer to consult this code of practice.

In the case of flame detectors, the code primarily advises that spacing should be in accordance with limits specified by the manufacturer. On a practical note, the code does advise, however, that, of course, there

---

[48] BS 6266:2002, *Code of practice for fire protection for electronic equipment installations.*

[49] *Code of practice for Category 1 Aspirating Detection Systems.* Issue 1. Kingston-upon-Thames: British Fire Protection Systems Association, 1996.

* The BFPSA has, since publication of BS 5839-1, been amalgamated with the Fire Extinguishing Trades Association (FETA) to form the Fire Industry Association (FIA).

should be a clear line of sight between all points within the protected area and one or more flame detectors, or (where the flame detectors are intended to protect a specific hazard) between a specific hazard and one or more flame detectors.

Although the code does not specifically recommend the provision of smoke detectors in ventilation ducts, or give guidance on the circumstances in which this practice might be appropriate, there are various reasons why smoke detectors might be installed in ventilation ducts. For example, this might be necessary to stop the recirculation of smoke by a recirculating air conditioning system. It might also be necessary in order to ensure that dampers are closed within air conditioning ductwork to stop the spread of smoke; this is sometimes necessary in premises in which people sleep. Advice on this issue is given in BS 5588-9.[50]

Where, for whatever reason, smoke detectors are installed within air extraction ducts, the code provides some practical guidance. Specifically, the smoke detectors or associated probes should be installed in straight stretches of ductwork, at a distance from the nearest bend, corner or junction of at least three times the width of the duct. This is to ensure that they are installed at a point where there is a homogeneous concentration of smoke, rather than at the turbulent areas close to bends, etc. In order to ensure that any duct probe properly protects the full area of the duct, the code advises that, normally, the probe should cover the wider dimension of the duct, such that the length of the probe is at least two-thirds of that dimension.

---

[50] BS 5588-9:1999, *Fire precautions in the design, construction and use of buildings. Code of practice for ventilation and air conditioning ductwork*. This code of practice will be withdrawn following the publication of BS 9999.

19. Control and indicating equipment

The design of control and indicating equipment is a matter for the relevant product standard, namely BS EN 54-2,[51] rather than for BS 5839-1. However, the code does address three matters in relation to control and indicating equipment, namely the siting of the equipment, the facilities provided for visual indication of fire signals and the facilities provided for control of the system.

Furthermore, even if the system uses control and indicating equipment that fully complies with BS EN 54-2 (and, possibly, even third-party certificated as complying), the control and indicating equipment may, *or may not*, comply with at least four specific recommendations of BS 5839-1. For full compliance with the code, therefore, it will be necessary to ensure that these additional recommendations are satisfied.

This is an unfortunate situation, in that it is quite possible that non-compliances with the code can result from the use of control and indicating equipment that fully complies with the product standard for such equipment. This is an unfortunate quirk of the European standardization process. Although, under agreements for standardization in Europe, the UK is obliged to publish the European standard for control and indicating equipment as the national British Standard, it has, regrettably, been considered necessary to incorporate these additional recommendations in the code to ensure the appropriate level of fire safety for systems installed in the UK.

Three of these additional recommendations have already been discussed. The first concerns the integrity of the system if a cross-connection occurs between a detector circuit and a sounder circuit. As discussed in Chapter 11, the code recommends that, in the event of such a fault, only the detector circuit and sounder circuit involved should be

---

[51] BS EN 54-2:1998, *Fire detection and fire alarm systems — Control and indicating equipment.*

affected; otherwise, the system should operate correctly. When control and indicating equipment is examined for compliance with BS EN 54-2, the testing or certification body would not confirm compliance with this recommendation. Moreover, it is difficult, if not impossible, to prove compliance during installation inspections. To some extent, therefore, reliance needs to be placed on information from the manufacturer of the control and indicating equipment.

The second 'extra' recommendation relates to the provision of zonal indicators. As discussed in Chapter 12, the code recommends that the primary indication of the area(s) from which a fire signal(s) has originated should comprise an indication of the detection zone. Moreover, for compliance with the code, it is not satisfactory for the method of indication to comprise purely text on the normal liquid crystal or vacuum fluorescent display provided on addressable systems. The code recommends that the form of zone indication should comprise a separate light-emitting indicator for each detection zone of the system, such that the indicating equipment is capable of simultaneous display of fire signals on every detection zone.

This will normally comprise a bank of LEDs, but could comprise an illuminated mimic diagram. Although much less likely, for compliance with this recommendation, the code would also accept a VDU provided that it could simultaneously display fire signals in all detection zones without manual intervention. In effect, therefore, the VDU could display a mimic diagram. However, because the reliability of a single VDU is not adequate, a back-up form of detection zone indication would then need to be provided for compliance with the code. This could comprise, for example, a second VDU or a printer configured to print out automatically the fire information. (A printer would not be acceptable on its own, as it, too, would not be sufficiently reliable.)

In very large premises, comprising a commensurately large number of detection zones, compliance with this recommendation could involve a very large indicator panel that would require a significant amount of space. However, in such premises, the code would accept a hierarchical system in which, for example, in the security control room for the complex, indication is limited to the *sector* of origin, rather than the detection zone of origin. The code defines a 'sector' as a subdivision of the protected premises normally containing several detection zones. It is also noted in the code that a sector may even comprise more than one building. There could then be an arrangement whereby further indicating equipment within each sector indicates the detection zones.

However, as has been stressed many times in this guide, it is very important to ensure that the design of the system takes full account of the fire strategy for the building or complex. Accordingly, clause 23 of the code, which provides recommendations for control and indicating equipment, recommends that the control and indicating facilities should be suitable for the fire and evacuation procedures intended for the building. In complex premises, the code stresses the need for adequate consultation between interested parties to ensure that appropriate control and indicating facilities are provided. Therefore, in the example of a hierarchical display, it would need to be ensured that, at a central point, limitation of indications to the sector of origin would be sufficient to enable those monitoring the system at this location to have sufficient information to implement fire and evacuation procedures.

The third 'extra' recommendation is the restriction in the delay between operation of a manual call point and sounding of alarms within the area in question. Although BS EN 54-2 permits this to be 10 seconds, BS 5839-1 recommends a maximum of three seconds. This was discussed in Chapter 16.

Clause 23 also contains the final additional recommendation that is over and above the requirements of BS EN 54-2. The clause recommends that an evacuation control be provided. This control should be clearly labelled to indicate its function and should be provided on, or immediately adjacent to, the control equipment to enable fire alarm sounders to be started. Since this control will not necessarily be provided on control equipment complying with BS EN 54-2, for compliance with the code it would be acceptable for the control to comprise a separate device, provided it is immediately adjacent to the control equipment.

The device could comprise a manual call point, provided the manual call point was clearly labelled to distinguish its function from that of other manual call points in the building. The evacuate control may be the same as the control provided to restart sounders after silencing, as its correct operation should not be dependent on the state of any silencing or disablement device. Although the code refers to fire alarm sounders in this recommendation, it is reasonable to assert that the same facility should be provided to start any pre-recorded evacuation message in a voice alarm system.

However, in buildings with phased evacuation, no single evacuation control should result in an evacuation signal in all alarm zones simultaneously, unless the stairway capacity of the building is sufficient to cater for simultaneous evacuation of the entire building (see also Chapter 15). Instead, a separate evacuate control should be provided for each part of the protected premises in which an evacuation signal needs to be given simultaneously.

It is necessary to restrict the operation of certain manual controls to authorized personnel. In the example of the security control room, this will normally apply, simply because access to the control room itself will be restricted.

Because the code specifically recommends zonal indication, it also recommends the provision of a zone plan on or adjacent to the indicating equipment. This could, of course, take the form of an illuminated mimic or the VDU representation described above. Otherwise, there will be a need for a correctly orientated plan of the premises, showing at least the building entrances, the main circulation areas and the division into detection zones. It should be noted that this recommendation will not be satisfied by the provision of a zone chart that simply describes the location of each zone; a correctly orientated plan is necessary.

Indicating equipment should be sited at an appropriate location for both staff and firefighters responding to a fire signal. The code suggests that this should normally be an area on the ground floor, close to the entrance of the building likely to be used by the fire and rescue service. However, an alternative is provision of indicating equipment in a continuously manned control room from, which, at least, initial control of any fire incident will be implemented. Where there are multiple entrances to a building, repeat indicating equipment might be necessary to assist the fire and rescue service. It should be noted that not all indicating equipment needs to be combined with controls that provide comprehensive control over all functions of the system. There is, however, a need for careful consideration of the fire strategy that will be adopted to ensure that the correct indicating facilities, and the correct control facilities, are provided at the appropriate locations.

The code also suggests, but does not positively recommend, that there may be benefit in locating indicating equipment at a position that will be visible to the fire and rescue service from outside the building. The philosophy here is that, if there is a facility for transmission of alarms to an alarm receiving centre, there is a possibility that the fire and rescue service may attend a fire alarm signal when the premises are unoccupied. If the officer in charge can see the zonal indicators and they indicate multiple zones in alarm, it may assist him in making a judgement as to whether there really is a fire and whether it may be advisable to force entry to the premises.

The environment in which the control and indicating equipment is to be installed should also be considered. For example, the ambient light level must be appropriate, so that indicators can be clearly seen, controls easily operated and instructions or legends easily read. Similarly, the noise level in the vicinity of the equipment should not be such as to prevent audible indications, such as a fault warning sounder, from being heard. Equipment that is likely to need routine attention for maintenance should be sited in readily accessible locations that facilitate safe maintenance work. It should be noted that this is not only a recommendation of the code, but is arguably necessary under relevant health and safety legislation.

The designer is also expected to consider the possible effects of fire on the control and indicating equipment. The equipment and its associated extra low voltage power supplies should be sited in areas of low fire hazard, so that the equipment is unlikely to be involved in a fire before adequate warning to occupants has been given. If the system incorporates automatic fire detection, consideration should be given to whether the areas in which any control and indicating equipment, associated power supplies and any other control facilities should be protected by automatic fire detection.

The code recommends such protection, unless the fire hazard in the area in which the equipment is installed is negligible and there is an adequate degree of fire separation between that area and areas of greater fire hazard. However, this recommendation does not apply if the area is continuously manned in the case of a Category P system, or is continuously manned when the building is occupied by any person in the case of Category L systems; in these cases, there is no benefit in the provision of automatic fire detection, since people will be present to detect a fire that might affect the equipment. Generally, these conditions will apply to the entrance foyer of a large building, in which it is, in any case, appropriate to install the control and indicating equipment. There may, therefore, not be a need for automatic fire detection in this area specifically to protect the control and indicating equipment; detection may, of course, be provided as part of the general fire protection of the building.

Special consideration needs to be given to premises in multiple occupation. For example, siting control and indicating equipment in the premises of one tenant is unlikely to be satisfactory, since the premises of this tenant might be unoccupied, making the equipment inaccessible, when other parts of the premises are occupied. The code recommends that, in premises in multiple occupation with communal parts, main control and indicating equipment should be located within a communal area, such as an entrance hall. Where no communal parts exist, the code recommends that the equipment should still be sited in an area to which access is possible at all times that the premises are generally occupied.

20. Networked systems

In recent years, the construction of large, complex buildings, such as shopping centres and multifunction entertainment complexes, has become commonplace. In these complexes, there are often several thousand automatic fire detectors. The number of detectors involved, and the distances between a central, focal point (such as a security control room) and the extremities of the complex, are such that it is often inappropriate to provide a single fire alarm control and indicating panel, to which a vast number of devices would then need to be connected via long runs of cable.

Under the above circumstances, a 'networked system' is commonly used. In such a system, a number of 'sub-panels' are distributed around the complex, and manual call points, detectors and fire alarm sounders are connected directly to these local panels. The local panels are then 'networked' by means of a data highway, and information from these sub-panels is relayed back to central equipment that provides the relevant degree of control and indication. The networked system may even serve a number of different buildings located on a single site.

Often there are two different ways of looking at a system that is configured in this way. First, the entire configuration of central equipment and sub-panels may be regarded as simply a single fire alarm system. If we take this view, the sub-panels are provided simply for engineering convenience. These sub-panels can then simply take the form of 'black boxes', with no local facilities for control or indication.

At the other extreme, one might view the configuration as a number of virtually independent fire alarm systems, each fully complying with the code. Thus, in this case, the sub-panels would incorporate all the control and indicating facilities recommended by the code and would, themselves, be sufficient to meet the specified fire safety objective, such as life safety or property protection. The purpose of the 'networking' may simply be to provide remote indication of alarm signals at, say, a gatehouse, over and above the minimum system requirements necessary to satisfy the recommendations of the code.

In practice, many networked systems fall between these two extremes. As always, however, the facilities provided, particularly at local sub-panels, need to be suitable and sufficient to support the relevant fire strategy. On the other hand, care needs to be taken to ensure that, in the event of fire, confusion does not result from operation of controls at a central point and (possibly conflicting) operation of controls at local sub-panels.

Particular care needs to be taken to ensure the relevant degree of integrity of the network itself. Commonly, examination of a networked system reveals that a data cable has been used for the network. Usually, the data cable in question is not fire resisting. In most cases, this will result in a serious non-compliance with the code, but this does depend on the way in which the system is viewed. If all sub-panels can function as 'stand-alone' fire alarm systems and do not depend on the network to facilitate primary alarm functions and compliance with the code, a communications failure on the network will have no significant effect. Under these circumstances, the code treats the network as an ancillary circuit.

More commonly, the cause and effect logic for the operation of the system does depend on the network, even if only to ensure that the fire and rescue service are summoned from a central control point in the event of fire. Under these circumstances, the network forms part of the critical signal paths and should be treated in the same way as any other fire alarm circuit to which the code applies.

Where sub-panels are simply 'black boxes', they need not even be visible to occupants, provided they are readily accessible for maintenance purposes. For example, in this case, the sub-panels are sometimes installed within electrical risers. In such a situation, it would be disconcerting for occupants to hear audible warnings from the sub-panels (e.g. in the case of system faults that are relayed to the central equipment). Accordingly, in this situation, the code permits audible warnings to be suppressed or disabled. For example, if the sub-panel happens to comprise a panel compliance with BS EN 54-2, any internal sounder required for compliance with this product standard could be disconnected.

If the network is not simply ancillary to full compliance with the code, the communications link between sub-panels should be monitored, regardless of whether it comprises wiring or radio transmission. Moreover, a fault on the communications link between sub-panels should not affect the operation of any sub-panel.

Also, in these circumstances, any cables used for the network should be fire resisting in accordance with the recommendations of the code (see Chapter 22). Clause 26 of the code divides fire resisting cables into two levels of performance, namely 'standard' and 'enhanced'. However, in the case of cables used for a network, standard fire resisting cables may be used in all circumstances in which the network is configured as a loop, and the incoming and outgoing sections of the loop follow diverse routings (except in the vicinity of the sub-panels), provided, also, that there will be no loss of communication to any sub-panel in the event of a single open or short circuit on the loop. It should be noted that this relaxation from the use of enhanced grade fire resisting cables in all circumstances applies only to the network itself; the wiring of other circuits connected to sub-panels (i.e. fire detection and sounder circuits) may, or may not, need to be wired in enhanced grade fire resisting cables, according to the relevant recommendations in clause 26 of the code.

Where the networked communications link constitutes only an ancillary circuit, the code still recommends that cables comply with the relevant recommendations of the code for fire alarm cables (see Chapter 22), but the cables need have no fire resistance if they do not form part of the critical signal paths or the relevant power supply circuits. In such a case, it may be possible to use a non-fire resisting data cable.

In some networked systems, a fire signal at one sub-panel will be transmitted around the network, or via the 'master' control equipment, for the purpose of initiating fire alarm signals at other sub-panels, from where the appropriate fire alarm sounders will then be driven. This can then delay the sounding of evacuation or alert signals in areas beyond that in which a manual call point is first operated. As discussed in earlier chapters, the delay between operation of the call point and sounding of an evacuation signal in, at least, the alarm zone in which the call point is located should not exceed three seconds. There is, of course, less urgency in the sounding of alarm signals in other alarm zones. However, in the case of a networked system, the code still recommends that appropriate alarm signals are given in these other alarm zones, beyond that in which the manual call point is located, within 10 seconds. This recommendation applies specifically to alarm signals generated by operation of a manual call point; the code makes no such recommendation in respect of alarm signals generated by automatic fire detectors.

In the case of large complexes of the type in which a networked system is likely to be used, often it will be appropriate for evacuation and alert signals to be given by a voice alarm system, rather than fire alarm sounders. Although clause 24 of the code, which deals with networked systems, makes no specific reference to voice alarm systems, it would be reasonable to assert that the same principles and recommendations should apply when a voice alarm system is used to give alarm signals, particularly as a voice alarm system may also be configured as a form of networked system.

21. Power supplies

In practice, the primary power supply for any fire alarm system will be derived from the normal 230 V mains supply serving the building. This supply will then be transformed and rectified at the fire alarm power supply equipment (to which BS EN 54-4[52] applies).

Two potentially conflicting considerations apply to this mains supply. First, even though, as discussed below, there will always be a standby supply in the form of batteries, it is highly desirable that the normal mains supply to the system is always available, so that there will only rarely be total reliance on batteries for the correct operation of the system. After all, albeit that proper maintenance is a prerequisite of compliance with the code, if the system is not properly maintained, on mains supply failure, the batteries too may fail to operate the system correctly. Moreover, as discussed below, batteries have only a finite capacity, on exhaustion of which, if the mains supply fault is not rectified, the system will fail to function.

The potentially conflicting requirement relates to electrical safety. As in the case of any electrical circuit, the cables serving the mains supply to the fire alarm system need proper protection against overload or short circuit, either of which will, therefore, ultimately, result in automatic disconnection of the circuit by the circuit protection. (If a power supply unit or standby batteries are housed in a separate enclosure from the control equipment, any interlinking cables would also need to be electrically protected against overcurrent; it would not, for example, be acceptable for remote batteries to be interconnected by cables without, for example, a suitable fuse in the circuit.)

Similarly, while it is undesirable for faults on other circuits and in other equipment to result in isolation of the mains power supply to the

---

[52] BS EN 54-4:1998, *Fire detection and fire alarm systems — Power supply equipment.*

fire alarm system, electrical safety considerations make it undesirable for the mains supply to the fire alarm system to remain live when the main isolator for the building has been switched off, so isolating all other electrical supplies; it might be regarded as reasonable for anyone operating the main isolator in the building to assume that all circuits in the building were isolated, and a live circuit to the fire alarm system might, under these circumstances, create the risk of electric shock.

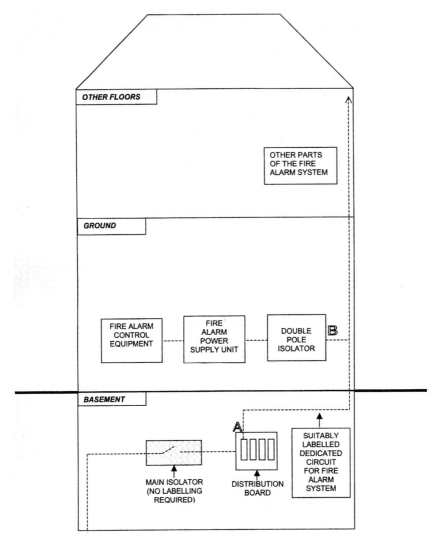

Figure 7 — Mains supply for fire alarm system

The manner in which the code resolves these issues is shown diagrammatically in Figure 7. This diagram is not reproduced from the code, but is merely the author's interpretation of the recommendations in the code, which are discussed below.

First, note that the mains supply to all parts of the fire alarm system should be supplied via an isolating protective device (such as a circuit-breaker) from the load ('dead') side of the main isolating device for the building. Even so, the code also contains a (slightly vague) recommendation that, where the user needs to isolate the supplies in the building during closed hours, a separate supply should be provided for the fire alarm system and that supply should not normally be isolated at these times. This does not, of course, necessarily conflict with the previous recommendation in relation to the main isolator, but it would necessitate a slightly different arrangement from that shown in the very simplistic arrangement contained in Figure 7, whereby, for example, a subsidiary isolator(s) serves all circuits other than the fire alarm system.

The code recommends that the 230 V final circuit(s) to all parts of the fire alarm system should be dedicated solely to the fire alarm system, and should serve no other systems or equipment. This differs from the practice in, for example, intruder alarm installations, in which the mains supply could be derived from, for example, a general electrical ring main. From point A in Figure 7, therefore, the circuit should be regarded as a dedicated fire alarm circuit, to which all the recommendations of the code regarding fire alarm circuits apply. Thus, for example, the cable between point A and the equipment that the mains supply serves should be fire resisting and segregated from the cables of other circuits (see Chapter 22).

The arrangement shown in Figure 7, whereby the dedicated 230 V mains supply emanates from the first electrical distribution board in the building's electrical distribution system, is, in fact, given in the code as a satisfactory example of compliance with the code. Nevertheless, the exact wording of the recommendations contained in the code does not make this a positive recommendation. The code merely recommends that the final circuits to all parts of the fire alarm system should be derived from a point in the building's electrical distribution system 'close' to the main isolating device for the building. It is not acceptable for the supply to be connected via a card or coin-operated meter, as this would, obviously, reduce the reliability of continuity of supply.

The code also recommends that, subject to compliance with other recommendations in the code and those of BS 7671,[53] the number of

---

[53] BS 7671, *Requirements for electrical installations. IEE Wiring Regulations.*

isolating devices between the incoming power supply to the building and the fire alarm power supply unit should be kept to the 'minimum practicable'. Particularly in a large building with a complex electrical distribution system, it will be for the designer to determine the interpretation of 'close' and 'minimum practicable'. No doubt, third-party certification bodies inspecting the work of electrical contractors and fire alarm companies will also wish to take a pragmatic, albeit stringent, approach to interpretation of these recommendations in actual buildings.

Furthermore, in a very large complex, such as a shopping centre or an airport terminal, strict compliance with the above recommendations might prove very onerous and expensive. For example, the complex might be served by a networked system (see Chapter 20), or there might be distributed power supply units around the building to drive fire alarm sounders within specific parts of the building, thereby minimizing long cable runs and voltage drop. Also, in some addressable systems, certain devices connected to detector loops, such as input/output units, require a mains power supply.

The question then arises as to whether it is necessary for the mains supplies to all such remote equipment to be derived from a single point in the building, close to the main isolator. The code, itself, acknowledges that, in these circumstances, a stringent limitation in the number of isolating devices between the incoming power supply and the various parts of the fire alarm system might be 'impracticable'. Thus, the code envisages that, in these circumstances, mains power supplies to parts of the system might be derived from one or more local distribution boards in the building. Nevertheless, the code regards such an arrangement as a variation that would require agreement of the interested parties, such as enforcing authorities and/or property insurers.

If the above variation is adopted, the code recommends that the number of isolating devices between the main incoming supply and the local distribution board should still be kept to the minimum practicable. It is also recommended that it be ensured that any need to isolate the supply to the local distribution board (e.g. for maintenance) will be infrequent, and that the risk of inadvertent isolation is low. Also, the final circuit derived from the local distribution board should be dedicated solely to the fire alarm equipment.

In addition, there will be a need to consider every isolator, switch and protective device between the main isolator and the local distribution board. Since any of these will isolate the mains supply to at least part of the fire alarm system, each one will need to be labelled in accordance with the recommendations of the code (see below), and they should all be inaccessible to unauthorized persons or protected against unauthorized operation (see below). The recommendations of the code in respect of residual current devices (see below) would also mean that no residual current device serving other circuits (e.g. serving all circuits connected to the local distribution board) serves the final circuit to the fire alarm system.

Regardless of the exact configuration that is adopted in respect of mains supplies, to avoid inadvertent isolation of the mains supply to the fire alarm system, every isolator and protective device that can isolate this supply should be clearly labelled, using durable fade resistant material:

- 'FIRE ALARM', in the case of a protective device that serves only the fire alarm circuit;
- 'FIRE ALARM. DO NOT SWITCH OFF', in the case of a switch (which may, or may not, incorporate a protective device) that serves only the fire alarm circuit;
- 'WARNING. THIS SWITCH ALSO CONTROLS THE SUPPLY TO THE FIRE ALARM SYSTEM', in the case of any switch that disconnects the mains supply to both the fire alarm system and to other circuits.

However, this recommendation does not apply to the main isolator for the building. The reason for this is that, whereas previous versions of the code accepted connection of the fire alarm system to either the 'live' or 'dead' side of this switch, the 2002 code recommends that the supply to the fire alarm system should, as in the case of all other circuits in the building, be connected to the 'dead' side. Accordingly, in installations designed in accordance with the 2002 code, it is reasonable to expect that anyone isolating all supplies to the building by use of the main isolator will appreciate that the supply to the fire alarm system is also affected. On the other hand, as noted above, particularly where several isolators have been permitted between the main isolator and the fire alarm power supply unit, each one of these must be appropriately labelled.

Every isolator, switch and protective device that is capable of disconnecting the mains supply to the fire alarm system, should be suitably located to make it inaccessible to unauthorized persons; alternatively, protection against unauthorized operation can be provided if operation requires the use of a special tool. In clause 25, the term 'special tool' is not defined, although the code gives the example of a key actuator (or 'secret key'). However, it would seem reasonable to use the explanation of the term 'special tool' contained in a note to subclause 12.2.2f)2), which relates to the use of a 'special tool' for removal of detectors. In that clause, a 'special tool' is described as a tool not likely to be carried by a member of the general public. Since various articles can be used as screwdrivers, slot-headed screws are deemed unacceptable in that clause as a means of prevention of unauthorized operation.

To further protect the integrity of the mains supply to the system, the code recommends against protection of the circuits supplying the fire alarm system by a residual current device (RCD), such as an earth leakage circuit breaker, unless the RCD is required for compliance with BS 7671. Even where, for reasons for electrical safety (e.g. the nature of the supply to the building and the arrangements for earthing), an RCD is required for compliance with BS 7671, it should be arranged that a fault on any other circuit or equipment in the building should not be capable of resulting in isolation of the supply to the fire alarm system. In practice, the most likely means of facilitating this level of security is to provide a separate RCD for the fire alarm system. (It should be noted that, under the latest (2008) edition of BS 7671, an RCD may be necessary for electrical safety if, for example, cables concealed in walls and partitions could be penetrated by nails, screws, etc.)

Ultimately, the mains supply will reach the power supply unit for the fire alarm system. At that point, it has become recognized custom and practice to provide an unswitched fused connection unit ('unswitched spur'). It has been traditionally accepted that a fire alarm system should not have a simple 'off switch', as would be found in general electrical equipment. It has also, previously, been deemed that the risk posed by the fire alarm power supply unit and control equipment are not such that a means of emergency switching is necessary for compliance with BS 7671.

The purpose of the local fused connection unit has, in practice, simply been to provide a convenient method of isolation of the mains supply during maintenance work on the fire alarm control equipment. This custom and practice, along with the associated philosophy, is now reflected in the code, which recommends that, to facilitate local isolation during maintenance, suitable means should be provided for isolation of the low voltage circuit that serves the power supply and control equipment. Since the objective of this means of isolation is safety during maintenance, the code recommends that *double pole* isolation be provided.

The code recommends that the above form of isolation should be provided for *all* parts of the system, in the vicinity of the equipment served. Specifically, it should not be necessary for maintenance technicians to access remote parts of the building (e.g. to search for means of isolation in a basement switch room, some distance from the fire alarm equipment), in order to isolate power supplies to equipment during maintenance. On the other hand, the recommendation described above, whereby unauthorized use of means of isolation should be prevented, applies to this facility, and it should be possible to lock the facility in both the 'normal' and 'isolate' positions to prevent unauthorized use.

Obviously, one means of satisfying the above recommendation would be to provide a lockable, double pole switch, suitably labelled, close to the equipment. However, it should be noted that, whatever facility is provided, it should be provided for all parts of the system. This must, surely, therefore apply to equipment such as loop-operated input/output units that require a mains supply direct to the unit.

It should be noted from the above recommendations that great importance is attached to maintaining the integrity of the mains power supplies. A philosophy whereby the importance of the mains supply is of limited importance, simply because standby batteries are provided, would not, therefore, be consistent with the spirit of the code. Thus, the code also recommends that, irrespective of the condition of the standby batteries, the mains power supply should be capable of supplying the maximum alarm load of the system.

The term 'maximum alarm load' is defined in the code: it is the maximum load imposed on a fire alarm system power supply under fire conditions, comprising the power required for simultaneous operation of all fire alarm devices, fire signals from all automatic fire detectors and manual call points in the building, any power drawn by other systems and equipment in the alarm condition and any power required for transmission of fire signals to an alarm receiving centre (ARC) (if a facility for this is provided). This is quite an onerous situation, in that, even when the batteries are 'flat', the mains power supply must be capable of supplying the power demand in the rather unlikely situation (at least in the case of a large building) in which fire alarm signals are being given by all manual call points and detectors, so that, for example, all zonal indicators are illuminated. In practice, this recommendation will have more of a bearing on the rating of the fire alarm power supply unit than the rating of the mains circuit supplying it.

With regard to the power supply unit itself, the batteries should, similarly, be capable of supplying the maximum alarm load of the system, in the event of mains failure. Transition between the normal supply and the standby supply, and vice versa, should not cause any interruption to the normal operation of the system or result in a false alarm. Separate protection should be provided for the mains supply and the battery supply, so that the operation of a single protective device cannot result in failure of both the normal and standby supply.

The presence of the normal or the standby supply should be indicated by a green indicator, located in a position that makes it readily obvious to any person responsible for monitoring faults on the fire alarm system. Effectively, this indicator is intended simply to provide an indication that power is being supplied to the system by one means or another; it is not a 'mains on' indicator that is intended to confirm that the mains supply is available. Failure of the mains supply will, of course, be indicated by an audible warning and visual 'fault' indication.

Since, as discussed below, it would be possible for the mains supply to fail when premises are unoccupied, and for the batteries to be exhausted prior to reoccupation, the location of the green indicator is important, as the absence of the indication will be the only means by which occupants will know that the fire alarm system is inoperative (perhaps as a result of a failure of only the final circuit serving the fire alarm system, while all other electrical supplies in the building are healthy). In practice, of course, the indicator is normally provided at the main fire alarm indicating equipment. Depending on the capacity of standby batteries (see below), it may, therefore, be very important that, after, say, a weekend or holiday period, the fire alarm indicating equipment in premises that are not continuously occupied is checked to ensure that the green indicator is present to indicate that the system has not suffered total power failure.

The standby batteries provided should be of the rechargeable type and have an anticipated life of least four years. Car batteries should not be used. The charger should be capable of recharging batteries (once they are discharged to their final voltage) to a capacity required for compliance with the code, after a charging period of 24 hours. If the power supply complies with BS EN 54-4, this recommendation will, in any case, be satisfied, but the recommendation appears in the code so that, if larger batteries than those specified in the original design are subsequently provided to cater for additional load, consideration will need to be given to the capability of the charger to recharge these larger batteries within the 24-hour period.

Often, the batteries used in fire alarm systems are only guaranteed for four years. As the batteries age, care will be needed to confirm that they are capable of holding their charge. For this reason, the code recommends that labels should be fixed to all batteries, indicating their date of installation. The labels should be sited such that they can be read without disturbing the batteries. Within their maintenance specifications, some users specify that batteries should be replaced as a preventative maintenance measure after a specified number of years; the recommendation for labelling of the batteries will also be of assistance in this respect.

Great care needs to be taken in specifying the duration for which standby batteries should be capable of operating the system, as the recommendations of the code vary, in a complex, albeit logical, way, according to the category of system and other relevant factors. These factors include the presence of a standby generator, the facility to transmit power supply fault signals to an ARC, the hours of occupation of the building, and also the nature of the fire alarm equipment served.

Consider, first, a Category M or Category L system. In both cases, the objective of the system is protection of life, and the function of the system is purely to evacuate occupants from the building in the event of fire. In the UK, failures in power supply to a building as a result of faults in the local electricity supply network rarely last more than a few hours; the standby batteries must be capable of operating the system during such failures, as the building might continue to be occupied.

However, a fault could occur in the electrical supplies within the building. It might reasonably be anticipated that such faults would be obvious to occupants, if present, and rectified quite quickly. Account also needs to be taken of the possibility of a fault on the final circuit serving the fire alarm system or on the mains part of the fire alarm power supply unit. In the latter case, there should be an arrangement in place, whereby, on a 24-hour basis, a technician from a maintenance organization, with whom there is an agreement, can attend the premises within eight hours of a call from the user.

In the light of the above considerations, the recommendations of the code in respect of standby battery capacity for Category M and Category L systems provide quite a generous factor of safety. The code recommends that the battery capacity should be sufficient to maintain the system in operation for at least 24 hours, after which sufficient capacity should remain to provide an evacuation signal in all alarm zones for at least 30 minutes.

However, the figure of 24 hours is reduced to six hours if the building is provided with an automatically started standby generator that provides power to the fire alarm system in the event of mains failure. It should be noted that the relaxation for buildings with automatically started standby generators can reasonably be expected to cater for all the scenarios described above, other than the exceptional case of a fault in the final circuit serving the fire alarm system, or within the fire alarm power supply unit, and the arrival of a maintenance technician after a period towards the maximum accepted by the code.

In practice, maintenance company response times are commonly shorter than eight hours in most areas of the country but, equally, it must be borne in mind that, according to the nature of the fault, some time will be required before repair of the fault. Thus, even if there is compliance with the code, in buildings with automatically started standby generators, there could be a need to evacuate occupants from a building if a mains power supply fault cannot be rectified within the period for which the standby batteries will operate the system. (As an aside, HTM 05-03 Part B[54] does not permit a relaxation from the 24-hour period in the case of hospitals, even though hospitals would generally have an automatically started standby generator.) If the relaxation for automatically started standby generators is to be adopted, care needs to be taken to ensure that the generator serves all mains circuits serving all parts of the fire alarm system (e.g. including distributed power supply units, etc.).

Compliance with the code and BS EN 54-2[55] will, of course, ensure that failure of the mains supply is indicated within 30 minutes of its occurrence. (In practice, in most systems, indication is given within a much shorter period.) However, if the fault occurs when the premises are unoccupied, the fire alarm system could obviously be inoperative when reoccupation occurs, unless this occurs within the period for which the standby batteries can operate the system. If the mains power supply failure affects other circuits in the building, the fault will, of course, be obvious. Therefore, the greatest risk is that associated with a fault on the dedicated circuit serving the fire alarm system.

In, for example, an office building that is unoccupied at weekends, the only indication to users that the system is totally inoperative will be the absence of the green power indicator discussed above. Possibly, the worst case scenario is that of a building with an automatically started standby generator and a six-hour duration standby battery; in this case, a fault on the fire alarm circuit during the night could result in the system being inoperative when occupants return on the following morning. This, again, highlights the need for the fire alarm indicating equipment to be checked each day in such cases.

Although not essential for compliance with the code, the above situation can be avoided if there are facilities for transmission of signals to an ARC. Often, even if such facilities are provided, only fire signals

---

[54] HTM 05-03 Part B, *Alarm and detection systems*. Published by the Department of Health in England and Wales. (In Scotland, the relevant code of practice is SHTM 82 published by NHS Scotland.)

[55] BS EN 54-2:1998, *Fire detection and fire alarm systems — Control and indicating equipment*.

are transmitted to the ARC. However, it is nearly always very simple to arrange for fault signals to be transmitted as well, as the transmitters used normally have the facility to transmit many different, separately identifiable alarm signals. If the premises are likely to be unoccupied for longer than the duration of the standby battery capacity at any time, and there is a facility for transmission of fire signals to an ARC, it is, therefore, of benefit to transmit power supply faults to the ARC, so that the user can be made aware of the fault. This would then obviate reliance on the absence of the green indicator as the sole form of warning that the fire alarm system is inoperative.

In the case of Category P systems, the objective is property protection, and the primary function of the system is to facilitate summoning of the fire and rescue service in the event of fire. Whereas, in the Category M or Category L system, failure of the fire alarm system while the premises are unoccupied does not immediately defeat the objective of the system, total failure of a Category P system at any time totally defeats the objective of the system.

Accordingly, the code recommends that, in the case of a Category P system, the battery capacity should be sufficient to maintain the system in operation for at least 24 hours, after which sufficient capacity should remain to operate all fire alarm devices for least 30 minutes. In the case of a Category P system, there is no relaxation for an automatically started standby generator.

Moreover, the minimum period of 24 hours' standby duration only satisfies the recommendations of the code for a Category P system if the building is continuously manned to such a degree, or is inspected outside normal working hours in such a way, that staff in the building would be aware of a power supply fault indication on the system within no more than six hours of its occurrence; there will then be 18 hours left to arrange for rectification of the fault. Alternatively, the 24-hour minimum duration satisfies the recommendations of the code if power supply fault signals are automatically transmitted to an ARC, which is instructed to notify a keyholder (and, possibly, the maintenance organization) immediately on receipt of a fault indication from the premises. Again, the latter arrangement provides a generous period for someone to attend the premises and rectify the fault.

In all cases other than those described above, even the period of 24-hour standby duration is insufficient to satisfy the recommendations of the code for Category P systems. In these other cases, the code recommends that battery capacity should be sufficient to maintain the system in operation for at least 24 hours longer than the maximum period for which the premises are likely to be unoccupied. However, an upper limit of 72 hours in total is recommended; thus, if the premises are likely to be unoccupied for longer than 48 hours, the battery capacity need only be sufficient to operate the system in the quiescent state for 72 hours. In either case, at the end of the standby duration, there should still be sufficient capacity to operate all fire alarm devices for at least 30 minutes.

The term 'likely' in the above recommendation is, obviously, open to interpretation, but, if, for example, the designer, on investigation, is made aware that the premises normally close for a week during the Christmas period, it would seem reasonable to specify a 72-hour duration battery, even if, for the rest of the year, the premises are continuously occupied around the clock. On the other hand, a lengthy unoccupied period as a result of, say, industrial action, could not reasonably be anticipated.

In the case of Category P systems, the code specifically recommends that, if the building is likely to be unoccupied for more than the duration of the standby battery capacity at any time, and there is a facility for transmission of fire signals to an ARC, power supply fault signals should also be automatically transmitted to the ARC, for immediate notification of a keyholder. There are two points to note about this recommendation. First, in the case of a Category P system, it is a specific recommendation; in the same circumstances, the code points out the benefits of the remote transmission arrangement in the case of a Category M or a Category L system, but the remote transmission facility is *not* a specific recommendation of the code.

Consider, therefore, the case of an office building that is normally occupied only between the hours of 9.00 a.m. and 6.00 p.m. on Monday to Friday. In the case of a Category M or Category L system for the premises, a standby battery duration of 24 hours will be necessary (or six hours if the premises are provided with an automatically started standby generator). If there is a facility for automatic transmission of fire signals to an ARC, the code acknowledges the benefit of transmission of fault signals to the ARC, but failure to provide this facility is not a variation from the recommendations of the code. In the case of a Category P system, a standby battery duration of 72 h will be necessary (with no relaxation for an automatically started standby generator), and, if there is a facility for transmission of fire signals to an ARC, there might, at first sight, be no need for transmission of fault signals to the ARC, since the premises are not unoccupied for longer than 72 h. However, if, as is likely, the premises will sometimes remain unoccupied on a Monday (e.g. on a Bank Holiday), fault signals should be transmitted to an ARC. In this case, as we are dealing with a Category P system, failure to do so would be a variation from the recommendations of the code.

The second point to note is that the code is, effectively, recommending that the user capitalize on an existing facility to transmit fire signals to an ARC; it is not recommended that a facility for transmission of signals to an ARC be provided specifically for transmission of power supply faults, if no facility is considered necessary for transmission of fire signals. Equally, as discussed in Chapter 13, the code already recommends that, except in the case of continuously occupied premises, Category P systems should incorporate a means for automatic transmission of fire signals to an ARC. (The same recommendation applies to certain Category L systems in non-domestic premises in multiple occupation.) However, if there is already a properly considered and documented variation from this recommendation (e.g. perhaps in the case of a Category P2 system with only a few detectors), the failure to transmit fault signals to an ARC need not be regarded as a further variation, even though the premises are unoccupied for a period longer than the standby battery duration, as there is not already an existing transmission facility on which to capitalize.

Often, equipment is provided over and above the minimum required to satisfy the recommendations of the code. For example, in a large building or complex, such as a shopping centre or large entertainments complex, colour graphics displays and text VDUs are provided over and above the basic BS EN 54-2 control and indicating equipment and zonal indications required to satisfy BS 5839-1. (Since the text and graphics VDUs are often driven from a separate PC, they are regarded as supplementary by the code, and the basic zonal indications should still be provided at an appropriate location.)

Often, these associated displays draw significant current, and compliance with the above recommendations would necessitate large standby batteries. The question then arises as to whether, since the additional equipment is not necessary for compliance with the code in the first place, the standby power supplies for it should comply with the recommendations of the code. In effect, the code describes three different situations, and provides different recommendations for each.

The first situation is one in which the equipment is not the normal method of indication of fire to those responsible for monitoring the system. For example, in, say, a security control room, it might be the case that security staff normally regard standard BS EN 54-2 control and indicating equipment as their 'interface' with the fire alarm system, while the graphics and text VDU sits in a corner, along with other building management system displays. Alternatively, a text VDU connected to a networked fire alarm system might reside within a manager's office or a maintenance engineer's office, as a secondary form of display to these persons if they happen to be present. In this case, there is no need for a standby supply, complying with the recommendations of the code, for the supplementary equipment.

The second (and more likely) situation is that the graphics/text VDUs are used by security control room staff as their primary indication of fire and its location. In this case, it is the BS EN 54-2 control and indicating equipment that 'sits in the corner'. Although the VDUs are not required for compliance with the code, since they are the normal method of indication, some delay or confusion might result if, in the event of fire, they are inoperative. Accordingly, the code recommends that, if the basic control and indicating equipment that is necessary for compliance with the code is suitably sited for use as a 'default' in the event of failure of the additional equipment, the capacity of the standby batteries serving the additional equipment should still be sufficient to operate the system in the quiescent mode for at least four hours. This should give ample time for those operating the system to come to terms with the need to use the 'default' equipment.

The third situation is one in which the additional equipment is the primary form of interface with those operating the system, and the basic control and indicating equipment is not suitably sited to enable effective control and monitoring of a fire incident. For example, it might be located within a plant room, so that it is still available, but is hardly convenient for control and indication in an emergency. In this third case, the code recommends that the standby power supplies for the additional equipment should satisfy all the recommendations of the code for equipment necessary for compliance with the code.

Traditionally, there has been some variation in the calculations used by designers in determining the battery capacity (in ampere-hours) required to satisfy the duration specified. This has meant that quotations from fire alarm contractors were not necessarily obtained on the basis of a 'level playing field', as one contractor might specify one size of standby battery, whereas another contractor might specify a different capacity. To avoid this situation, Annex D of the code provides a formula for calculation of the battery capacity of valve regulated lead acid batteries (the most common type used in fire alarm systems) to achieve a specified standby duration and alarm duration. As Annex D is normative, failure to use this formula constitutes a failure to comply with the recommendations of the code.

The formula in question is: $C_{\text{MIN}} = 1.25(T_1I_1 + DI_2/2)$

where:

C_{MIN} is the minimum capacity of the battery when new at the
20-hour discharge rate and at 20 °C (in ampere-hours)
T_1 is the total battery standby period, in hours
I_1 is the total battery standby load, in amperes
I_2 is the total battery alarm load, in amperes
D is a de-rating factor.

Most of the factors in the above formula are self-explanatory. The figure
of 1.25 is simply a 'fudge factor' to allow for battery ageing.

The de-rating factor is intended to take into account the fact that the
effective capacity of a battery depends on the rate at which it is discharged. Battery capacity is normally quoted at the 20-hour discharge
rate. Thus, a 20-ampere-hour battery would be capable of providing
one amp for 20 hours. However, it would not be capable of providing
20 amperes for one hour. The de-rating is needed in cases in which the
alarm current is sufficiently high to reduce the effective capacity below
its nominal value.

There is, therefore, need for something of an iterative calculation.
If, when $D = 1$, $C_{MIN}/20$ is equal to or greater than I_2, no de-rating
is required; a figure of 1 can be adopted for D. Otherwise, D can be
obtained from battery manufacturer's data; manufacturers provide a
series of curves for battery capacity at various rates of discharge. In
practice, this is quite complicated, and, accordingly, the code recommends that, instead, a 'default' figure of 1.75 may be adopted for D.
It is the latter practice that is normally adopted, and, in practice, the
major factor in the equation is still T_1I_1. The capacity required for the
30-minute full alarm load is usually quite small compared to T_1I_1, and
it makes little difference whether this figure is multiplied by 1 or 1.75;
there will, nevertheless, be cases where the use of 1.75, as opposed to 1,
necessitates the use of larger batteries.

22. Cables and wiring

The code deals with cables, wiring and other interconnections in clause 26. The first point made within that clause is that interconnections need not specifically use cables; radio or fibre optics can be used. Although the code contains no specific recommendations for fibre optic connections, the commentary of clause 26 points out that they need to provide at least equivalent integrity and reliability to other cables recommended for the same purpose. In the case of radio-linked systems, a separate clause of the code contains specific recommendations for such systems (see Chapter 23).

The intent of clause 26 is to ensure the integrity and reliability of fire alarm circuits before, and to a sufficient extent during the course of, any fire. As discussed in Chapter 11, the code ensures that, under normal circumstances, the time for which the system, or any part of it, is disabled as a result of a fault on wiring is minimized by circuit monitoring, to which the recommendations of clause 12 apply.

Clause 26 endeavours to ensure that the probability of faults is minimized. Its key recommendations in this respect relate to protection of cables against mechanical damage, protection of cables against damage by fire, segregation of fire alarm circuits from other circuits, and identification of fire alarm circuits so that they can be distinguished from other circuits.

The cables should also, of course, be suitable, electrically, for their purpose; there is, therefore, a need to consider conventional electrical engineering issues, such as voltage drop, current carrying capacity, impedance and, where appropriate, ability to transmit data at the relevant speed without corruption.

The code specifically recommends only three types of cable, namely mineral insulated copper sheathed cables (complying with

BS EN 60702-1),[56] cables complying with BS 7629[57] and armoured fire-resistant cables complying with BS 7846.[58] However, the code also accepts the use of cables rated at, at least, 300/500 V that provide the same degree of safety to that afforded by conforming to BS 7629, so precluding any obstacle to the use of new forms of cable. It should be noted that any requirements of the above standards in respect of fire resistance can be ignored, as resistance to fire is separately specified in BS 5839-1 (see below).

In practice, most designers will specify either mineral insulated copper sheathed cables or proprietary fire resisting cables conforming to BS 7629 (often described as 'soft-skinned' cables). Traditionally, the choice has been largely a matter of preference on the part of the designer. Mineral insulated copper sheathed cables are less likely to need additional mechanical protection and have a very long history of performing extremely well in real fires, often well beyond the duration necessary to ensure that the objectives of the fire alarm system are satisfied. On the other hand, the newer proprietary fire resisting cables conforming to BS 7629 have now been in existence for many years without any evidence to suggest that their performance in real fires is inadequate. The total cost of installation of these cables (comprising material cost plus labour cost) is often lower than in the case of mineral insulated copper sheathed cables, and these cables are sometimes easier to retrofit in an existing building. With certain exceptions, the choice of cable type, within the range of cables accepted by the code, remains largely a matter of 'taste' on the part of the designer.

To ensure mechanical strength, the code recommends that, whatever cable is used, all conductors should have a cross-sectional area of at least 1 mm^2. To avoid the risk of mechanical damage to the cables, they should not be installed within the same conduit as the cables of other services. Where the cables share common trunking with other cables, a separate compartment of the trunking, separated from other compartments by a strong, rigid and continuous partition, should be reserved solely for fire

---

[56] BS EN 60702-1:2002, IEC 60702-1: 2002, *Mineral insulated cables and their terminations with a rated voltage not exceeding 750 V. Cables.*

[57] BS 7629-1:1997, *Specification for 300/500 V fire resistant electric cables having low emission of smoke and corrosive gases when affected by fire — Multicore Cables.*
BS 7629-2:1997, *Specification for 300/500 V fire resistant electric cables having low emission of smoke and corrosive gases when affected by fire — Multipair Cables.*

[58] BS 7846:2000, *Electric cables. 600/1000 V armoured fire-resistant cables having thermosetting insulation and low emission of smoke and corrosive gases when affected by fire.*

alarm cables. The purpose of this recommendation is to avoid damage to the fire alarm cables when modifications are carried out to other circuits (e.g. other cables are stripped out). When a new fire alarm system is retrofitted to a building, it would, of course, be possible to consider a variation from this recommendation for economy of installation, particularly in the case of mains supply cables for the fire alarm system; care might, however, be required in the case of other circuits in order to avoid any chance of electromagnetic interference to fire alarm circuits from circuits of other services.

Mineral insulated copper sheathed cables and steel wire armoured cables may be used throughout all parts of the system without additional mechanical protection, except in particularly arduous conditions. The code recommends that other cables should be given mechanical protection in any areas in which physical damage or rodent attack is likely. More specifically, other than in relatively benign environments in which cable is clipped directly to robust construction, mechanical protection should be provided for these other cables in all areas that are less than 2 m above floor level.

The term 'relatively benign environments' is not specifically defined, but, since the code gives the example of offices, shops and similar premises, in many situations, other than certain factories, warehouses and similar premises, it will be possible to install the so-called 'soft-skinned' cables without additional mechanical protection. However, where the environment is not 'relatively benign', additional protection to these cables will be necessary, at least, everywhere that cables run less than 2 m above floor level; it should be noted that this will include at least part of each 'drop' to a manual call point, since the latter devices are generally installed around 1.4 m above floor level.

For the purposes of the above recommendation, additional protection may be provided by running the cable on cable tray, 'chasing in' within the building structure, or by installation of the cables in conduit, ducting or trunking. If, however, particularly arduous conditions might be experienced (such as impact by forklift trucks or goods trolleys), additional, robust protection is recommended by the code in the form of burying the cable in the structure of the building or installation in *metal* conduit or trunking.

To further ensure the integrity of the fire alarm circuits, the code recommends that cables should be installed without external joints wherever practicable. Where jointing of cables is necessary, other than in the case of joints at or within components of the system, the terminals used to joint the cables should be constructed of materials that will withstand a similar temperature and duration of temperature to that of the cable itself. This recommendation is likely to preclude the use of plastic terminal blocks. Ceramic terminal blocks could, however, be used. The joints should be enclosed within junction boxes and labelled with the words 'FIRE ALARM', to assist in the identification of fire alarm circuits.

In recent years, there has been much controversy regarding the performance required from fire alarm cables during the course of a fire. The 1988 version of BS 5839-1 divided fire alarm circuits into two groups, namely those required to operate for a prolonged period during the course of a fire and those not required to do so. No fire performance requirements were recommended for the latter group of cables, but the 1988 version of the code recommended that the former cables should either comprise mineral insulated copper sheathed cable or cables capable of achieving a certain performance if tested in accordance with BS 6387,[59] but other types of cable could also be used provided they were suitably protected against fire by burial in the structure of the building or separation from any significant fire risk by structural fire protection.

The controversy that has raged in recent years concerns the manner in which cables are tested in accordance with BS 6387. The tests specified in BS 6387 include one to verify resistance to fire alone. There is then a further test to verify resistance to fire in conjunction with water spray (reflecting the fact that, during a fire, water will be discharged onto the fire from extinguishers, hose reels and/or sprinkler heads), and a third test to verify the resistance of the cable to fire in conjunction with mechanical shock (reflecting the fact that, during a fire, objects may fall).

The controversy has centred around the matter of whether all three tests should be carried out on a single sample of cable or whether, as actually happens, a separate sample is used for each of the three tests. Particularly, it has been claimed that, generally, mineral insulated copper sheathed cables can pass all three tests even if they are carried out on a single sample of cable, whereas it is claimed that this is not generally true of soft-skinned cables.

This controversy has been resolved in the 2002 version of the code, which also, to some extent, simplifies the recommendations in respect of the fire resistance of cables. First, the code recommends that all cable systems used for all parts of the critical signal paths, and for the low voltage mains supply to the system, should be fire resisting. It

---

[59] BS 6387:1994, *Specification for performance requirements for cables required to maintain circuit integrity under fire conditions*.

should be noted that this recommendation applies to the cable itself; protection of a non-fire resisting cable by building construction will not satisfy the recommendations of the code. It should also be noted that, as discussed in Chapter 21, this recommendation applies to the entire length of mains supply cable to the system, from the point at which the circuit is first dedicated to the fire alarm system (see Chapter 21). The cables recommended by the code should also be used for the circuits between any separate power supply units and the control and indicating equipment.

However, the code now divides fire resisting cables into two types, according to their level of fire resistance, namely 'standard fire resisting cables' and 'enhanced fire resisting cables'. The code specifies performance levels for each of the two groups of cables. Rather than these performance levels relating to BS 6387, the tests relate to BS EN 50200[60] in conjunction with additional performance recommendations specified in BS 8434-2[61] (for cables of enhanced fire resistance). The performance levels themselves were developed largely by determining the level of performance that can, in the case of enhanced fire resistance, reasonably be expected in the case of a mineral insulated copper sheathed cable, and that can, in the case of standard fire resistance, reasonably be expected of any of the existing proprietary fire resisting cables that have been certificated as conforming to BS 7629.

Several 'soft skin' cables have now been tested and certificated by a third-party certification body in accordance with the recommendations of the code for enhanced fire resistance, using the tests of BS 8434-2. Therefore, it is possible to obtain 'soft-skinned' cables of enhanced fire resistance.

The code acknowledges that cables capable of complying with the recommendations for standard fire resistance are expected to include some that have been commonly used for many years for circuits in fire alarm systems that must operate for a prolonged period during a fire, without any evidence from real fires that satisfaction of the objectives of the fire alarm system necessitates a higher performance. However, the code recognizes that the level of fire resistance described as 'enhanced'

---

[60] BS EN 50200, *Method of test for resistance to fire of unprotected small cables for use in emergency circuits.*

[61] BS 8434-2:2003, *Methods of test for assessment of the fire integrity of cables — Test for unprotected small cables for use in emergency circuits — BS EN 50200 with a 930 °C flame and with water spray.*

is desirable in certain situations. Four such situations are described in the code, and these are reproduced from the code in full below:

1) in un-sprinklered buildings (or parts of buildings) in which the fire strategy involves evacuation of occupants in four or more phases;
2) in un-sprinklered buildings of greater than 30 m in height;
3) in un-sprinklered premises and sites in which a fire in one area could affect cables of critical signal paths associated with areas remote from the fire, in which it is envisaged people will remain in occupation during the course of the fire. Examples may be large hospitals with central control equipment and progressive horizontal evacuation arrangements, and certain large industrial sites; the former is the more common application.
4) in any other buildings in which the designer, specifier or regulatory authority, on the basis of a fire risk assessment that takes fire engineering considerations into account, considers that the use of enhanced fire resisting cables is necessary.

It should be noted that, in the first three specific cases, sprinkler protection would obviate the need for use of cables of enhanced fire resistance. It is considered that, in a sprinklered building, the fire risk, the likelihood of fire development and the likely exposure of cables to fire make the use of cables of standard fire resistance acceptable. However, for the purpose of this recommendation, the code advises that a building should be regarded as sprinklered only if an automatic sprinkler installation complying with the recommendations of BS 5306-2[62] is provided throughout the building. It is not, however, necessary for the additional recommendations of BS 5306-2 for 'life safety installations', to be implemented in order for the relaxation in the code to apply.

The reason for the use of enhanced fire resisting cables in un-sprinklered buildings in which there is evacuation in four or more phases is simply that, in these situations, occupants will be expected to remain in the building for some time after fire is detected. Since a full Category L1 system is not always provided in buildings with phased evacuation (for example, Approved Document B under the Building Regulations in England and Wales specifies only that the L3 standard of BS 5839-1 be satisfied in a phased evacuation building), the fire,

---

[62] BS 5306-2:1990, *Fire extinguishing installations and equipment on premises — Specification for sprinkler systems.* Although BS 5839-1 still refers to this code of practice, it has now been superseded by BS EN 12845.

to which fire alarm cables could be exposed, could, in any case, have already been burning for some considerable time before detection. It is obviously essential that the system is capable of reliably giving warning to occupants during the very last phase of the evacuation. It is also important that there is a high reliability that indication from automatic fire detectors of fire spread can be given at the control and indicating equipment.

In a large building with phased evacuation, a networked fire alarm system might be provided (see Chapter 20). In this case, individual, self-contained fire alarm systems might serve parts of the building that are evacuated in less than four phases, even though the entire building is evacuated in four or more phases. In these cases, cables of enhanced fire resistance need not be used for the systems themselves, but there might be a need to use cables of enhanced fire resistance for the network. Even this would not be necessary if the network is configured in a loop, with diverse routing of incoming and outgoing circuits, and if the loop is designed in such a way that there will be no loss of communication to any sub-panel in the event of a single open or short circuit on the loop. Figure 8, which is reproduced from the code, shows this situation. It should be noted that, although in this figure, for simplicity, each self-contained system is shown as serving only two floors, in practice each system could 'drive' up to three phases of evacuation, which would, typically, comprise six floors.

The recommendation for cables of enhanced fire resistance in un-sprinklered buildings of greater than 30 m in height simply reflects the greater risk associated with tall buildings. In the case of tall office buildings, phased evacuation is often used in any case, and the recommendation relating to phased evacuation will already apply. It should also be noted that, for example, Approved Document B under the Building Regulations in England and Wales would not permit new buildings of greater than 30 m in height to be un-sprinklered, unless the buildings were of the 'other residential' nature, such as hotels, hostels, etc. (Approved Document B does specify that flats or maisonettes in blocks over 30 m in height should be sprinklered, but the recommendation does not relate to the common parts, but only to the flats. In Scotland, the equivalent guidance recommends sprinkler protection for flats in blocks above 18 m in height.) It is, nevertheless, important that the recommendation for use of cables of enhanced fire resistance in un-sprinklered buildings of greater than 30 m in height be borne in mind when retrofitting fire alarm systems in tall buildings that might not have required sprinkler protection at the time of construction.

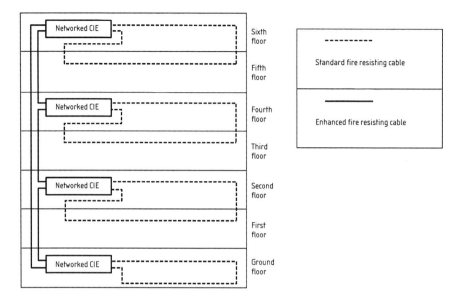

Figure 8 — Example of a networked fire alarm system in
a multi-storey building, showing standard cable grade for
local wiring and enhanced grade for network cable

The third situation, in which cables of enhanced fire resistance are specified above, often occurs in hospitals. In a hospital, the principle of progressive horizontal evacuation applies. This means that, in the first stages of a fire, patients are moved horizontally, through a set of fire resisting doors, into an adjacent 'sub-compartment'. Only if the fire continues to grow and threaten this adjacent fire compartment will these patients be further evacuated. Similarly, patients in the remainder of the hospital will not ever be evacuated unless they are threatened by the fire.

Progressive horizontal evacuation differs from phased evacuation in that, in a phased evacuation building, the intention is to evacuate all occupants in the event of fire, but merely to do so in a number of discrete phases. In progressive horizontal evacuation, the intention is, if possible, never to evacuate the majority of occupants. If, subsequently, at what could be a much later stage, evacuation of areas remote from the fire is necessary, any cables required for this purpose must remain undamaged. It is for this reason that cables of enhanced fire resistance are specified in the code, unless the premises are sprinklered. In practice, HTM 05-03 Part B now recommends the use of cables of enhanced fire resistance for hospitals.

A similar situation to that described for hospitals can apply in a very long complex of (generally low rise) interconnected buildings within an industrial complex; it may be unnecessary to evacuate the areas most remote from a fire, but, equally, there will be a need for a facility to do so at an advanced stage in the fire if this becomes necessary. However, if the hospital or single range of buildings were served by a networked system, and each of the independently evacuated sections were served by an individual, self-contained fire alarm system, cables of enhanced fire resistance would not be necessary except, possibly, in the case of the network cables. Thus, the considerations applicable to networked systems, described for phased evacuation buildings, apply in this situation.

What then of a large site, with many *separate* buildings, all served by a single fire alarm system, with cables for one or more buildings running through other buildings? This situation is not clearly addressed in the code. However, in fire safety design, account is not normally taken of a situation in which two independent fires occur at the same time. Accordingly, pragmatism would seem to dictate that if the separation between buildings is such that, in the event of fire in one building, evacuation of other buildings could not be anticipated, even at an advanced stage of the fire, the use of cables of enhanced fire resistance would seem to be unnecessary.

With regard to the fourth of the situations in which the code recommends that cables of enhanced fire resistance should be used, the reason is that, in some fire engineering solutions, a reduction in the normal level of other fire protection measures may be acceptable to an enforcing authority, provided an automatic fire detection system is installed. In such a case, clearly the reliability of the automatic fire detection system must be of a high order, since, for example, normal provisions for means of escape may have been relaxed on the basis that the system will operate when required. In these circumstances, the code leaves it to the enforcing authority to determine whether, as part of the fire engineering solution, cables of enhanced fire resistance will be necessary to satisfy legislation.

In the same way that any joints in cables should not compromise the fire resistance of the overall cable system (see above), methods of cable support should be such that circuit integrity is not reduced. The methods of support should withstand a similar temperature, and duration of temperature, to the cable itself, while maintaining adequate support. As pointed out in the code, this recommendation, in effect, precludes the use of plastic cable clips, cable ties or trunking, where these products are the sole means of cable support.

In February 2005, a fire occurred in a flat within a block of flats in Stevenage, Hertfordshire. The fire resulted in the deaths of two fire-fighters and one member of the public. It is known that, during the incident, one of the two fire-fighters was entangled in fire alarm cables within the common parts of the block, support for which had failed as a result of fire damage to their supporting plastic trunking. Although the use of plastic trunking as the sole means of support for fire alarm cables does not satisfy the recommendations of the code (primarily to prevent loss of circuit integrity), the April 2008 amendment to the code now draws attention to the hazard of falling cables to fire-fighters, so emphasizing the need to avoid plastic components as the sole means of support. The amendment also cites inadequately supported cables as a significant departure from the recommendations of BS 5839-1, to which a newly appointed maintenance contractor should draw to the attention of the user (see Chapter 34). Fire resistance of cable support is also a matter that the designer might want to draw to the attention of an installer.

Finally, there remains the matter of protecting fire alarm cables from any detrimental influence of other circuits. The code recommends, therefore, that, where multi-core cable is used for interconnection of fire alarm circuits, none of the conductors should be used for circuits other than those of the fire alarm system. To avoid electromagnetic interference with the fire alarm signals, care needs to be taken that any recommendations by the manufacturer of the fire alarm equipment in respect of separation of fire alarm cables from the cables of other services are followed.

Furthermore, fire alarm cables carrying power in excess of extra-low voltage (e.g. at 230 V) should be segregated from extra-low voltage fire alarm circuits (e.g. 24 V circuits). However, the code recognizes the four types of cable specified within clause 26 and described above, as themselves, a suitable form of segregation, subject to conformity to any recommendations by the manufacturer of the fire alarm equipment in respect of separation for the purposes of avoiding electromagnetic interference. Nevertheless, the code recommends that the mains supply to any control, indicating or power supply equipment should not enter the equipment through the same cable entry as cables carrying extra-low voltage. Within the equipment itself, low voltage and extra-low voltage cables should be kept separate to the extent practicable.

Having segregated the fire alarm circuits from other circuits and, in the case of trunking, kept the fire alarm cables within a separate compartment from other circuits, it is important that this situation is maintained. It is also important that there is no interference with fire alarm circuits as a result of confusion between these circuits and other circuits. Accordingly, the code recommends that all fire alarm cables should be of a single, common colour that is not used for cables of general electrical services in the building. While a note in clause 26 of the code states that the colour red is preferred, it would be possible to comply with the code by using another colour, provided the same colour is not used for cables of other electrical services in the building.

23. Radio-linked systems

The previous chapter of this guide considered the recommendations of the code in respect of cables. However, the code does not specifically recommend that cables are used throughout a fire alarm system. Instead, radio communication can be used for communication between control equipment and the manual call points, fire detectors and fire alarm devices linked to the control equipment. In large buildings, in which the distance between devices and control equipment (and/or the building construction itself) precludes adequate strength of radio signals from devices existing at the control equipment, radio relay units can extend the range of the system.

The relay units may comprise 'black boxes' with no other function than to extend the range of the system, or they may, in fact, comprise local control and indicating panels; in the latter case, there is, in effect, a form of networked system. The code recommends that, where there is a network of control and indicating equipment, the system specification should define whether there is to be one master panel, at which all controls and indications are available, or whether some control and indication is to be possible at sub-panels.

Radio-linked fire alarm systems were first recognized in the 1988 version of BS 5839-1, which accepted radio communication between control equipment and manual call points/fire detectors. Since then, the use of radio-linked systems has grown, and a greater variety of products has become available. Radio-linked fire alarm sounders have also become available and, indeed, are the norm in radio-linked systems. Clause 27 of the code provides recommendations for radio-linked systems, and it accepts that, as well as detectors and manual call points, fire alarm devices (e.g. fire alarm sounders) may communicate with control equipment by means of radio-links.

Experience suggests that there are both advantages and disadvantages in the use of radio instead of hard wiring. However, the code does not consider these, nor does it need to do so, since clause 27 provides recommendations for systems that are radio-linked, rather than providing recommendations in respect of the situations in which radio-linked systems are, or are not, appropriate. It is, therefore, a matter for the designer to decide whether to use a radio-linked system or a 'hard-wired' system; this will be, largely, a matter of personal 'taste'.

In the experience of the author, one of the main advantages of radio-linked systems is ease of retrofitting in heritage buildings and other buildings in which the installation of cables would cause disruption and be intrusive to the character of the building. Thus, radio-linked systems are commonly used to protect stately homes and country houses. Installation time is also greatly reduced. For example, in one project with which the author was involved (a large hotel), it was estimated that a radio-linked system could be installed and commissioned within three weeks, whereas, to install and commission a hard-wired system would have required at least three months. In another project, a radio-linked system was selected to provide a single, integrated fire alarm system to be installed throughout a number of separate blocks of luxury flats that could not easily have been linked by wiring and that had, in any case, only recently been redecorated, making wiring undesirable.

The much shorter installation time required for a radio-linked system might suggest that the cost of installation and commissioning would be much cheaper than in the case of a hard-wired system, particularly as installation of wiring probably accounts for around 50% of the total cost of such a system. However, the equipment itself will be more expensive, since every device incorporates a radio transmitter. In practice, whether a radio system will be significantly cheaper or even more expensive will depend on the particular building, the need or otherwise for radio relay units and the ease with which wiring can be installed. If life cycle cost is taken into account, consideration would also have to be taken of the cost of battery replacement, particularly in the case of radio-linked sounders, in which batteries will have a shorter life than in the case of radio-linked manual call points or automatic detectors. Overall, therefore, on a life cycle basis, there could be a cost penalty for the benefit of easier installation and any lower installation cost.

At the time of writing, the most common radio-linked systems installed are those manufactured by a small number of specialist firms. Since radio transmission protocols are not standardized throughout the industry, if a radio-linked system is chosen by the designer, choice of product will be very limited, although radio-linked systems can be provided and installed by numerous fire alarm companies. There will, nevertheless, be a much greater choice of product and availability of leading edge detection technologies in the case of hard-wired systems.

It is possible to 'mix and match' hard-wired equipment and radio-linked equipment. Indeed, the code recognizes that radio communications may be used to link a small number of detectors and other components to what is essentially a wired system. This could, for example, enable fire alarm equipment in a remote building to be linked by radio to a main, hard-wired system. In practice, this situation is very uncommon, but the recommendations of clause 27 of the code would apply to the radio-linked part of such a system.

The need for clause 27 and its recommendations that are specific to radio linked systems arises from the fact that some of the recommendations of the code, applicable to wired systems, are unsuitable for, or cannot be applied to, radio-linked systems. The obvious aspects of a radio-linked system to which the normal recommendations of the code cannot be applied comprise the power supplies for the radio-linked devices, which will normally comprise primary batteries, and monitoring of the connection between the devices and the control equipment. However, there is still a need for a radio-linked system to afford reliability and integrity in the protection it offers, equivalent to the levels of reliability and integrity recommended for hard-wired systems.

As discussed in Chapter 10, reliability begins with product design and performance. Accordingly, the code recommends that components of a radio-linked system should comply with BS EN 54-25.[63]

As discussed above, the main aspects of radio-linked systems to which the general recommendations of the code cannot readily be applied are power supplies and monitoring. Accordingly, for radio-linked systems, the code accepts the use of batteries as the normal power supply for all components, other than control and indicating equipment. However, there should still be at least two independent power supplies for all radio-linked components (which is not always necessary for compliance with BS EN 54-25). In practice, the two power supplies will normally comprise a primary battery plus a second primary battery. The code would, nevertheless, permit a mains supply as the normal supply, and a battery as the standby supply. It would also accept a secondary battery as the standby supply. Moreover, capacitors with an appropriate specification are accepted as an alternative to secondary batteries. In practice, since the main benefit of a radio-linked system

---

[63] BS EN 54-25, *Fire detection and fire alarm systems – Part 25: components using radio links.*

is the almost total absence of any wiring, it is unlikely that these other options will occur.

Primary batteries will, of course, eventually become exhausted. Obviously, adequate warning of impending battery failure is necessary. However, conceptually, this is a natural condition in the life of a radio-linked system, as opposed to the occurrence of an unpredicted defect. Accordingly, the code recommends that, although power supplies incorporating one or more primary batteries should give at least 30 days' warning of impending failure of each battery, this should be indicated specifically as a low battery warning condition at the control and indicating equipment, rather than as a fault condition.

Obviously, such an indication should receive attention within a relatively short time, albeit that, in view of the 30 days' quiescent operation that remains, battery replacement is not urgent. Unfortunately, some users tend to wait until there are numerous low battery indications on the system before calling the maintenance organization, so minimizing the cost of maintenance charges. In the opinion of the author, this is hardly within the spirit of the code, and, indeed, it could be argued that periodic replacement of batteries before low battery indications are prevalent would be a more suitable preventative maintenance measure, particularly since the code recommends that primary power supplies should have a minimum, normal operational life of three years (over a normal temperature range) before the low power condition is signalled.

However, if the user does ignore the low battery indication(s), the code contains a further 'long stop' recommendation. The code recommends that, at the point at which the power supply(ies) to any radio-linked component can maintain the component in normal operation for no more than seven days and, in addition, in the case of fire alarm devices, 30 minutes in the alarm condition, a *fault* warning should be given at the control and indicating equipment. Thus, at this stage, the low battery indication is escalated to a fault indication, necessitating more urgent attention.

With regard to monitoring, compliance with the code does not require quasi-continuous transmissions between radio-linked components and control equipment. Were this required, there would be significant potential for clash of signals from different radio-linked components and, consequently, spurious fault signals at the control and indicating equipment. Accordingly, the code recommends only that a fault that gives rise to loss of communication with a radio-linked component should be indicated at the control and indicating equipment within two hours of its occurrence.

This does mean, of course, that, for example, an area or room could be left devoid of protection by a specific fire detector for up to two hours as a result of a communication fault, whereas, in the case of a hard-wired system, indication of loss of communication would be given within 100 seconds. Does this mean a lower standard of reliability in the case of radio-linked systems? In theory, the answer must be yes, and the two-hour period is simply a compromise between the need for frequent monitoring and the need to avoid signal clash.

However, in practice, any difference in reliability is probably of no significance. Transmission faults should be rare occurrences. Fires, themselves, are rare occurrences. The probability of the fire within the two-hour maximum 'window' before a transmission fault is detected is arguably an event of diminishingly small probability. (If, for example, an arsonist were to remove a detector head, a fault signal would be given, and the recommendation of the code in respect of all systems, namely that the fault indication be given at the control equipment within 100 seconds, still applies.)

Moreover, it could be argued that there is a greater need for continuous monitoring of hard-wired systems, since the medium of communication (i.e. the wiring) can be interrupted by mechanical damage; this is not possible in the case of a radio-linked system. Perhaps the closest analogy that would apply in the case of a radio-linked system would be a change to the building structure that affects the radio signal strength (e.g. enclosure of a detector within metal partitioning), or the closure of a metal shutter at the end of the working day. Again, however, the likelihood of a fire within a short period of this occurring must be regarded as extremely low, and, once the problem was identified, suitable action can reasonably be anticipated.

A further argument in favour of permitting this minor relaxation in the case of radio-linked systems is that, in some circumstances, were it not for the benefits of a radio-linked system in avoiding cables, the user might not be prepared to install a system at all, in which case there would never be any protection!

Even in a radio-linked system, there will be a need for some wiring. Specifically, there will be a need for a mains supply circuit to the control and indicating equipment. Obviously, this circuit will be monitored in the same manner as the supply to the control and indicating equipment of a hard-wired system. A radio-linked system may, in addition, require antennae external to components. The cables of such antennae should be monitored for open and short circuits, so that a fault condition is given at the control and indicating equipment within 100 seconds of such an event. All antennae, themselves, should be so arranged that special tools are required for disconnection or removal of the outer housing.

If external antennae are used, the cable obviously forms part of the critical alarm path. Accordingly, as well as the need for monitoring of the cable, there will be a need to protect the cable against the effects of fire. Ideally, each antenna cable should be fire resisting in accordance with the recommendations of the code. In practice, a suitably fire resisting cable of the coaxial type normally used is very uncommon. Accordingly, the code permits a relaxation for these cables, such that they do not need to be fire resisting provided they are routed through areas of low fire risk, or are protected against exposure to fire. Protection can be provided by burial in at least 12 mm of plaster or by separation from any fire risk by materials that would afford a fire resistance of at least 30 minutes if tested in accordance with the relevant part of BS 476.[64] (This form of protection was accepted for all cables in the 1988 version of the code, but is only accepted in the 2002 version for antennae cables in radio-linked systems.)

A further potential fault mode that is unique to radio-linked systems is 'jamming' of transmissions by other radio signals. Accordingly, the code recommends that, after 30 seconds of continuous interference to the transmitted signal that can compromise the performance of the fire detection and fire alarm system, a fault indication should be given at the control and indicating equipment within a further 100 seconds. It should be noted that this does not mean that a fault indication need only be given after 130 seconds of continuous interference, but merely that, after 30 seconds of continuous interference, a fault indication should be given, albeit not necessarily immediately but within 100 seconds.

A further relaxation, based on compromise between conflicting objectives, is required to minimize unnecessary drain of batteries in a radio-linked system, so preventing premature failure of the batteries. Thus, as discussed in Chapter 14, in certain circumstances, subject to the agreement of the enforcing authority, radio-linked sounders should silence automatically after 30 minutes. Also, after detection of fire, a detector LED need only remain illuminated for 20 minutes, after which it may automatically extinguish.

It was asserted earlier in this chapter that it is important to ensure adequate radio reception (i.e. signal strength) throughout all interconnected parts of the radio-linked system. Accordingly, the code devotes considerable attention to this matter. Clause 27 recommends

---

[64] BS 476, *Fire tests on building materials and structures.*

that installation of a radio-linked system should only take place after a comprehensive radio survey has been undertaken. The purpose of the survey is to ensure adequate signal strength for communication between components and to ensure that no other sources of radio-transmission could interfere with, or block, radio communication between components in the system. The radio survey test equipment should be approved by the manufacturer and regularly calibrated, with the date of calibration, and the date when the next calibration is due, marked on the equipment.

During the initial radio survey, radio signal strength readings should be recorded and kept for future reference. Thereafter, at commissioning, details of the signal level received at each of the receiver units from all radio devices should be measured and recorded, along with background radio noise level. The signal levels should be kept on site with the system log book. Signal levels should then be checked, again, at the time of each service visit.

24. Electrical safety and electromagnetic compatibility

Electrical safety is discussed in clause 29 of the code, while electromagnetic compatibility is discussed in clause 28. These two clauses are the final clauses of Section 2 of the code, which is addressed specifically to the 'designer'.

Clause 29 is primarily concerned with avoidance of electric shock. Accordingly, the clause recommends that the system design should be such as to satisfy the relevant recommendations of BS 7671.[65] The code recommends that the instructions of the manufacturer of the control and indicating equipment should be followed, particularly in respect of earthing arrangements, and that circuit protective conductors should be adequately rated. Since earthing is a matter of general electrical engineering, it is not considered further in this guide.

As discussed in Chapter 22, the code recommends segregation of low voltage and extra low voltage fire alarm circuits. If any extra low voltage fire alarm cables share the same wiring containment with other cables, the cable insulation of the fire alarm cables should be rated for the highest voltage. In practice, this will inevitably be the case, but, normally, 'shared containment' (e.g. installing fire alarm cables within the same trunking compartment as other cables) should be avoided (see Chapter 22).

The code also gives consideration to the possibility of electric shock to persons making contact with live terminals when detectors are removed (however unlikely this may be). Thus, it is recommended that, for extra low voltage circuits with removable components (e.g. detectors or parts of detectors) that expose to touch conductive circuit parts

---

[65] BS 7671, *Requirements for electrical installations. IEE Wiring Regulations. Seventeenth edition.*

at ELV potential, all relevant power supplies should not only comply with BS EN 54-4,[66] but they should incorporate safety isolating transformers complying with BS EN 61558.[67] It should be noted that this latter recommendation goes beyond the requirements for compliance with BS EN 54-4. In addition, under these circumstances, in wet areas, unless circuit voltages are less than 15 V ripple free DC or 6 V a.c. r.m.s. (which is unlikely), either a tool or special technique should be necessary to remove parts exposing ELV parts, or the parts should be positioned out of reach of persons other than authorized personnel. For the purposes of this clause, the code notes that wet areas include those containing a bathtub or shower basin, swimming pools, hot air saunas, agricultural and horticultural premises, abattoirs, cold stores and certain food preparation areas.

Finally, as discussed in Chapter 21, consideration needs to be given to protection of maintenance engineers against shock. Therefore, means should be provided for double pole isolation of the mains supply to all parts of the system. These isolation facilities should be suitably sited, in the vicinity of the equipment served, for use by maintenance technicians without the need for access to remote parts of the building. The facility should be lockable to prevent unauthorized use (see also Chapter 21).

Electromagnetic compatibility probably first became a major issue in fire alarm system design with the advent of addressable fire alarm systems in the early 1980s. Even in the case of conventional systems, the explosion in the use of mobile telephones brought with it problems of interference with fire alarm systems, in addition to the problems already experienced from two-way radio transmitters.

Often, when problems of electromagnetic interference to fire alarm systems as a result of 'pickup' from the cables of other services arises, a philosophical difficulty can arise in apportionment of 'blame'. On the one hand, it is sometimes argued that manufacturers of fire alarm systems are perfectly well aware that fire alarm cables will, in practice, run in close proximity to other cables in, at least, parts of a building at some time during the lifetime of the system, even if not when cables are installed initially. It can also reasonably be anticipated that mobile telephones and two-way radios will often be used in close proximity to fire alarm equipment. Thus, it is argued that prime responsibility for avoidance of problems as a result of electromagnetic interference should lie, or at least begin, with the equipment manufacturer.

---

[66] BS EN 54-4:1998, *Fire detection and fire alarm systems — Power supply equipment.*

[67] BS EN 61558, *Safety of power transformers, power supply units and similar.*

Certainly, in this connection, experience suggests that immunity to electromagnetic interference can vary considerably from one system to another. This has made it difficult for the code to make specific, definitive recommendations on measures to avoid electromagnetic interference to the fire alarm system. The code points out that it is necessary to ensure compliance with any more specific recommendations of the fire alarm equipment manufacturer. The manufacturer should, in any case, provide suitable guidance for compliance with the Electromagnetic Compatibility Regulations 1992, the effect of which has probably been to improve immunity of fire alarm systems to electromagnetic interference.

The more 'purist' view is that there should always be good segregation between fire alarm cables and the cables of other services, so that potential for interference is minimized. The code acknowledges that this is an ideal, but one that is difficult to satisfy in real installations, particularly where fire alarm cables are retrofitted.

Nevertheless, the code does give some practical guidance. The importance of correct earthing is noted, and care is advised in the case of systems that manufacturers advise are sensitive to multiple screen earths. Screen continuity is also deemed to be important, and exposures of cores outside of the screen should be kept to a minimum, consistent with practical installation requirements. All cables specifically recommended by the code do, in any case, provide a degree of screening, and cables that do not comply with the recommendations of the code should only be used with the prior agreement of all interested parties, and their use should be recorded as a variation. Quality of terminations is also important. For mineral insulated copper sheathed cables, terminations of sheaths should be effective around the entire 360° of the sheath, while, for other cables, care should be taken to ensure that the screen of the cable is continued to an appropriate terminal in the control panel or device.

As indicated above, the code does acknowledge that, for example, in order to ensure economy of installation, separation between fire alarm cables and cables of other services throughout an entire installation might not be practicable. However, the commentary of clause 28, notes the importance of ensuring that fire alarm cables do not run unnecessarily long distances in close proximity to high current power cables, particularly if these serve high inductive loads.

There is a tentative suggestion within the commentary that an 'unnecessarily long distance' might be more than 35 m in aggregate, but the technical committee responsible for the code did not feel sufficiently confident about this figure to include it within a positive recommendation. The commentary, of course, is not part of the code that should be subject to audit. It is, however, recommended that, where it is necessary to cross fire alarm system cables with those that can potentially cause interference, the cables should be crossed at right-angles, so minimizing the extent to which separation at these points is not maintained.

25. False alarms and their limitation

Chapters 9 to 24 of this guide have addressed topics covered within Section 2 of BS 5839-1, which contains design considerations and is addressed to 'the designer'. In moving on to consider limitation of false alarms, we move on to Section 3 of the code. This section, which is one of the seven sections into which the code is divided, is concerned solely with the subject of limitation of false alarms; this gives some insight into the importance attached to this subject by the technical committee responsible for the code. Thus, within this chapter of the guide, we will be considering the material within clauses 30 to 35 of the code, whereas previous chapters have each addressed only one or two clauses.

The fact that limitation of false alarms is addressed in Section 3, rather than in Section 2, is not intended to imply that limitation of false alarms is not a matter for the designer. Indeed, the opposite is true; the code asserts that the major part of responsibility for limitation of false alarms rests with the designer. Indeed, this is the very reason for the close proximity of the relevant section of the code to the section on design. However, the separation of the two sections arises from an intention that responsibility for limitation of false alarms should not rest solely with the designer. Rather, the code adopts a 'cradle-to-grave' approach to limitation of false alarms, attributing responsibility for this matter to every party involved in the specification, design, installation, commissioning, management at operational level and maintenance of the fire alarm system.

It should be noted that, in imposing responsibility for limitation of false alarms, the term 'specification of the fire alarm system' precedes the term 'design of the fire alarm system'. Often, the terms 'design' and 'specification' might be regarded as virtually synonymous. However, the separate use of the two terms in this context is based on an acknowledgement within the code that it is not, of course, the designer that creates the demand for the system in the first place.

Often, the system is required by enforcing authorities, using the powers granted to them by legislation; obvious examples include the automatic fire detection system installed within a hotel, or a house in multiple occupation. Similarly, a property insurer may require provision of an automatic fire detection system as a condition of insurance.

The code recommends that, when imposing requirements for automatic fire detection, enforcing authorities and property insurers should take the guidance contained in Section 3 of the code into account, so that, subject to the overriding need for adequate protection of life and/or property, the form of detection specified does not have the potential to create an unacceptable rate of false alarms. There is little doubt in the mind of the author that over-specification of smoke detection by enforcing authorities in circumstances in which it is almost bound to create false alarm problems is a contributory factor to the unacceptable rates of false alarms now experienced from automatic fire detection systems on a national basis.

One example with which the author was concerned was a large, newly built student hostel, in which, during the first year following occupation, 115 false alarms occurred. The university in question considered that the main design and build contractor was responsible for this situation, as the contractor had responsibility for design, installation and commissioning of the system (which had been subcontracted to others). Certainly, at first sight, there was some merit in this argument. The subcontractor had installed optical smoke detectors close to the doors to the en suite showers within each student's bedroom. The resulting false alarms were somewhat predictable.

The contractor blamed the students and, by implication, the university's management of the building. Again, there was some merit in this argument. A proportion of false alarms occurred as a result of the students' activities, such as smoking, cooking toast and burning incense.

On the other hand, the role of the fire and rescue authority in creating the situation might reasonably be questioned. Contrary to the guidance issued by the Home Office to fire and rescue authorities at that time, the fire and rescue authority had demanded smoke detection within each bedroom, rather than heat detection as recommended by the Home Office, as a prerequisite to certification of the hostel for the purpose of letting rooms to members of the public during university vacations. The room volume was relatively small, the room height was low and there was not a great deal of ventilation. It was possible to create, repeatably, conditions in which, following prolonged operation of the shower, a cloud of steam rolled over the entire ceiling of the room immediately that the door to the shower was opened. While an optical smoke detector placed in close proximity to the shower was possibly the worst practice that could have been adopted, it is unlikely that an ionization chamber smoke detector placed anywhere within the room would have been sufficiently immune from malperformance, and false alarms, in this scenario.

Moreover, a fire alarm system should be 'fit for purpose', and account should be taken of the likely occupants of the building and their activities. After dealing with a great number of colleges and universities over many years, the author is firmly convinced that smoke detectors and students do not make a good mixture! It is an interesting philosophical point as to whether the student activities should be modified to take account of the fire alarm system or vice versa.

The need for enforcing authorities to adopt a responsible attitude to limitation of false alarms within the requirements they impose, and the associated recommendations within the code, introduce, in effect, an interesting concept, which has never arisen in previous versions of the code, namely compliance of an enforcing authority with the recommendations of the code. The very first recommendation of clause 30 is that enforcing authorities should take the guidance of Section 3 of the code into account when imposing requirements for automatic fire detection. Could this mean that, say, a fire and rescue authority might have a liability in civil law for the consequences of an unacceptable rate of false alarms, if it could be shown to the satisfaction of a court that this situation arose from a failure on the part of the fire and rescue authority to take the guidance in Section 3 of the code in account? Until such a case comes before the courts, perhaps brought by a company whose trade has been affected by persistent false alarms, there cannot be an answer to this question, but the spectre of such a case is an interesting one!

Similarly, as noted in the code, the same care needs to be taken by property insurers when they impose requirements for automatic fire detection. Again, this introduces the concept of compliance with the code by the property insurer when making requirements. It would, for example, hardly be appropriate for the insurer to specify a system for the purpose of protecting the client's property and minimizing the potential for business interruption by fire if the system installed then, itself, is a cause of constant business interruption. In practice, in difficult environments, it is probably easier to reconcile the requirements for property protection with the requirement to minimize false alarms than to reconcile the latter with requirements for protection of life. The need for automatic fire detection to protect property often arises when people are not present and processes are not operating, so false alarms are much less likely, whereas protection of people clearly must be provided only when people are present.

Notwithstanding the above considerations, it would be wrong to consider the role of the enforcing authority or the property insurer out of context. Most requirements imposed by these parties will normally be fair, reasonable and unlikely to, in themselves, cause unacceptable rates of false alarms. However, even in the short time between publication of the code and the drafting of this guide, designers have raised the question of the action they should take if they believe that the system that must be designed to satisfy requirements of enforcing authorities, insurers or, indeed, users themselves, is likely to be unduly prone to false alarms. This scenario is not explicitly considered in the code, but an appropriate action would clearly be to draw the attention of the relevant specifier to the potential problem before design begins.

If designers feel strongly that, notwithstanding their concerns, they are required to design systems that will obviously create unacceptable rates of false alarms, it would seem appropriate to record variations from the recommendations of the code, even though this may require the agreement of the very party whose recommendation is the cause of the problem! The situation should, however, rarely arise and designers should, in any case, endeavour to ensure that any reasonable requirement for protection can be reconciled with limitation of false alarms, even if by, as a form of last resort, the use of 'alarm filtering' (see below).

Thus, the designer is considered to be the key player in the limitation of false alarms. It is a specific recommendation of the code that the system designer should ensure that the system design takes account of the guidance contained in Section 3 of the code. The certificate of compliance that the designer must complete not only certifies that the design complies with Section 2 of the code, it also certifies that account has been taken of the guidance in Section 3. More specifically, the design certificate contains various tick boxes that the designer must consider and tick as appropriate to indicate which of various specific actions have been taken within the design to ensure that false alarms are limited. A further informative annex (Annex E) sets out in schematic form the thought processes involved in ensuring that system design is sufficiently immune to false alarms.

The modular certification schemes published by British Approvals for Fire Equipment (BAFE) enable third-party certification bodies to certificate fire alarm designers, regardless of whether the designers are a fire alarm contractor (in which case the firm will also be certificated for installation, commissioning and, usually, maintenance of systems) or a consulting practice that is independent of any fire alarm manufacturer or installer. In order to achieve certification, the designer will need to demonstrate to any third-party certification body operating the scheme that, in the case of systems designed in accordance with BS 5839-1, their designs take account of Section 3 of the code. In subsequent inspections of installations, the third-party certification body will audit the compliance of the design with the recommendations in that section.

The code considers the role of the installer in limiting false alarms as much less significant. The logic is that the role of the installer is simply to install the system in accordance with the requirements of the designer. However, when the installer comes to install the system, it could well be the case that only then do circumstances that could give rise to false alarms come to light. It is also possible, of course, that the designer has overlooked some matter that should have been considered in the design if false alarms are to be limited. Accordingly, the code recommends that, where an installer identifies any circumstances that might lead to a high rate of false alarms, the designer, purchaser, or user should be informed accordingly.

Nevertheless, the code makes it clear that this does not imply that it is the responsibility of the installer to verify or certificate compliance of the system design with the code. It is the designer who is expected to have the appropriate expertise, rather than the installer, who may simply be a general electrical contractor. On the other hand, the code does acknowledge that any installer purporting to have specialist capability in installation of fire alarm systems needs to have a good understanding of the guidance in Section 3 of the code. Again, it might, therefore, be reasonable for a third-party certification body to take issue with an installer that dutifully implements the designer's requirements without highlighting any really obvious potential for false alarms to the relevant party.

Commissioning of a system primarily involves setting a system to work. Accordingly, the code acknowledges that, as in the case of the installer, it is not the responsibility of the commissioning engineer to verify or certificate compliance with the system design with the recommendations of the code. However, commissioning is also a final 'safety net' that is the last opportunity for weaknesses in the system to be identified before handover to the purchaser or user. Moreover, one can reasonably expect greater expertise on the subject of false alarms, and their avoidance, on the part of a fire alarm commissioning engineer than in the case of a non-specialist installation contractor. Indeed, the code recommends that any person responsible for commissioning a fire alarm system in accordance with the recommendations of the code should possess, at least, a basic knowledge and understanding of Section 2, Section 3 and Section 4 'Installation' of the code.

In view of the above considerations, the code recommends that a special check is carried out as part of the commissioning process to ensure that there is no obvious potential for an unacceptable rate of false alarms. Within the model certificate of commissioning, the commissioning engineer is specifically required to record that, taking into account the guidance in Section 3 of the code, no obvious potential for an unacceptable rate of false alarms has been identified.

What then if the commissioning engineer does identify a potential problem in this respect? First, this should be documented for referral to the designer, user or purchaser. The commissioning certificate itself is a suitable medium for recording this information, since it contains a section in which work that should be completed before or after the system becomes operational should be recorded. Again, third-party certification bodies operating the BAFE modular schemes are likely to wish to see evidence that, in the case of companies certificated for commissioning of fire alarm systems, commissioning engineers pay adequate heed to the above recommendations, and to the importance of identifying potential causes of false alarms as part of the 'special check' incorporated within the commissioning process.

Realistically, commissioning engineers may wish to be very sure of their ground before, in effect, challenging designers in respect of the adequacy of the design to minimize false alarms. Particularly in the case of contracts for supply and commissioning of a system, the commissioning engineer's firm is unlikely to have had significant contact with the designer during the design stage. The company will never have had an opportunity to inspect the system until the point of commissioning, at which time, often, the purchaser is anxious for handover to take place and the installer is awaiting final payment. The designer may either have long since ceased to have any involvement with the contract or may be acting on behalf of the purchaser to facilitate handover of the system.

Inevitably, it will be difficult for the commissioning engineer to ignore totally the commercial pressures that exist. Given that his/her company was not responsible for the design, should he/she risk upsetting all parties involved on the basis of a mere suspicion that activities in the building or the siting of smoke detectors just a little too close to environmental influences (such as steam or smoke) that may give rise to false alarms will result in an unacceptable rate of false alarms, particularly as one or more of the parties that might be upset (such as the designer or the purchaser) could well have been very influential in the selection of the company to supply and commission the system? If capital works, or a delay in completion of the project, would be the outcome of addressing the commissioning engineer's concerns, prudence might preclude the commissioning engineer from voicing concerns that could be deemed, or proved by subsequent experience, to be unfounded.

The code offers a solution for situations in which the commissioning engineer is not sufficiently confident to recommend changes to the system. The principle is introduced whereby, where there is cause for concern regarding possible potential for false alarms but it is not definite enough to warrant action at commissioning, the concern is recorded, so that particular attention can be given to the matter in examining the false alarm record at the time of the first (and, if necessary, subsequent) service visits. Thus, the model commissioning certificate contains space for an entry under the heading 'The following potential causes of false alarms should be considered at the time of the next service visit: …'. This further ensures continuity in the 'cradle-to-grave' consideration of false alarms, to which reference has already been made.

Clause 43 of the code encourages the purchaser or user to consider, under some circumstances, the need for 'verification' of the installed system's compliance with the code, as a further process following commissioning. The concept of verification is discussed in Chapter 32 of this guide. However, at this stage, it should be noted that clause 30 recommends that any person responsible for verification should verify, as far as reasonably practical, that adequate account has been taken of Section 3 in the design, installation and commissioning of the system. Moreover, the model verification certificate contained within Annex G of the code requires the person carrying out verification to confirm (or otherwise) that, in his/her opinion, there is no obvious potential for an unacceptable rate of false alarms. Thus, here again, there is a further opportunity for the potential for false alarms to be identified.

Whether verification is carried out or not, the code recommends a formal 'acceptance' process, in which there is a formal handover of the system to the purchaser or user. The code recommends that the designer and the supplier of the system should jointly provide the user (or his/her representative) with sufficient information to enable a user who is unfamiliar with the technology of fire alarm systems to limit the rate of false alarms. Accordingly, the code recommends that, as part of the acceptance process, the purchaser or his/her representative should ensure that this information has been provided to the user and that the user has an adequate understanding of the measures necessary to prevent false alarms. Again, the model acceptance certificate contained in Annex G requires the party accepting the system to confirm (or otherwise) that sufficient representatives of the user have been properly instructed in the use of the system, including avoidance of false alarms.

In theory, therefore, given the attention that has been focused on false alarms by each of the parties described above, the user should be presented with an operational system that will not be unduly prone to generating false alarms. The code then, logically, places various responsibilities on the user to ensure that this position is maintained. However, the code is realistic enough to acknowledge that, during the lifetime of the system, circumstances may arise in which the rate of false alarms becomes unacceptable. It is important that, when such circumstances arise, prompt and appropriate action is taken, so that the situation does not continue indefinitely.

In practice, in the experience of the author, based on many investigations of 'troublesome' installations, the key to successful investigation of a false alarm problem is *information*. Unfortunately, when an on-site investigation is carried out, such information is, often, sadly lacking. Often, by the time the users arrange for an investigation of the situation by a competent person, they have already come close to the end of their tether, and information about the detail and circumstances of each false alarm is frequently, at best, anecdotal.

In the light of the above comments, the code provides useful recommendations in respect of the responsibility of the user. Clause 30 of the code recommends that the user should arrange for suitable investigation and, if appropriate, for action to be taken on *every occasion* that a false alarm occurs. Examples of appropriate action given in the code comprise managerial changes within the building, modifications to the fire alarm system, or an investigation by the organization that maintains the system. So that adequate information is available for those who may have to investigate false alarms, the code recommends that the user should record appropriate details regarding *every false alarm* that occurs. The relevant information is set out in clause 30 of the code. Moreover, the model system log book contained in Annex F of the code contains a section dedicated to the recording of false alarms, and the headings within this section are conducive to recording of appropriate information.

One piece of information that the code advocates be recorded (if known) for each false alarm is the category of false alarm. In this connection, the code acknowledges that most false alarms arise from a combination of environmental influences, fire-like phenomena, inappropriate action by people in the building and accidental damage, rather than from faults in equipment. Thus, the code recognizes four different categories of false alarm, albeit that the generic term 'false alarm' is used in the code to describe any fire signal resulting from a cause(s) other than fire.

The four categories of false alarms are described and defined as follows:

1) *unwanted alarms*, in which a system has responded, either as designed or as the technology may reasonably be expected to respond, to any of the following:
    - a fire-like phenomenon or environmental influence (e.g. smoke from a nearby bonfire, dust or insects, processes that produce smoke or flame, or environmental effects that can render certain types of detector unstable, such as rapid air flow);
    - accidental damage;
    - inappropriate human action (e.g. operation of a system for test or maintenance purposes without prior warning to building occupants and/or an alarm receiving centre);
2) *equipment false alarms*, in which the false alarm has resulted from a fault in the system;
3) *malicious false alarms*, in which a person operates a manual call point or causes a fire detector to initiate a fire signal, whilst knowing that there is no fire;
4) *false alarms with good intent*, in which a person operates a manual call point or otherwise initiates a fire signal in the belief that there is a fire, when no fire actually exists.

Consideration of the above categories of false alarm indicates the importance of recording of the category of false alarm for each false alarm incident, when this information is available (perhaps only after investigation by a competent person, such as a maintenance technician). There is a tendency for users, and even enforcing authorities, to regard a fire alarm system that produces an unacceptable rate of false alarms as in some way defective. In practice, most false alarms are 'unwanted alarms', and the definition of this category of false alarm is such as to make clear that no 'blame' can, or should, be attached to the system. (The same is, of course, true of malicious false alarms and false alarms with good intent, although this truism will be much clearer to the user.)

It is also important to note that the definition of unwanted alarms necessitates that, in recording the category of false alarm, some understanding of fire detection technology is necessary, as these false alarms are not limited to environmental influences that are, at least to a lay person, fire or smoke-like in nature. For example, ionization chamber smoke detectors may become unstable and produce false alarms when subjected to rapid airflows. Obviously, the ionization chamber smoke detector is not designed to detect rapid air flows, but, equally, since instability when exposed to rapid air flows is an inherent feature of the detection technology, the system cannot reasonably be 'blamed' for the false alarms that then result.

Traditionally, and quite understandably, there has been a tendency for false alarms to be regarded as equipment faults if those responding to the alarm signal can find no obvious cause. This has, for example, almost certainly tended to result in an overestimation of the importance of equipment faults as a source of false alarms within national fire statistics. The officer in charge of a fire appliance does not have the expertise, time or resources to investigate the cause of a false alarm to which the fire and rescue service have been summoned and, in the absence of any obvious cause, the temptation to assume that equipment is faulty is obvious.

However, the code specifically recommends against the assumption that, in the absence of other information, a false alarm must have arisen from an equipment fault. Instead, the code recommends that, where any doubt exists regarding the cause of a false alarm, the cause should be recorded as 'unknown'. To aid those with greater expertise, completion of the model log book requires that the user record activities in the area if the cause of a false alarm is recorded as unknown.

In practice, of course, it would be unrealistic to expect every user in the land to devote the attention to the matter of false alarms that would occur in an ideal world. The user's main concern, after a false alarm occurs, is to resume normal activities, particularly if these are of a profit-making nature. Once activities have resumed, the user may not have the time or expertise to carry out any form of in-depth investigation, and there will often, understandably, be a reluctance to pay the call-out charges for the attendance of a maintenance technician. Therefore, in practice, the most that can probably be expected from even the most responsible user is that the relevant information is recorded for future consideration and that any obvious cause of a false alarm is suitably addressed.

A maintenance technician should, however, have a good standard of expertise in the causes of false alarms. Indeed, the code specifically acknowledges that periodic inspection and servicing needs to be carried out by a competent person with specialist knowledge of fire detection and alarm systems, including knowledge of the causes of false alarms.

Thus, the periodic servicing recommended in the code (see Chapter 34) provides an excellent opportunity for ongoing monitoring of the rate of false alarms by a competent person and for preliminary investigation of, and suitable action on, unacceptable rates of false alarms before the 'end of tether' that often first prompts concerted action by the user arises. For this to be effective, however, it is absolutely essential that the user complies with the recommendations of the code in respect of recording false alarms.

Thus, the code recommends that, at the time of *every* service visit, the system false alarm record should be checked carefully. The code identifies three matters that should be brought to light by this check.

First, the rate of false alarms during the previous 12 months, expressed as number of false alarms per 100 detectors per annum, should be determined by the service technician. The code recommends that this rate should be recorded in the log book by the service technician. In addition, completion of the model certificate of inspection and servicing, contained in Annex G of the code, requires that the number of false alarms during the previous 12 months be recorded, along with the number of false alarms per 100 automatic fire detectors per annum to which the gross number of false alarms equates. (In the case of Category M systems, this latter conversion is not, of course, applicable.) Unfortunately, in the experience of the author, six years after the original publication of the current version of BS 5839-1, this recommendation is frequently ignored by maintenance organizations. Equally, failure of many users properly to record false alarms in the log book for examination by the service technician does not assist matters.

Secondly, at the time of each service visit, it should be determined whether, since the time of the previous service visit, two or more false alarms, other than false alarms with good intent, have arisen from any single manual call point or fire detector (or detector location).

Thirdly, it should be determined whether any persistent cause of false alarms can be identified from a study of the false alarm log. The purpose of this check by the service technician is to determine the need for, and nature of, any action to reduce the frequency of false alarms. Great hope is pinned on this process of monitoring by service technicians, and, accordingly, a quite onerous burden is placed on the service technician. Indeed, the code recommends that, *as part of the service work*, a *preliminary investigation* should be carried out if any one or more of four circumstances is found to apply, namely:

1) the rate of false alarms over the previous 12 months has exceeded one false alarm per 25 detectors per annum;

2) eleven or more alarms have occurred since the time of the previous service visit, i.e. typically, within the previous six months;
3) two or more false alarms (other than false alarms with good intent) have arisen from any single manual call point or fire detector (or detector location) since the time of the last service visit;
4) any persistent cause of false alarms is identified.

It cannot be stressed strongly enough that checking whether any of the above four circumstances pertain, and, if so, carrying out the preliminary investigation, is an inherent part of compliance with the recommendations of the 2002 version of the code in respect of servicing. These actions should be taken unilaterally by the service technician, without the need for special instruction by the user, in all cases in which it is claimed, or required contractually, that servicing is carried out in accordance with BS 5839-1:2002. The corollary is that, for example, a service contract that regards this as an 'optional extra' is effectively a service contract that contains an option for servicing that fails to comply with the recommendations of the code, which could have civil, legal and insurance implications.

Equally, it should be noted that the investigation required for compliance with the code, under the circumstances defined, is described as 'preliminary'. The code recommends that the user should be informed of the outcome of the investigation and be given appropriate advice, but, of course, this advice might simply be that there is a need for a more in-depth investigation. The circumstances in which an in-depth investigation is required are also defined in the code. Before we consider these circumstances, it is relevant to consider 'benchmark' rates of false alarms that can reasonably be anticipated from a fire alarm system.

The code notes that, in 2000, fire and rescue services in the United Kingdom attended over 250,000 false alarms from fire alarm systems. (Since the code was published, the figure has continued to rise. In 2004, there were 286,200 such false alarms, although, in 2005, there was a slight decrease to 285,200.) The code further asserts that this level of false alarms is no longer regarded as acceptable by central government, fire and rescue services or the committee responsible for the code itself. Accordingly, the code advises that systems in which the parties responsible have not taken adequate care to limit false alarms, and systems that produce unacceptably high rates of false alarms, need to be regarded as not complying with the code. Such a non-compliance could bring with it civil liability and implications for insurance of the property, as well as possible action by enforcing authorities. Indeed, the code notes that, in the future, it is possible that a fire and rescue authority will take appropriate action if a fire alarm system consistently produces false alarms at unacceptable rates.

This, therefore, introduces the concept of an 'acceptable' rate of false alarms. In this connection, the code is realistic enough to acknowledge that, while any false alarm is undesirable, it must be accepted that, particularly in installations that incorporate a large number of automatic fire detectors, complete elimination of false alarms is impossible. The best that can be expected is that the rate of false alarms from any installation falls within limits defined as 'acceptable'.

How is this acceptable rate to be defined, given that the code notes that little information is available as to the 'average' rate of false alarms from fire alarm systems, and that a benchmark against which false alarm performance can be judged cannot be defined with any real precision? The approach adopted in the code is that, effectively, the rate of false alarms that can be anticipated will be somewhat specific to each installation. Factors that will affect the number of false alarms include the environment (including the electromagnetic environment), activities in the building, the level of occupation of the building and the standard of management in the building, the latter of which will affect matters such as control over third parties (e.g. contractors), and the potential for malicious operation of manual call points.

However, the code suggests that a key factor will be the number of automatic fire detectors in the installation. Thus, the code advises that the number of false alarms that can be anticipated is virtually proportional to the number of automatic fire detectors installed. This is because each detector can be considered as a potential generator of false alarms as a result of environmental factors and activities within the area of the detector, as well as, of course, the possibility of a detector fault. A specific 'constant of proportionality' is not given in the code, and, indeed, the code notes that the ratio of false alarms to number of detectors in the installation will depend on the extent to which smoke detectors are used; systems that are purely manual, or in which heat detectors are used, should not normally produce many false alarms.

As a guide, however, the code suggests that, in a relatively benign environment, in which there is no tendency for dust, fumes or insects to occur, and in which there is a good standard of management, false alarm rates equal to, or less than, one false alarm per 100 detectors per annum are possible. While this figure is not intended as a norm or 'average', it might, therefore, be regarded as an ideal target for false alarm management under ideal conditions. A more realistic expectation on industrial sites with shift working is suggested by the code to be one false alarm per 75 detectors per annum. (This figure is now used in the NHS, as a target to which false alarms should be reduced in a hospital.)

The code does not, however, suggest that the above figures are easily achievable. On the other hand, it does suggest that, in general, false alarm rates of one false alarm per 50 detectors per annum can be readily achievable with modern technology systems, unless there are severe environmental challenges for automatic fire detection. There is a tentative suggestion in the code that this rate might, therefore, be quite reasonable and 'acceptable' on an industrial site with processes that create an unfavourable environment for automatic fire detectors. On the other hand, it is suggested that this rate might not be 'acceptable' in a controlled environment, such as a computer room.

Thus, these figures now provide the user with some form of target, however imprecise it might be, at which to aim in any initiative to reduce false alarms. However, the lack of precision in these figures, and the number of variables that will affect the false alarm rate in any specific installation, are such that it would not be reasonable to deem the rate of false alarms as unacceptable simply because these particular figures are not reached. Nevertheless, since the code introduces the concept of an 'acceptable rate of false alarms', there must be some (much higher) rate of false alarms that does not simply fall short of the possible target ideal, but that is quite positively unacceptable.

The code defines such a level. The advice given is that, in general, in systems with more than 40 automatic fire detectors, a rate of more than one false alarm per 20 detectors per annum is never to be regarded as acceptable, particularly if the false alarms result in evacuation of the premises or summoning of the fire and rescue service. In premises with 40 automatic fire detectors or less, three or more false alarms per annum is to be regarded as unacceptable. It is these figures that are, therefore, used as the basis for the 'trigger' at which an in-depth investigation by suitable specialists should be carried out.

Specifically, the code recommends that, in systems that incorporate more than 40 automatic fire detectors, the user should instigate an in-depth investigation by suitable specialists if, in any rolling period of 12 months, either:

1)   the average rate of false alarms exceeds one false alarm per
     20 detectors per annum; or
2)   three or more false alarms are initiated by any single manual call
     point or automatic fire detector (or detector location).

In systems that incorporate 40 or less automatic fire detectors, the in-depth investigation should be instigated by the user if, in any rolling 12-month period, three or more false alarms occur.

It should be noted that, whereas the service engineer is expected to carry out a preliminary investigation if there are more than 10 false alarms since the time of the previous service visit, the in-depth investigation recommended in the case of serious false alarm problems is not triggered by any specific number of false alarms, but only by a 'rate' of false alarms. This is simply an acknowledgement of the fact that, as discussed above, the number of false alarms will be related to the number of detectors. In a system with 5,000 smoke detectors, the occurrence of 10 false alarms between service visits may constitute a good level of immunity to false alarms. With regard to the special in-depth investigation, the code suggests that this may be undertaken by the servicing organization, the manufacturer of the system or a suitably qualified third party (such as a consultant). (Some fire and rescue services now downgrade, or withdraw, response to calls to an actuating fire alarm system if false alarm rates, expressed in terms of numbers of false alarms per total number of detectors, exceed limits in guidance published by the Chief Fire Officers' Association.)

As has been stressed in this chapter, if false alarms are to be minimized, the key parties in the evolution of the system from original specification to ongoing operation must be conversant with the major causes of false alarms. The code defines the parties that must have this familiarity with the subject as any person responsible for specification, design, commissioning or maintenance of systems. To aid these parties, clause 33 of the code lists recognized causes of unwanted alarms. Most readers of this guide will be familiar with the 20 recognized causes of unwanted alarms listed in clause 33 of the code, and, therefore, they need not be repeated here. It should, however, be noted that the code acknowledges that most of these causes can be minimized by appropriate choice of detection system and suitable management arrangements.

Equipment false alarms, associated with faults in equipment, can, on the other hand, be minimized by choice of good quality equipment that satisfies the appropriate product standards. Third-party certification of the equipment provides a form of warranty of compliance. Once the equipment has been installed, regular servicing is important to ensure continuing satisfactory operation.

As noted in the code, the third category of false alarms, namely malicious false alarms, most commonly occur in certain public buildings, such as shopping centres, places of entertainment, certain public houses, public car parks and sports centres, and in educational establishments, such as universities and schools. These false alarms generally involve operation of manual call points.

The fourth category of false alarms, namely false alarms with good intent, is difficult to prevent and is, in any case, unlikely to present a significant problem. Moreover, it is generally undesirable to attempt to minimize false alarms with good intent, since the principles of fire safety dictate that it is entirely appropriate for people to raise the alarm, by operating a manual call point, if they suspect that there might be a fire. The code notes, therefore, that it is important that people are never discouraged from doing so.

In practice, if anything, there is a need positively to encourage people to operate the fire alarm system if they suspect that there is a fire. Experience shows that, in many real fires, there is a reluctance on the part of occupants to take the critical step of operating the fire alarm system. People are afraid of looking silly or causing needless disruption that might prove to be unwarranted. Therefore, while outside the issue of fire alarm system design, it should, in passing, be noted that it is essential that staff are instructed, and periodically reminded during fire training, to operate the fire alarm system immediately in the event of a suspected, or confirmed, fire.

Although expertise on the causes of false alarms and their limitation will generally reside primarily with the parties defined above, even at the design stage it might be appropriate to involve the end user in consideration of this matter. In this connection, the code suggests that it should be confirmed, before design begins, that automatic fire detection will be of a value that outweighs the potential for false alarms. In general, of course, this will be the case, but, in the case of some simple small buildings in which all areas are occupied on a 24-hour basis, automatic detection may be of little benefit to fire safety. Other than in such rare cases, it will, of course, be inappropriate to avoid fire detection as the means of limiting false alarms.

However, the code does advocate that, at the design stage, the designer makes at least a qualitative judgement as to the likely frequency of false alarms. In the case of very large systems with many smoke detectors, it might even be appropriate for the designer to provide the user with guidance on the approximate rate at which false alarms could occur. This might then identify the need for incorporation of measures within the design to limit the number of false alarms; an example might be 'filtering measures', which are discussed later in this chapter.

This quite onerous duty on the designer might, at first sight, appear somewhat theoretical, academic and idealistic. Certainly, it will hardly be appropriate for the designer of a fire alarm system for a small shop, which might comprise only two or three manual call points, half a dozen detectors and a few bells, to engage in dialogue with the user regarding the anticipated number of false alarms and special design measures for their avoidance! However, in the experience of the author, this guidance in the code is practical and sensible in the very large installations to which the guidance refers.

One example with which the author had experience involved a new and very large landmark public building, in which were to be incorporated around 4,000 detectors (almost all of which were smoke detectors). The original system design specified that, on operation of any one detector, there should be an immediate evacuation of part of the building, as well as summoning of the fire and rescue service. Prior to the opening of the building, the author was involved in assisting the occupier in formulation of a fire evacuation strategy. The occupier was advised that, given the very large number of smoke detectors, a significant number of false alarms could reasonably be anticipated, purely on a statistical basis.

Understandably, the occupier wished to have some grasp of the likely frequency, and was advised that one false alarm every 10 days could reasonably be anticipated, at least during the early period of occupation. This figure horrified the occupier, who considered that evacuation of even part of the building at such a frequency would be totally unacceptable. As a result of these discussions, the fire strategy was significantly modified, and a 'staff alarm' (see below) was incorporated. The result was that, during the first year or so of occupation, false alarms did, indeed, occur at approximately the predicted rate, but very few of these resulted in evacuation or summoning of the fire and rescue service.

Thus, by adopting an approach that is now advocated in the code, system performance that was highly satisfactory to both the user and the fire and rescue service was achieved, whereas, undoubtedly, major frustrations and dissatisfaction would otherwise have arisen. As a footnote, it is somewhat sad to record that, some time later, during a tour of the building organized for members of a professional body, a relatively senior fire officer was heard to mutter the question to his colleagues as to why someone could not just 'fix' the system, rather than introduce delays in evacuation; such is the level of misunderstanding that abounds on the matter of false alarms, even by those who should be better educated in the subject!

Throughout this chapter, there has been reference to limiting, minimizing and avoiding false alarms. We now need to consider the practical measures that can be adopted for this purpose. One entire clause (clause 35) of Section 3 of the code is devoted purely to measures to limit false alarms. Such is the weight attached to this matter, that clause 35 is five pages long and contains no less than 30 specific recommendations for consideration by the relevant parties.

Clause 35 of the code subdivides the measures advocated into eight groups, namely:

- siting and selection of manual call points;
- selection and siting of automatic fire detectors;
- selection of system type;
- protection against electromagnetic interference;
- performance monitoring of newly commissioned systems;
- filtering measures;
- system management;
- regular servicing and maintenance.

The 30 specific recommendations are not intended to constitute definitive 'rules'. On the other hand, they cannot be ignored if the various stages in system evolution and use are to comply with the code. Thus, the code recommends that the 30 recommendations in question be taken into account by any parties responsible for specification, design, commissioning or verification of a fire alarm system, and by maintenance organizations at the time of consideration of false alarm problems.

The recommendations for suitable siting and selection of manual call points relate primarily to avoidance of exposure of call points to accidental damage and malicious operation. Principally, this involves care in siting within certain high risk areas. As examples of areas in which there might be exposure to accidental damage, the code quotes areas in which trolleys or forklift trucks are used, and sports halls and gymnasia, in which ball sports are played. As examples of areas in which there is significant potential for malicious operation of call points, the code suggests shopping malls, some public houses, cinemas, theatres, nightclubs, schools, universities, certain public entertainment premises and public car parks.

In the case of shopping malls, the code recommends that manual call points should not be located within the malls themselves. This also accords with the recommendations of BS 5588-10.[68] In certain of the public premises described above, the code recommends that, subject to the agreement of all relevant enforcing authorities, it might be appropriate either to omit manual call points from areas accessible to

---

[68] BS 5588-10:1991, *Fire precautions in the design, construction and use of buildings — Code of practice for shopping complexes*. BS 5588-10 will be withdrawn after the future publication of BS 9999.

the public or to site them so that they are accessible only to authorized persons, provided there is adequate surveillance of the entire premises by people or CCTV and that manual call points are provided at suitably staffed locations. For example, it is not uncommon, in the case of certain public houses, to locate manual call points behind the bar.

Where mechanical damage is likely, the code refers to the use of guards. Hinged covers are also advocated for consideration as a form of guard and as a measure to limit malicious false alarms in the case of schools, universities, certain public entertainment premises and public car parks. Again, however, this would require the agreement of all relevant enforcing authorities, as the manual call points would not then comply with the requirements of BS EN 54-11[69] for type A manual call points, and agreement of a variation from the normal recommendations of the code would be necessary. In the case of public car parks, the code suggests that consideration might also be given to the use of a suitable emergency voice communication system (e.g. emergency telephones or an intercom system) in lieu of manual call points. This would also require approval of enforcing authorities, and it would be appropriate for such a system to comply with BS 5839-9.[70]

Ingress of moisture into a manual call point can cause malperformance of the device. In the case of an addressable system, such an event can cause various random fault and fire signals. Accordingly, the code recommends that, in areas in which manual call points are exposed to moisture, suitably moisture-resistant devices should be used. In practice, the performance would be specified by means of a relevant IP rating, e g. IP X5. As examples of such areas, the code gives external locations, wet areas of industrial buildings, food-processing areas that are subject to periodic washing down and certain kitchens. A practical example would be the case of breweries, where there are often 'wet' areas. In many kitchens, ingress of water is not a recognized problem, but it is not unknown for condensation to create problems for manual call points, and water could, of course, occur in washing-up areas.

In the case of automatic fire detectors, it should be noted that the code refers to 'selection and siting', whereas, in the case of manual call points, the term used was 'siting and selection'. This reversal of words is not accidental. In the case of manual call points, the code regards

---

[69] BS EN 54-11:2001, *Fire detection and fire alarm systems — Manual call points.*

[70] BS 5839-9:2003, *Fire detection and alarm systems for buildings — Code of practice for the design, installation, commissioning and maintenance of emergency voice communication systems.*

the siting of the devices as the critical factor, whereas, in the case of automatic fire detectors, greater emphasis is placed on selection.

However, as discussed above, if it is known that the provision of automatic fire detectors is likely to result in a high level of unwanted alarms, the first question that the designer should ask is whether, in fact, the provision of automatic fire detection is necessary. In this context, the 'necessity' will depend on the objectives of the fire alarm system, which should be clearly understood by the designer. Earlier in this chapter, the obvious example of a situation in which automatic fire detection is not necessary was suggested to be small, continuously occupied premises. However, there are more subtle situations in which the need for automatic fire detection might be questioned.

For example, the author's consulting practice was involved in providing independent advice on false alarm problems experienced within a food processing plant. The problem was clearly related to the environment, which was not conducive to the use of smoke detection. The objective of the system was property protection, rather than life safety, the latter of which would have necessitated only a manual fire alarm system (at least for compliance with legislation). Accordingly, the obvious alternative form of detection was heat detection. However, the premises were fully sprinklered, and a sprinkler head is simply a form of heat detector. Since operation of the sprinkler system resulted in a signal at the fire alarm system, it was questionable as to whether the slightly earlier warning afforded by heat detectors would have been of major advantage. Moreover, the nature of the fire hazard and fire load were not such that the development of a fire large enough to operate heat detectors (or sprinklers, which were primarily a 'long stop') was likely. Here then is an example of a situation in which the benefits of automatic fire detection might reasonably be questioned.

Over the last two decades, because of its greater sensitivity, smoke detection has become something of the 'default' form of fire detection, with heat detection specified only if it is obvious that smoke detectors would result in false alarms. However, the code recommends that, for systems complying with the 2002 version, consideration should be given to the use of heat detection, before smoke detection is specified. Thus, the code recommends that, before use of other types of fire detector, it should be confirmed that the use of heat detectors would not satisfy both the objectives of the fire alarm system and the recommendations of the code.

This recommendation has a bearing on, for example, the type of detector used within bedrooms in sleeping risks, which has been discussed at length elsewhere in this guide. In short, if the objective is purely to provide a warning to persons beyond the room of fire origin in the event of fire, it is likely that heat detection would be satisfactory. Indeed, it could be argued that, by specifying smoke detection under these circumstances, enforcing authorities and designers might be regarded as failing to comply with the recommendations of clause 35 of the code.

Unless there is an equipment fault, if heat detectors do generate false alarms, it is likely that the reason is either a high ambient temperature or rapidly fluctuating ambient temperatures. To avoid such false alarms, the code provides guidance on the 'headroom' that should exist between ambient temperatures and the temperature of operation of heat detectors. Rate of rise heat detectors should not be installed in locations in which rapid fluctuations in temperature may occur. Examples given in the code comprise kitchens, boiler rooms, loading bays with large doors to open air and lantern lights.

A common perplexity to face designers is the type of smoke detector that should be specified, i.e. optical or ionization chamber. Although, in earlier clauses of the code, guidance is given on considerations to take into account in respect of effectiveness in detection of fire, clause 35 of the code provides guidance on considerations in respect of false alarms that should be taken into account in selecting point and optical beam smoke detectors. The information is presented in the form of a table, which indicates situations in which smoke detectors should never be installed and situations in which smoke detectors should be avoided if possible. Further information is given on the type of smoke detector that should be avoided in a number of false alarm-prone situations. In the case of optical beam smoke detectors, the code also recommends suitable mounting to avoid misalignment of the beam due to movements in the structure to which the transmitter and receiver are mounted. It is also recommended that these detectors are not installed in areas in which obstruction of the beam may occur in normal circumstances.

Most aspirating smoke detection systems are considerably more sensitive than normal point-type smoke detectors. Indeed, the high sensitivity of these devices is the most common reason for them to be specified, e.g. in critical electronic equipment rooms. However, the code advocates that special consideration is given to ensure that the high sensitivity does not result in unwanted alarms. In this connection, aspirating smoke detection is sometimes specified in circumstances in which its advantage is not so much its high sensitivity, but the opportunity to install relatively 'invisible' fire detection that will not affect the ambience of, say, a stately home.

In these circumstances, high sensitivity is not required in order to satisfy the objective of the system. Accordingly, in such cases, the code advocates the use of aspirating systems that can be arranged to provide sensitivity equivalent to that of point smoke detectors complying with BS EN 54-7,[71] since, were it not for the visual impact of point detectors, they might well have satisfied the fire safety objective quite adequately.

Carbon monoxide fire detectors are sometimes specified in situations in which smoke detectors or heat detectors could be used, simply to avoid the false alarms that might arise from smoke detectors, but to provide much more sensitive detection than could be afforded by heat detectors. However, it is important to take account of circumstances that might result in unwanted alarms from these detectors. Normally, such circumstances will be those in which carbon monoxide is generated, such as badly ventilated kitchens, areas in which vehicle or other exhaust fumes occur and some laboratories. The code also recommends that the guidance of the manufacturer on avoidance of unwanted alarms should be taken into account, particularly in relation to locations in which contamination of the electrochemical cell could result in unwanted alarms.

Similarly, it is a simple truism that infrared and ultraviolet flame detectors should not be located in areas in which sources of infrared or ultraviolet radiation create the potential for unwanted alarms. The mere presence of infrared radiation itself, however, does not necessarily generate potential for unwanted alarms, as various techniques can be adopted to prevent this, e.g. generation of fire alarm signals from infrared flame detectors only if the infrared radiation sensed has the characteristic flicker frequency of a diffusion flame. Accordingly, the code recommends that the guidance of the manufacturer of the detector, in respect of sensitivity of detectors to other non-fire sources of radiation, should be taken into account.

The code regards analogue fire detection systems as less prone to unwanted alarms than conventional fire detection systems. When analogue fire detection systems were first introduced in the 1980s, such an assertion, albeit that it was also made within the 1988 version of the code, was open to debate. A number of poorly designed analogue systems were prone to software problems and electromagnetic interference that actually made them less stable than simpler, conventional systems. However, in the case of the current generation of analogue systems, the assertion will generally be valid. Even the simple pre-alarm warning incorporated within many analogue systems provides an opportunity

---

[71] BS EN 54-7:2001, *Fire detection and fire alarm systems — Smoke detectors — Point detectors using scattered light, transmitted light or ionization.*

for the user to investigate a situation that, had it been permitted to continue, would have resulted in a false alarm.

In view of the above considerations, the code recommends that, unless there are overriding considerations, systems that incorporate a high number of smoke detectors should be of the analogue type. It is for the designer to determine what constitutes a high number of smoke detectors, but a relatively tentative suggestion within the code is that a high number might be regarded as more than 100 detectors.

Arguably, the future for reduction of false alarms lies in the use of multi-sensor detection systems that incorporate measures to filter out false alarms from environmental influences that principally affect only one of the sensors incorporated within each detector. It should, however, be noted that not all multi-sensor detection systems incorporate such measures; some multi-sensor detectors use the multi-sensor feature primarily to offer good sensitivity to a broader spectrum of fires.

However, the code recommends that, in systems that incorporate a very high number of automatic fire detectors (other than heat detectors), the use of systems that include multi-sensor fire detectors and incorporate suitable measures to minimize the potential for unwanted alarms should be considered at the design stage. Again, only tentative advice on what constitutes a 'very high number' of detectors is offered in the code; more than 1,000 detectors is suggested as constituting a very high number. However, looking to the future, the code suggests that, as standards for multi-sensor fire detection systems are produced, and more proprietary systems become available, more definitive advice might be given and the definition of 'very high number' might be reduced, if evidence of significant improvements in unwanted alarm immunity can be established for these systems.

It was asserted in an earlier chapter that modern fire alarm systems are less susceptible to electromagnetic interference than the systems of 10 to 20 years ago. However, the code recognizes electromagnetic interference as a potential cause of unwanted alarms. The code recommends that, in order to minimize the potential for unwanted alarms from electromagnetic interference, the recommendations of clause 28 of the code should be followed; these were discussed in Chapter 24. In addition, it is recommended that the designer should take into account the likely sources of electromagnetic radiation in the building. These include mobile telephones, two-way radios, mobile telephone base stations (which are often found now within buildings) and other high power transmitters.

In some cases, very high electromagnetic field strengths might occur. Examples are radio transmitter sites, airport terminals and radar stations. In these cases, the code recommends that guidance should be sought from the system manufacturer, who may be able to recommend special measures, such as the provision of filters on external circuits, to reduce the potential for unwanted alarms. In the case of an existing building, where unusually high field strengths occur, the code recommends that information be provided to the system manufacturer regarding the field strengths that exist. This, effectively, implies that measurements should be carried out in these cases.

Sometimes, false alarms occur in the early life of a system. This can arise from 'infant mortality' of components, poor siting of detectors that was not identified before handover, and environmental influences that were not appreciated prior to handover. These early problems are sometimes attributed to 'settling in' of the system, but are really more accurately the result of previously undetected problems. In order to prevent these problems causing false alarms, the code recommends that, in the case of systems incorporating more than 50 automatic fire detectors, a 'soak period' should follow commissioning. A soak period is defined in the code as a period after a fire alarm system has been commissioned, but prior to handover, during which the system's performance in relation to false alarms and faults is monitored. Thus, other than in the case of small systems, handover, as envisaged in the code, is not complete until the end of the soak period.

The code recommends that the duration of the soak period should be at least one week, but the actual period should be defined by the designer and incorporated within any tender specification. On the model design certificate, the designer is required to indicate whether no soak test is necessary, based on the number of automatic fire detectors, or to define the period for the soak test. Where a soak test is required, since it will immediately follow commissioning, the model certificate of commissioning also contains a space in which the period of any required soak test should be recorded.

Obviously, until successful completion of the soak test, the system should not be regarded as the means of giving warning of fire in the building. Thus, during this period, each manual call point should bear an indication that it is not to be used. In practice, this means that, in the programme for a new building project, allowance would have to be made for the soak period before occupation of a building. Where an existing fire alarm system is being replaced by a new system, strip out of the old system clearly should not begin until the completion of the new system's soak test. Practical difficulties may, however, arise in complying with the code if the new system uses the wiring of the old system.

The code defines the criteria for successful completion of the soak test, namely that:

1) during the soak period, no false alarm occurred; or
2) investigation of all false alarms that occurred, by the supplier of the system, has identified the cause of every false alarm and enabled any relevant measures to be taken to minimize potential for similar false alarms to occur in the future.

The code does not, however, state the manner in which matters should proceed if, according to the above criteria, the soak test is not successfully completed. Such circumstances could, however, possibly delay handover of the system. Moreover, a note within the code points out that a purchasing specification might require that, on completion of any relevant measures, a further soak test be carried out. This, however, would be a matter for the specifier to define at the tender stage.

Even if all the above recommendations for limitation of false alarms are dutifully followed, the code acknowledges that the rate of false alarms (e.g. expressed as one false alarm per n detectors per annum), or the sheer number of false alarms, might be unacceptable. The code envisages that the unacceptable extent of false alarms might be anticipated at the design stage or that it might only come to light after operational experience. For example, if there is a large number of automatic fire detectors, the number of false alarms that might be anticipated by the designer, even at the initial design stage, might be regarded by the user as unacceptable, even though the rate is well within the definition of acceptability given in the code.

Under these circumstances, the code suggests that 'filtering' measures might be appropriate, particularly in installations with a very large number of automatic fire detectors, which the code suggests might be, for example, more than 1,000 detectors. Two forms of 'filtering' are described in the code.

The first (and, in practice, the less common) form of filtering is the use of a 'time-related system'. In such a system, the form of protection varies on a time-related basis. For example, smoke detectors may be disabled automatically during normal working hours, so that, in effect, the system is Category M during working hours and Category M/P outside normal working hours. This technique could not, of course, be applied if the function of the automatic fire detection were life safety, as it would, obviously, be needed when people were present.

Other forms of time-related system include those in which detector sensitivity is reduced at certain times, such as during working hours, and multi-sensor systems in which one of the sensors is disabled (or reduced in sensitivity) at certain times. In the latter case, if, say, smoke sensors are disabled during normal working hours, but protection at these times by heat detectors is still required, the detector spacing should follow that recommended for heat detectors, rather than that recommended for smoke detectors.

In all of the above examples, the causes of false alarms are not eliminated or reduced; it is merely that the false alarms are 'filtered out' by preventing response to the causes of false alarms at certain times of day. It goes without saying, however, that the modified form of response, and associated reduction in the level of protection, need to be understood by, and be acceptable to, the relevant interested parties.

The second form of filtering involves the use of a 'staff alarm'. The code defines a staff alarm as a restricted alarm, following the operation of a manual call point or automatic fire detector, given to certain staff in the premises to permit investigation prior to evacuation. There are, however, two points to note, immediately. First, as indicated in a note to the definition in the code, the use of staff alarms in response to signals from manual call points is not generally acceptable. This issue was discussed in Chapter 15.

Secondly, although the definition refers to a delay in evacuation, quite often the summoning of the fire and rescue service (whether via the public emergency call system or via an alarm receiving centre) is also delayed, so that summoning of the fire and rescue service does not occur unless and until an evacuation is initiated; the code notes, however, that this may, or may not, be the case. Equally, the code suggests that it might be preferable to delay the summoning of the fire and rescue service until the expiry of the investigation period if the fire and rescue service attendance time is less than the investigation period; otherwise, in these circumstances, at the time of arrival of the fire and rescue service, investigation is still underway, the premises are still fully occupied and no audible fire alarm signal is sounding. The arrival of the fire and rescue service under these circumstances may not only be unwarranted, but it may cause confusion.

Staff alarms are becoming quite common in large, complex buildings that are protected by a high number of automatic fire detectors, particularly smoke detectors. Indeed, as suggested earlier in this chapter, they are quite often a major consideration within the fire strategy for complex buildings, even at the initial design stage. The use of a staff alarm does, however, necessitate a good standard of management. There must be sufficient staff to investigate, and to manage the situation thereafter, at all times that the staff alarm arrangement applies, and there must never be any suggestion that staff might simply endeavour to cancel the alarm during the investigation period and then investigate at leisure. In practice, the staff alarm normally applies at all times, but there is no reason why, in certain premises, it should not only apply at certain times of the day, such as normal working hours, in which case the system is also a time-related system.

Initiatives to minimize false alarms to which the fire and rescue service are summoned tend to favour the arrangement in which the 'delay' incorporated within a staff alarm applies at least to summoning of the fire and rescue service, regardless of whether or not it applies to an audible evacuation signal. In practice, the need for, and acceptability of, the investigate period to apply to evacuation of the premises and summoning of the fire and rescue service need to be considered separately.

For example, in a Category P system, the prime purpose of the system is to summon the fire and rescue service in the event of fire. Care needs to be taken that, in consideration of a 'false alarm strategy', the fire strategy is not compromised to an unreasonable extent. Consideration needs to be given to the likely damage that will occur in the event of fire during the 'end-to-end' time from ignition of a fire, detection by the system, possible expiry of the potential investigate period, summoning of the fire and rescue service, the attendance of the fire and rescue service and the start of extinguishing action by them.

On the other hand, as noted in the code, the delay pending investigation might only apply to the summoning of the fire and rescue service. In the latter case, the building, or part of it, would be evacuated when the system operates, but summoning of the fire and rescue service would be delayed pending an investigation to determine whether the signal is merely a false alarm. Equally, care needs to be taken in the case of premises in which early attendance of the fire and rescue service to extinguish any fire can be critical to life safety (e.g. hospitals and residential care homes).

Although filtering should, arguably, always be considered at the design stage in systems with very large numbers of smoke detectors, filtering measures should not be regarded as an 'easy' option to mask shortcomings in system design that could be improved by other means. This view is echoed in the code, which recommends that filtering measures should only be adopted under the following circumstances:

1) after consultation and agreement with all relevant enforcing authorities; and
2) in the case of Category P systems in which it is proposed to incorporate an investigation period prior to the summoning of the fire and rescue service, after consultation with the insurers; and

3) where it is considered that either the rate of false alarms (expressed as number of false alarms per 100 detectors per annum) or the actual number of false alarms, cannot be limited to a level acceptable to the user and the fire and rescue service by other means; and

4) where it is considered that the incorporation of filtering measures does not negate the objectives of the system in terms of protection of life, property, business continuity or the environment.

As already suggested, point 4) above cannot be stressed strongly enough. Fires are very rare events in the experience of building occupiers and managers. Sadly, false alarms are only too frequent an experience. This often leads users to develop a so-called fire strategy that is, in reality, a strategy for minimizing the effects of false alarms. The natural concern on the part of users to avoid the effects of false alarms sometimes blinds them to the need for a strategy that will be robust in ensuring the safety of people in the event of an actual fire. A good false alarm strategy is not necessarily a good fire safety strategy!

Even so, properly designed filtering measures do incorporate safeguards to ensure that potential delays in implementing fire procedures in the event of fire are minimized. For example, the code recommends that filtering should not be applied to signals initiated by manual call points. Thus, during the investigation period, if anyone in the building, including those investigating the alarm signal, discover a fire, the alarm can be raised quickly by use of any nearby manual call point. (As discussed in Chapter 15, a staff alarm is sometimes accepted as the response to operation of a manual call point in public entertainment premises, but this is not primarily for the purpose of filtering out false alarms, but to enable predetermined staff actions to be put in place to assist the public with evacuation.) As was also discussed in Chapter 15, staff alarms should only be used where staff, including any night staff, are sufficient in number and fully trained in the action they are to take in the event of fire.

A further common safeguard incorporated within staff alarm arrangements is coincidence detection. When this arrangement applies, although only a staff alarm results from the operation of a single automatic fire detector, operation of any two detectors will result in a full fire alarm condition. The value of coincidence detection is acknowledged in the code, albeit that it is not specifically recommended that it should always be incorporated within a staff alarm arrangement. (Sometimes, coincidence detection is described, incorrectly, by people as 'double knock'.)

The code also recommends that, if the fire and rescue service is not summoned immediately at the start of any investigation period associated with a staff alarm, it is essential that they are summoned immediately on expiry of this period. A note in the code acknowledges that reliability and compliance with this recommendation can be aided by the use of facilities to transmit signals automatically to an alarm receiving centre on expiry of the investigation period. Some fire and rescue authorities actually advocate this in a staff alarm arrangement.

There is an implicit acknowledgement in the code that filtering might be adopted by the alarm receiving centre, albeit that this arrangement is not explicitly discussed within the code; the code merely recommends that any arrangements for filtering of automatic summoning of the fire and rescue service by an alarm receiving centre should comply with BS 5979.[72] Filtering of alarm signals at the alarm receiving centre, in the form of a telephone call to the protected premises to verify that the alarm is genuine, is commonly used in respect of intruder alarm signals. It is much less common for this to apply to fire alarm signals, but such an arrangement is not precluded by BS 5979. Care would, however, be necessary to ensure that filtering did not occur at the protected premises and also, subsequently, at the alarm receiving centre, as this would be likely to cause an unacceptable delay in transmission of signals to the fire and rescue service.

Automatic sprinkler systems are not prone to false alarms. False alarms as a result of water discharge from sprinkler heads is extremely rare, and, when it does occur, it is normally the result of significant events, such as mechanical damage (e.g. by forklift trucks), corrosion of heads in aggressive environments, freezing of unheated pipework, etc. However, false alarms do sometimes occur in systems that are supplied from water mains, as opposed to the now more common form of supply, namely a water storage tank and pumps. In systems supplied directly from towns' mains, the pressure in the main may rise at night as a result of low demand. This increase in pressure can lift the clack of the alarm valve, permitting water to flow through the pipework that serves the hydraulic alarm gong. The normal means of providing a signal from a sprinkler system to a fire alarm system comprises a pressure switch within this pipework. Accordingly, a false alarm can arise under these circumstances.

The code therefore recommends that, where a signal from an automatic sprinkler system that is supplied from water mains is used as an input

---

[72] BS 5979, *Remote centres receiving signals from fire and security systems – Code of practice.*

to the fire alarm system, there should be liaison with the organization responsible for installing or maintaining the sprinkler system to minimize potential for unwanted alarms as a result of water pressure surges. In practice, this is achieved by a hydraulic or electronic time delay facility, and consideration of these measures is recommended by the code under such circumstances. The hydraulic time delay comprises a small reservoir within the alarm line, which must be filled before water 'overflows' further down the alarm line. An electronic time delay, which is probably more common, is usually achieved by use of a pressure switch that incorporates a variable time delay (for which the pressure sensed must exist) within the switch; a similar arrangement could be applied at the fire alarm control equipment, but, philosophically, as the problem is one associated with the sprinkler installation, it is normally at the sprinkler installation that the matter is addressed.

The code also makes recommendations for ongoing management of the fire alarm system by the user. As the user is unlikely to possess, or read, the code, it is, as discussed earlier, important that the designer and supplier of the system inform the user regarding these recommendations. The recommendations in question are intended to ensure that, for example, contractors are properly apprised of the measures necessary to minimize false alarms during building work; various measures that are appropriate during such work are recommended in the code. The code also highlights the importance of ensuring that staff in the building are aware of the presence of automatic fire detection, so that they can avoid actions that could cause false alarms. Staff also need to be informed when routine testing or maintenance work might cause the occurrence of a fire alarm signal. More generally, the building, and any plant in the building, should be adequately maintained to ensure that leaking roofs, steam leaks, etc. do not cause unwanted alarms.

When false alarms do occur, the code recommends that suitable action should be taken by the user. Relevant actions were discussed earlier in this chapter, but it should be stressed that, at the very least, this should comprise recording of the false alarm and all relevant associated information in the system log book.

Finally, in order to limit false alarms, the code recommends that servicing and maintenance of the system should be carried out by a competent organization. Recommendations for maintenance (including servicing) are contained within Section 6 of the code; the relevant clauses are discussed later in this guide.

26. Installation work

Installation is the subject of an entirely independent section of the code, namely Section 4. This reflects a principle that has been stressed throughout this guide, namely the subdivision of the code into sections that are primarily addressed to various different parties. Thus, Section 4 is addressed primarily to the installer of the system.

The responsibilities imposed on the installer by the code are relatively minimal, at least in comparison with the responsibilities placed on all other relevant parties, namely the designer, the commissioning engineers and the maintenance organization. Thus, Section 4 of the code is only just over three pages long, thereby representing only 2% of the contents of the code by length. This current chapter of the guide is concerned with only two of the three clauses into which Section 4 is divided, namely clause 36, which is entitled 'Responsibility of installer', and clause 37, which is entitled 'Installation practices and workmanship'.

Fire alarm systems are commonly installed by electrical contractors, and the code does not expect such a contractor to have specialist knowledge in the design of fire alarm systems, although many may well have considerable knowledge. Thus, the code stresses that it is not, in general, the responsibility of the installer to check or verify whether the design of the system complies in full with the recommendations of the code, unless, of course, the installer is also the designer. This is something of a reversal of the situation in respect of the 1988 version of the code, which placed virtually all burdens on a party known as 'the installer'. It is, therefore, very important that, as recommended in clause 6 of the code, responsibilities for design, installation and commissioning are clearly defined and documented before an order is placed for the system.

What, then, is expected of the installer? Primarily that he/she installs the system fully in accordance with the requirements of the designer and follows good practice in installation work. However, the code does not make life quite that simple for the installer! The code acknowledges that, in practice, compliance with a number of recommendations in Section 2 of the code impact on installation and compliance may, therefore, be delegated by the designer to the installer. However, this needs to be made clear in any specification or contract, so that the installer accepts responsibility for the issues in question, and it is necessary for the installer to be competent to address the issues in question. Such issues will, therefore, often be limited to matters that it is reasonable to expect any competent electrical contractor to address. An example is cable routes; often, these are not determined by the designer, but are left to the installer to determine. Under these circumstances, in a specification, the designer may refer to clause 26 of the code, which, although this lies within Section 2 of the code, could reasonably be imposed, in part, on the installer. Methods for supporting cables should also be well within the understanding of the installer, but the designer might wish to emphasize the need for fire performance of supporting methods.

At the design stage, it can be very difficult for the designer to ensure compliance with all recommendations of Section 2. The obvious example in this respect concerns sound pressure levels; the number and siting of sounders is often more of an art than a science, and it might be reasonable, within a specification, to require that the installer carry out measurements of sound pressure level, before commissioning, so that any additional sounders required can be installed before the somewhat late stage in a project at which commissioning is carried out. Similarly, information on final fit out might not be available at the design stage and, accordingly, it might be reasonable to expect an installer to be aware of the need to avoid siting detectors too close to partitions, etc.

Even so, the code considers, in effect, that the designer should not glibly assume that the installer of the system will have expertise in the design of fire alarm systems. Therefore, it is the responsibility of the designer to provide sufficient information and guidance to the installer to enable the installer to satisfy the relevant recommendations of Section 2.

Equally, the code suggests that, if the installer *is* aware of shortcomings in the design, particularly those arising from features of the building that might not have been known to the designer, then, simply as a matter of good practice, the installer should draw these to the attention of the designer, user or purchaser. This includes shortcomings or conditions in the building that might result in an unacceptably high rate of false alarms. For example, the code would appear to expect the installer to know the basics of manual call point siting and to ensure compliance with the relevant recommendations of the code, other than recommendations relating to the model of call point used and system performance parameters, such as the delay between operation of a call point and the sounding of the alarm signal.

Notwithstanding that the recommendations within Section 2 are concerned with design issues, the code defines, quite specifically, those recommendations within Section 2 of the code with which the installer should comply. The code also recommends that the installer should ensure that, to the extent appropriate, there is consultation with all relevant interested parties; this was discussed in Chapter 8. These parties might include the designer, the user or purchaser, the supplier of the system and any relevant consultants.

This begs the question as to what should happen if, say, the designer does not specify the provision of one or more manual call points at relevant exits from the building. It has been asserted numerous times within this guide that the installer is not responsible for full design verification. Yet, within clause 36, there is a recommendation to the installer that the installation of manual call points should be in accordance with the various recommendations for manual call point siting that are contained within the design section of the code. Is this an anomaly? At first sight, it might seem so. However, in effect, the technical committee responsible for the code have apparently taken the view that any contractor installing a fire alarm system should be capable of checking the very basics of manual call point provision.

Moreover, only seven recommendations in respect of manual call points are referenced within Section 4 for attention by the installer, and two of these relate to matters of installation detail that can properly be considered to be within the remit of the installer. The need for consideration of the other five recommendations by the installer can probably best be justified in the case of a new building, in which, at the design stage, inadequate information might have been available to the designer to enable travel distances to manual call points to be accurately calculated (e.g. because layout of partitioning was not known), activities within certain areas (e.g. high hazard areas that necessitate provision of a local call point) might not have been known and, possibly, even the number and locations of exits might have changed during the building project.

The above justification for the responsibility placed on the installer to check manual call point siting does not, by itself, resolve the issue as to the action that the installer should take if the specification of the designer is found to be non-compliant with the relevant recommendations at the time of installation. While the code does not explicitly explore this issue, pragmatism would seem to dictate that the action that is appropriate will depend on the installer's judgement as to how the non-compliance has arisen. For example, if the installer's judgement is that it has obviously arisen from the final internal fit out, probably the most appropriate action is to draw the issue to the attention of the designer (if still involved in the project), the user or the purchaser. On the other hand, the installer might consider that the non-compliance, is, in fact, an intentional variation from the recommendations of the code on the part of the designer; the design certificate should, in this case, be the first port of call for the installer, as it should show such a variation.

Moreover, the code notes that a designer might accept responsibility for variations from some of the recommendations in Section 4 (including the recommendation for the installer to comply with the recommendations of Section 2 in respect of manual call point provision) and communicate this in the form of specific written requirements, e.g. within a specification. Thus, if, for example, on design drawings the designer has omitted a manual call point from an exit that was clearly shown on the design drawings, it would seem reasonable for the installer to interpret this as an intentional variation and to follow the requirements of the specification. However, this variation would need to be deemed as a variation not only from the recommendations of Section 2 but the recommendations of Section 4. Accordingly, there would be a need for the variation to be identified in the installation certificate issued by the installer.

The relatively minimal expertise in design that the code expects of installers is even clearer when we consider the recommendations of Section 4 regarding the installation of point heat, smoke and carbon monoxide detectors. In this case, the recommendation of the code is that the installer should, at least, ensure compliance with only three specific recommendations in Section 2, namely those related to the distance at which the detectors should be installed below ceilings, the 500 mm spacing that should be maintained between detector locations and walls, partitions or obstructions to the flow of smoke and hot gases, and the recommendation for spacing detectors sufficiently far away from inlets from forced ventilation systems. These are recommendations that, arguably, quite properly fall within the scope of consideration at the installation stage.

Similar, very basic recommendations are made to the installer regarding the need to ensure compliance with certain recommendations of Section 2 in respect of siting beam-type smoke detectors, line heat detectors and smoke detectors in ventilation ducts. In the case of beam-type smoke detectors and line heat detectors, it would seem that the code has considered it appropriate to recommend that the installer consider certain additional practical siting issues, which might have been equally appropriate to consider in the case of point detectors. For example, in the case of beam-type smoke detectors, the code recommends that the installer should ensure compliance with a recommendation that storage racks reaching within 300 mm of the ceiling should be treated as walls; in the case of point detectors, the code does not specifically recommend that compliance with the latter recommendation be ensured by the installer. This is either a minor anomaly within the code or an implication that, in the case of these more specialist forms of fire detection, a slightly greater expertise is necessary on the part of the installer. On the other hand, there can be no argument that the installer should, as recommended in the code, ensure that 'special' requirements for siting of beam-type smoke detectors, such as mounting transmitters and receivers on solid construction, are followed.

Often, the installer of the fire alarm system is responsible for provision of the mains power supplies to the system, particularly if the installer is an electrical contractor. The code recommends that the installer of the mains power supplies to the fire alarm system should ensure that the supplies comply with the recommendations of the code for such supplies. Sometimes, the installer of the fire alarm system does not install the mains power supply for the system; this can arise if the user has provided the mains power supply for the purpose. In this case, the code does not specifically recommend that the installer of the system verify compliance of the mains power supply with the code. However, this will be checked at commissioning (see Chapter 28).

Obviously, the installer will be responsible for fixing control, indicating and power supply equipment. The code recommends that all such equipment that is likely to need routine attention for maintenance should be sited in readily accessible locations that facilitate safe maintenance work. (This might, in any case, be regarded as a requirement of the Construction (Design and Management) Regulations.) It is further recommended in the code that all metallic parts of the installation, including conduit, trunking, ducting, cabling and enclosures, should be well separated from any metalwork forming part of a lightning protection system.

With regard to the installation work, the code expects little more than that the installer should comply with the requirements of BS 7671,[73] albeit that, where any conflict between BS 5839-1 and BS 7671 exists

---

[73] BS 7671, *Requirements for electrical installations. IEE Wiring Regulations. Seventeenth edition.*

(which is unlikely), BS 5839-1 should take precedence. Particular conventional good practices that are highlighted in clause 37 of the code, include proper fixing of cables, so that, for example, they do not rely on suspended ceilings for their support, avoidance of unnecessary joints, proper arrangements for earthing, with care taken to ensure the electrical continuity of electromagnetic screens, including metallic sheaths of cables.

Recommendations are also given in clause 37 for fire stopping of penetrations for cables, conduits, trunking or tray, and for fire stopping within ducts, trunking, shafts, etc. that pass through floors, walls, partitions or ceilings. Recommendations are also given to ensure that cables are not damaged as they pass through penetrations in construction and that penetrations in external walls are suitably sleeved.

Again, clause 37 recommends consideration of some of the recommendations in Section 2 of the code. However, once again, these are primarily recommendations that relate to practical installation considerations, such as segregation, protection of cables against mechanical damage and support of cables, rather than matters of fundamental design, such as whether cables should be of standard or enhanced fire resistance; the latter issue is purely one for the designer to specify.

Generally, it is the responsibility of the installer to provide 'as fitted' drawings of the system, showing the locations of equipment, cable routes, cable sizes and types, etc. The view taken in the code is that, by default, unless it has been agreed that the preparation of 'as fitted' drawings is to be the responsibility of others, it is the responsibility of the installer to supply these to the purchaser or user of the system. Presumably, however, where the installer acts as a subcontractor to others, it is reasonable that provision should be via the principal contractor. On completion of installation work, the installer should also issue a certificate of installation. Annex G of the code contains a model certificate for this purpose.

27. Inspection and testing

The third and last clause of Section 4 of the code, clause 38, deals with inspection and testing of wiring. This clause is included within Section 4 because, of course, this work is normally carried out by the installer.

In practice, any competent contractor who installs electrical wiring, whether as part of a fire alarm installation or any other form of electrical installation, will 'Megger' test the wiring to confirm that the insulation resistance is adequate. The code recommends that insulation testing should be carried out at 500 V d.c., unless the cables are not rated for mains voltage; in practice, cables used within the system will be rated for mains voltage, albeit that fire alarm systems operate at extra low voltage.

The necessity of testing cables at 500 V is often queried, given that the circuits will be operating at extra low voltage. One reason is that the technical committee responsible for the code have always considered that this initial 500 V test is useful in identifying incipient defects that might not come to light from testing at a much lower voltage and that might not be identified by the system's fault monitoring; problems might, however, arise during the lifetime of the system. Previous versions of the code have recommended that the 500 V insulation resistance test be carried out every five years. In practice, this was very rarely carried out at all during the lifetime of the system, as, to do so, would require disconnection of devices to avoid damage. Accordingly, the 2002 version of the code only recommends that the 500 V test be carried out on completion of wiring, or sections of wiring, usually with equipment disconnected and prior to completion of the entire system.

The code recommends that insulation resistance be measured between conductors, between each conductor and earth, and between each conductor and any screen. In practice, when such a test is carried out on newly installed wiring, a reading of infinity will be obtained, or, at least, the meter will indicate a higher resistance than the 100 MΩ that is often the maximum value that the meter can accurately read. Although this will invariably be achieved with properly installed and undamaged cable, such high resistance is not necessary for operation of the system. Moreover, compliance with BS 7671[74] would necessitate only a resistance of 1.0 MΩ. However, the code recommends that the insulation resistance measured in these tests should be at least 2 MΩ.

The figure of 2 MΩ is quite arbitrary, but is set at a higher level than specified in BS 7671 because, in practice, if such low insulation resistance is found in newly installed cables, it almost implies the existence of a potential fault that might result in instability in the degree of insulation resistance afforded. Moreover, the code does contain a 'health warning' in the form of a note that draws attention to the fact that, in large systems, the insulation resistance would need to be much higher if control and indicating equipment has a means for sensing resistance between conductors and earth, otherwise nuisance fault indications might result. On the other hand, for a small non-addressable system of up to about four zones, 2 MΩ might be acceptable.

Since the installation is an electrical installation to which BS 7671 applies, obviously, further tests should be carried out to ensure compliance with BS 7671. Thus, the code draws attention to the need for earth continuity testing and, in the case of mains supply circuits, for measurement of earth fault loop impedance.

Since the insulation resistance tests need to be carried out with equipment disconnected, further tests might need to be carried out on the final completion of the system. The code makes the installer responsible for carrying out these tests, unless there is specific agreement that they will be carried out as part of the commissioning process. In the case of an addressable system, normally the manufacturer will specify a maximum resistance for any loop. Thus, one of the further tests recommended by the code is measurement of the resistance of any circuit for which a maximum circuit resistance is specified by the manufacturer or supplier. A check for correct circuit polarity is also recommended. As a final 'catch all', the code also recommends that the installer carry out any other tests specified by the manufacturer of the system, unless, again, there is specific agreement that these tests will be carried out as part of the commissioning process.

The results of all tests described above, should be recorded and made available to the commissioning engineer. Thus, completion of the model installation certificate contained in Annex G requires that the

---

[74] BS 7671, *Requirements for electrical installations. IEE Wiring Regulations. Seventeenth edition.*

installer confirm that wiring has been tested in accordance with the recommendations of clause 38 and that test results have been recorded. The model certificate contains space for the installer to record the person to whom these test results have been provided.

28. Commissioning

Commissioning and handover are the subject of Section 5 of the code, thus, following the modular approach of the code, introducing further parties in the chain that exists between initial specification of the system and final operational use. Commissioning is the subject of clause 39 within Section 5.

Commissioning is defined in clause 3 of the code as the process by which it is determined that the installed system meets the defined requirements. While this may appear to be a very broad duty, in practice the code tends to regard commissioning as merely setting the system to work and verifying that it operates correctly in the manner designed. The commissioning engineer is also expected to ensure that installation workmanship is generally of an adequate standard and that all relevant documentation has been handed over to the user.

However, the code acknowledges that it is not, in general, the responsibility of the commissioning engineer to verify compliance of the design, or of the installation work, with the recommendations of the relevant sections of the code, i.e. Sections 2 and 4 respectively. Equally, the code recognizes that, as in the case of installation, it may be difficult to ensure that the system complies in full with certain recommendations of Section 2 until the time of commissioning; adequacy of sound pressure levels is an obvious example (unless adequacy of sound pressure levels throughout the building has been carefully checked during the installation process). Similarly, as discussed in Chapter 26, information about structural features of the building, or final layout, might not have been available to the designer. Commissioning is, in effect, the final 'safety net' for obvious shortcomings in design to be identified.

Thus, a commissioning engineer needs to possess at least a basic knowledge of fire alarm design practices and of the recommendations of the code in respect of design and installation. In order to commission the system properly, the commissioning engineer will need to be furnished with the specification for the system. The commissioning engineer should also have a basic knowledge and understanding of Section 3 of the code, and of the recommendations it makes in respect of limiting false alarms, so that he/she can verify compliance with, at least, the principles discussed in Section 3.

In considering the suitability of companies for certification under third-party certification schemes, no doubt, in the case of companies that have fire alarm system commissioning within their scope, the third-party certification bodies will wish to confirm that commissioning engineers have the necessary competence, as described in the code. In carrying out inspections of commissioned installations, a degree of 'fault' may be attributed to the commissioning engineer if, at least, obvious non-compliances with certain recommendations of Sections 2, 3 or 4 of the code have not been identified at commissioning, particularly if unintentional non-compliances have arisen as a result of circumstances of which it would not be reasonable to expect the designer to have been aware.

The code sets out a list of 27 matters that are to be checked during the commissioning process. These, obviously, include testing all devices in a suitable manner and confirming that the system's 'cause and effect', as specified by the designer, is correctly programmed and demonstrated as compliant with the specification; thus, it should be confirmed that, for example, every manual call point and automatic fire detector, on operation, results in the correct zone indication, correct text display (if the system is addressable), and that all plant shutdowns, etc. operate correctly.

The code also recommends that sound pressure levels throughout all areas of the building are checked for compliance with the recommendations of the code. If the installation incorporates a voice alarm system, it should be confirmed that intelligibility is satisfactory. (Guidance on the latter matter is contained in BS 5839-8,[75] which, in most circumstances, only expects a subjective assessment of intelligibility.) A check is also necessary to ensure that no changes to the building, since the time of original design, have compromised the compliance of the system with the code, e.g. by a final fit out that affects the adequacy of device siting.

As in the case of the installer, the commissioning engineer is not expected to confirm that the siting of all devices meets the detailed

---

[75] BS 5839-8, *Fire detection and alarm systems for buildings — Code of practice for the design, installation and servicing of voice alarm systems.* In 2008, BS 5839-8:1998 will be superseded by BS 5839-8:2008.

design recommendations of the code. For avoidance of doubt as to the commissioning engineer's responsibilities in this respect, the code specifies the particular recommendations within Section 2 that should be verified at commissioning. The recommendations that are cited relate primarily to practical considerations, such as proximity of detectors to walls, partitions, obstructions and air inlets. Similar practical considerations in the siting of control, indicating and power supply equipment are recommended for verification, along with a check that a suitable zone plan is displayed.

The commissioning engineer is also expected to inspect the mains power supplies, as far as is reasonably practicable, to ensure compliance with the recommendations of the code. The need for this check at commissioning should be noted, as past custom and practice has been for the commissioning engineer to ignore mains power supplies, as outside the scope of his/her consideration. The code also recommends that the commissioning engineer confirm that standby power supplies comply with the recommendations of the code for these supplies. This will require measurement of quiescent and alarm currents, and the use of the formula given in Annex D of the code (see Chapter 21). It is recommended in the code that, in the course of these measurements, the commissioning engineer confirm that the load currents in all circumstances are close to the predictions used by the designer to determine the specified battery capacity. The code is silent on the matter of what the commissioning engineer is expected to do if the two do not closely coincide, but presumably it would be reasonable to confirm that there is some valid reason for this.

A check should also be carried out to ensure, as far as is reasonably practical, that the correct cable type has been used throughout the system and that installation workmanship complies with the relevant recommendations of the code. It should be noted that, at commissioning, very little of the cable may be visible, and certainly it will be difficult to confirm that every length of cable is suitably supported. However, for compliance with the code, presumably, at least, an element of 'sampling' would be appropriate if possible.

In the case of radio-linked systems, the code recommends that a check be carried out at commissioning to ensure that radio signal strengths are adequate throughout all areas of the protected premises to ensure reliable operation of the system. In Chapter 23 of this guide, this check was considered in more detail.

Often, batteries are not fitted until the time of commissioning. The age of a battery is often regarded as some indication of its future reliability. Indeed, some users actually specify that batteries should be changed every few years as a preventative maintenance measure. Accordingly, the code recommends that labels, visible when batteries are in their normal position, should be fixed to batteries, indicating the date of installation.

More generally, while, as has been constantly stressed in this guide, it is not the responsibility of the commissioning engineer to verify or certify compliance of the system design with the code, the code does recommend that the commissioning engineer confirm that there are no obvious shortcomings in compliance with Section 2 of the code. Thus, it would be expected that the commissioning engineer identify the existence of unprotected areas within a Category L1 or P1 system, or obvious errors in the spacing or siting of detectors. It is, however, probably not reasonable to expect the commissioning engineer to identify minor departures from, for example, the 7.5 m and 5.3 m 'rules' relating to the maximum distance of any point from the nearest smoke detector or heat detector respectively.

In Chapter 27, it was noted that there might be agreement that certain tests, which could be undertaken by the installer, should be undertaken by the commissioning engineer. An obvious example is measurement of loop resistance. Therefore, either these tests should be carried out at commissioning, or the commissioning engineer should confirm that adequate records exist. More specifically, the code recommends that the commissioning engineer confirm that adequate records of insulation resistance, earth continuity and, where appropriate, earth loop impedance tests exist. It is also recommended that the commissioning engineer confirm that all relevant documentation has been provided to the user or purchaser; the nature of this documentation is discussed in the next chapter of this guide.

On completion of commissioning, as in the case of all the discrete stages identified in the code, a commissioning certificate should be issued. Completion of the model certificate contained in Annex G requires that the commissioning engineer confirm that the system has been commissioned in accordance with the code, other than any recorded variations from the recommended commissioning process. Completion of the certificate also requires that it be confirmed that all equipment operates correctly, installation work is, as far as can be reasonably ascertained, of an acceptable standard, that there is no any obvious potential for an unacceptable rate of false alarms and that the required documentation has been provided to the user. The certificate should also record an appropriate period for which a soak test should be carried out (see Chapter 25). As discussed in Chapter 25, there is also space on the commissioning certificate for the commissioning engineer to record potential causes of false alarms that, while not warranting specific action at the time of commissioning, should be considered at the time of the next service visit to determine whether false alarm problems are arising.

29. Documentation

Frequently, even large, responsible fire alarm contractors are somewhat 'scrappy' in respect of documentation presented to the user or purchaser at handover. It is not at all unknown for retentions in a contract to be retained well after the system has become operational, simply because, under the contract, completion of the fire alarm project includes handover of proper documentation. Sometimes, it almost seems as though, unless the retention is high enough, in the closing stages of a project the contractor would almost rather waive collection of the retention than put together the documentation required under the contract.

In a highly modular contract, in which design, installation, supply and commissioning are undertaken by a number of different parties, more than one party may be involved in provision of the documentation recommended by the code. To address this point, the code notes that the responsibility for provision of documentation needs to be defined before an order for the system is placed. In addition, the organization to which each form of documentation is provided needs to be defined in any contract for design, supply, installation and commissioning of the system. For example, some documentation might be provided to a main contractor (e.g. by an installation subcontractor), rather than directly to the user or purchaser. Therefore, as noted in Chapter 28, at commissioning it needs to be ensured that, either the documentation has been provided to the relevant parties, or that any absent documentation is identified for appropriate action.

Clause 40 of the code defines the documentation that should be provided to the purchaser or user of the system. Since the recommendations of this clause do nothing else, other than list the relevant documentation, the clause is quite short. However, the devotion of an independent clause within the code to the subject of documentation, and the mirroring of that approach within this guide, is intended to highlight the importance of proper documentation and, hopefully, to improve the quality of documentation handed over at the end of projects in the future.

Accordingly, it is probably of value to list, within this chapter of the guide, the documentation that the code recommends be provided to the purchaser or user of the system on completion of the system, as this forms a useful checklist. The documentation comprises the following.

- Certificates for design, installation and commissioning of the system.
- An adequate operation and maintenance (O&M) manual for the system.
- 'As fitted' drawings.
- A log book.
- A record of any agreed variations from the original design specification.
- Such other records as are required by any purchase specification.

Separate certificates may exist for design, installation and commissioning (i.e. if each of these processes is undertaken by a different party). Model certificates are contained within Annex G of the code, but as this is an informative annex, rather than a normative one, the certificate used need not comply exactly with the format of the model certificate. However, the certificate used should contain the relevant information shown in the model certificate. If more than one of these three processes, including all three of them, are undertaken by a single party, there would seem no reason for that party to issue separate certificates for each of the processes involved; it would seem reasonable, and probably more convenient for the recipient in any case, to provide a single certificate that covers the processes for which the signatory has been responsible.

Possibly, one of the most inadequate documents handed over by fire alarm contractors is the O&M manual. Often, any manual that is handed over contains nothing more than 'glossy' data sheets on the products provided. It should, therefore, be stressed that this would not be a satisfactory O&M manual for compliance with the recommendations of the code; the code recommends that the O&M manual should provide information, *specific to the system in question*, and that the information provided should include the following:

1) the equipment provided and its configuration, including, for radio-linked equipment (but not radio-paging systems provided for deaf or hard of hearing people), the background RF noise level and attached signal strengths;

2) use of all controls;
3) recommendations for investigation of a fire alarm or fault signal after the incident is over and the building is declared safe for reoccupation. (This is not, however, intended to be the emergency or evacuation plan, which is the responsibility of the occupant to formulate.);
4) recommendations for investigation in the event of a false alarm;
5) routine weekly and monthly testing of the system by the user or his/her appointed agent (the relevant information should accord with the recommendations given in clause 44 of the code);
6) service and maintenance of the system in accordance with Section 6 of the code;
7) avoidance of false alarms (based on the information contained in Section 3 of the code);
8) the need to keep a clear space around all fire detectors and manual call points;
9) the need to avoid contamination of detectors during contractors' activities;
10) the importance of ensuring that changes to the building, such as relocation of partitions, do not affect the standard of protection;
11) other user responsibilities described within Section 7 of the code.

'As fitted' drawings are another 'Cinderella' area in many contracts, with drawings either not provided or barely meeting the definition for 'as fitted'. Again, to improve this situation, the code is very specific as to the minimum information that should be provided on all 'as fitted' drawings. This comprises:

1) the positions of all control, indicating and power supply equipment;
2) the positions of all manual call points, fire detectors and fire alarm devices;
3) the positions of all equipment that may require routine attention or replacement (the obvious example is short circuit isolators);
4) the type, sizes and actual routes of cables.

Although (sometimes only after prompting) contractors are willing to show the types and sizes of cables, the matter of cable routes is often contentious. Frequently, they are missing from drawings or, at best, comprise straight lines drawn between devices, often extending outside the curtilage of an irregularly shaped building! The wording 'actual routes' in the code is, therefore, worthy of note. Indeed, the code does amplify this term within a note, which asserts that cables routes shown need to comprise a *reasonable representation* of the route followed, such as to enable a competent person to locate the cable in the event of a fault or need for modification or extension of the system.

The note goes on to point out that a simple schematic showing the sequence in which the devices are wired, is unlikely to satisfy this recommendation, other than in small, simple systems. Thus, within the code there is something of a 'test', against which 'as fitted' drawings can be judged. The question that needs to be considered is whether a competent person could, perhaps during a maintenance call-out, find every section of cable by reference to the 'as fitted' drawings.

A further note in the code points out that, in the case of extensions or alterations, existing 'as fitted' drawings need to be updated. Again, this is an important point, as, in practice, it is common to find 'as fitted' drawings on site that barely resemble a system that was installed many years previously and has been subject to major modification.

It should also be noted that compliance with the code does involve provision of a log book to the user or purchaser. A model format for this log book is given in Annex F of the code, although, as this is in an informative annex, the log book need not follow the exact format of that shown in the annex. However, for compliance with the code, the format must be such that all events, including fire alarm signals, fault signals, system tests and maintenance visits, can be recorded.

The format of the model log book contains three different sections relating to maintenance work, false alarms and events other than false alarms or maintenance work. Certainly, there is great value in recording false alarms in a separate section from other events, since, as discussed in Chapter 25, there will be a need for careful scrutiny of these records by the service technician at the time of each service visit.

The code provides no further information as to the form that the record of agreed variations from the original design specification should take. There is, however, space within the model installation certificate for variations from the specification to be recorded. This might, or might not, alone be sufficient to meet the spirit of the relevant recommendation. Presumably, the recommendation to record agreed variations from the original specification is to ensure that there is a suitable audit trail to assist any third party in following the route by which the final installation design has been achieved, if this does not accord with the original specification.

With regard to other records required by the purchase specification, in the case of a simple system installed on behalf of a relatively uninformed user or purchaser, the purchase specification will probably not call for any additional records. However, a concerned and interested purchaser may require further records. Examples given in the code are insulation resistance test records and commissioning records. Some large purchasers require sight of these at handover. Since, normally, third-party certification bodies demand that contractors keep records of insulation resistance tests and commissioning, it should not be difficult for contractors to provide these to the user or purchaser if required to do so.

30. Certification

Certification is the subject of just one short clause of the code, namely clause 41. However, as in the case of 'Documentation', the devotion of an entire clause of the code to this subject, and the parallel adopted in this guide, highlight the importance attached by the code to proper certification.

In previous versions of the code, the issue of a single certificate was envisaged following completion of installation and commissioning. This certificate, however, primarily verified that the design of the system complied with the recommendations of the code. As noted in the previous chapter, the 2002 version of the code envisages separate certification of design, installation and commissioning, for which, clause 41 suggests that three separate certificates ultimately need to be issued; in practice, there would seem to be no harm in combining these in situations where all three processes are undertaken by one organization, provided the three processes are, in effect, separately certificated within the one document.

It is primarily the design certificate that confirms compliance of the design with the vast majority of the recommendations contained in the code. Regardless of whether this certificate has been properly issued, the installer can, and should, issue an installation certificate, which primarily confirms that the system was installed in accordance with the specification and the recommendations of Section 4 of the code. Similarly, the commissioning engineer can, and should, quite independently issue a commissioning certificate, which primarily confirms only that the system has been commissioned in accordance with the recommendations of the code. However, as discussed in Chapter 28, commissioning in accordance with the code does include some consideration of matters addressed in Sections 2, 3 and 4 of the code.

The modular form of certification advocated in the 2002 version of the code is primarily intended to ensure that certification is much more meaningful than it has been in the past. For this to be the case, as noted in the code, it is important that whoever signs the certificates is competent to confirm that the recommendations of the code in respect of the process to which the certificate refers have been satisfied, or that variations have been agreed. Indeed, there is a thinly veiled warning within the commentary of clause 41 to the effect that the purchaser or user might rely on the certificates as evidence of compliance with legislation, and that liability could arise for anyone that issues a certificate without due care in ensuring its validity. Such liability might arise not only in civil law, but in criminal law; the author is aware of one situation in which the Trading Standards department of the local authority considered prosecution of a contractor for issuing BS 5839-1 certificates in respect of installations that were likely not to comply with the code. With the demise of certification under the Fire Precautions Act 1971, and the reliance now placed on fire risk assessments by employers, landlords, etc., there may, now, be greater dependence of these parties on certificates of compliance for relevant fire protection installations.

Certification, as envisaged in the code, does not, however, end with the commissioning process. As discussed in the next chapter of this guide, 'acceptance' is considered to constitute a formal process and it, too, should be the subject of certification. In this case, the code recommends that the organization bearing contractual responsibility to the purchaser for the system should issue a certificate of acceptance to the purchaser for completion. Thus, Annex G of the code contains a model acceptance certificate.

In previous chapters of this guide, there has been frequent reference to 'the purchaser or user'. When this term was used, as in the case of the code, the context in which it was used would probably be sufficient, in the case of an actual project, for it to be obvious whether it was to the purchaser or the user that any recommendations in question referred. It should be noted, however, that the acceptance certificate should be issued to the purchaser, not the user. The purchaser and user may, of course, be the same party, but, where they are not, in the case of the acceptance certificate the code does not offer the alternative of issue of the acceptance certificate to the user. However, as discussed in the next chapter of this guide, as part of the acceptance process, the purchaser will need to consider the requirements of the user, e.g. in terms of handover of documentation to the user.

The code also makes provision for a further, optional stage, termed 'Verification'. Verification is discussed in Chapter 32 of this guide. At this stage, it should be noted that, if verification, as defined in the code, is carried out, a verification certificate should be issued, and, again, Annex G of the code contains a model verification certificate.

The system will need to be inspected and serviced periodically throughout its lifetime. Accordingly, Annex G also contains a model certificate of inspection and servicing. The certificate confirms that relevant details of the work carried out and faults identified have been entered in the system log book, records the number of false alarms during the previous 12 months and contains a conversion of this number into a 'rate' (see Chapter 25) and indicates any further work or action considered necessary.

During the lifetime of the system, it may also be subject to modification. The code contains particular recommendations that need to be taken into account when a system is modified; these are discussed in Chapter 35 of this guide. At this stage, it should be noted that, when a system is modified, a modification certificate should be issued, and a suitable model certificate is shown in Annex G of the code. The certificate confirms that, following the modifications, the system has been tested in accordance with relevant recommendations of the code and that 'as fitted' drawings and other system records have been updated as appropriate. An important feature of the modification certificate is also that it confirms that the modifications have introduced no additional variations from the code, other than those specifically recorded in the modification certificate.

31. Acceptance by the user or purchaser

The code regards the process of 'acceptance' as an independent formal process in the chain of events between specification of a system and the system becoming operational. In turning our attention to acceptance, we are now dealing with the last of the 'compulsory' processes that are required to take place for compliance with the code.

While formal handover of the system may involve either the purchaser or the user, the process of formal acceptance, as envisaged in the code, is the responsibility of the purchaser or their representative. Although the purchaser and user will often be the same party, particularly in the case of purchase by a small firm, in some projects there can be a very clear distinction between the purchaser and user. For example, the purchaser may be the head office project engineering team of a large corporate body, whereas the user would be the management of the site or building in which the fire alarm system is installed. Of course, there is nothing to stop the purchaser nominating the user as their representative.

As noted in the code, in the case of a small, simple building, acceptance might involve little more than a brief inspection of the system by the user, demonstration of its operation by the commissioning engineer, and handover of the relevant documents to the user; there is nothing in the code that necessitates the purchaser or user having any particular degree of expertise in fire alarm systems. However, in the case of large, complex systems, the purchaser or his/her representative is likely to be well informed, and may wish to witness relevant tests as part of a formal and structured acceptance procedure. This requirement should not be 'sprung' on the contractor at the end of a project. The code recommends that the purchase specification should define the acceptance procedures required by the purchaser, including any tests that are to be witnessed and details of the witnessing procedure; for example, there will be a need to define the extent of notice that needs to be given to the purchaser before tests that he/she wishes to witness are carried out.

The code recommends just seven matters with which the purchaser or his/her representative should be satisfied before accepting the system. These comprise:

1) that all installation work appears to be satisfactory;
2) that the system is capable of giving a fire alarm signal;
3) that any facility for remote transmission of faults and alarms to an alarm receiving centre operates correctly;
4) that the following documents have been provided to the purchaser or user:
   - 'as fitted' drawings;
   - operating and maintenance instructions;
   - certificates of design, installation and commissioning;
   - a log book that complies with the recommendations of the code in terms of its format;
5) that sufficient representatives of the user have been properly instructed in the operation of the system, including, at least, all means of triggering fire signals, silencing and resetting the system and avoidance of false alarms;
6) that the nominated person has been advised of their responsibilities and how these might be discharged;
7) that all relevant tests, defined in the purchase specification, have been witnessed.

In the case of a small system, the check of installation work will probably be no more than a quick walk round the installation. In large projects, the purchaser will probably wish to pay greater attention to the standard of workmanship to ensure that it meets his/her standards. In a small system, confirmation of system operability need only comprise, say, operation of a manual call point by the commissioning engineer to demonstrate that the system does work and, if there is connection to an alarm receiving centre, that the alarm receiving centre receives the signal correctly; if fault signals are also transmitted to the alarm receiving centre, the correct transmission of a fault signal should be demonstrated to the purchaser. In the case of large projects, the purchaser will probably wish to, at least, witness the operation of a sample of manual call points and automatic detectors. Indeed, the purchaser might wish to witness test operation of all devices. This again highlights the need for the purchaser's requirements in this respect to be clearly identified in the purchase specification.

In the case of, say, a small shop, it is probably sufficient that the manager and perhaps one or two other members of staff are instructed in the operation of the system. As noted in the code, however, in the case of large complex systems there will probably be a need for a formal training course for a number of people. Again, requirements for user training should be defined in the purchase specification.

The 'responsible person', to which there is reference above, is defined in the code as the person having control of the building and/or premises, whether as occupier or otherwise, or any person designated by the person having control of the building and/or premises to be responsible for the fire alarm system and the fire procedures. The code notes that the responsible person might, or might not, be the person responsible under fire safety legislation for compliance with legislation. In practice, other than in small premises, the responsible person, defined in BS 5839-1, is unlikely to be the responsible person, defined in the Regulatory Reform (Fire Safety) Order 2005. The responsibilities of the BS 5839-1 responsible person are described in clause 47 of the code and discussed in Chapter 36 of this guide.

On completion of acceptance, the purchaser or their representative should sign an acceptance certificate, issued by the organization bearing contractual responsibility to the purchaser for the system. The nature of this certificate was discussed in the previous chapter of this guide.

32. Verification

There has been frequent reference in this guide to the modular approach to design, installation and commissioning adopted in the code. It has also been asserted that the reason for this approach in the code is that it reflects common practice in fire alarm projects, particularly those involving large new buildings. The code does, however, recognize that this approach to a project provides scope for certain issues to 'fall down the cracks' at the interface between one module and the next.

Thus, system design might be compliant with the recommendations of the code in relation to the drawings and other information provided to the designer at the design stage. The installer might then correctly install the system strictly in accordance with this design. The organization carrying out commissioning may have had little or no previous input to the project, as their contract may simply be for supply of the system and commissioning after installation.

Sections 4 and 5 of the code do recommend that a certain amount of checking is carried out by installers and commissioning engineers to ensure that the basic design recommendations of the code are satisfied. However, it is accepted in the code that it is not the responsibility of the installer or the commissioning engineer to identify shortcomings in design. Thus the code suggests that a purchaser might consider that, as a result of division of responsibilities for design, supply, installation and commissioning (or for any other reason), there is significant potential for the installed system to deviate from the recommendations of the code. In these circumstances, 'verification' should be obtained from a single organization, which should then issue a single verification certificate. The purpose of verification is to confirm that, as far as can reasonably be determined, the system complies with all recommendations of the code, or that variations have been agreed and documented in accordance with the recommendations of the code.

This advice then begs two questions, namely who should carry out the verification and how far should their verification work go in establishing compliance of the installed system with all recommendations of the code? The first of these questions is answered within clause 43 of the code, which deals with the matter of verification. The code suggests that the verifying organization may be one of those involved in the design, supply, installation or commissioning processes (e.g. the system supplier or the designer) or an independent third party (such as a consultant).

With regard to the second question, the code is realistic enough to acknowledge that it is unlikely that any one organization, particularly a third party, will be able to verify in full the compliance of the system with every recommendation of the code. Moreover, this degree of scrutiny may be unnecessary. For example, the modular approach to the project has no real bearing on the quality of installation work. Therefore, if an installation certificate has been issued by a responsible contractor, and no significant shortcomings in the quality of installation work have been identified at commissioning, the need for, or value of, further inspection of wiring as part of a further verification process is arguably doubtful, particularly as there may be difficulty in carrying out such an inspection where wiring is concealed from view.

For these reasons, the code stresses that the scope and extent of the verification process need to be subject to agreement between the purchaser or user and the organization responsible for verification. This is particularly important advice that should be carefully followed to avoid dissatisfaction with the quality of the verification on the part of the purchaser or user, resultant disputes between these parties and potential liability for the verifying organization. The code also advises that an indication of the scope and extent of the verification process needs to be given in the verification certificate or associated documents; associated documents could, for example, comprise a report, which begins with a clear statement of the work carried out.

The need, or otherwise, for verification is a matter for the purchaser or user. This will probably depend on many factors, such as the nature and complexity of the building and the fire alarm system, the purchaser's perception of the skills of the designer, installer and commissioning organization, and his/her perception of the scope that exists for errors or omissions to have occurred. However, the code does positively recommend that, where a purchaser or user considers that, as a result of division of responsibility for the design, supply, installation and commissioning processes, there is *significant* potential for the installed system to deviate from the recommendations in the code, verification of compliance should be arranged. Thus, it could be argued that, if the purchaser is well aware of the potential for this problem, but decides against verification, the purchaser has failed to comply with the recommendations of the code.

Moreover, some purchasers or users may feel that, notwithstanding that the project may not have been modular in terms of responsibilities, verification could be of value as a 'comfort factor'. The code also notes that a verification certificate can be of value to an enforcing authority or property insurer.

The code recommends that any person responsible for verification should be competent in the design of fire alarm systems in accordance with the code and be familiar with relevant installation practices. While, as already noted, the scope and extent of the process needs to be agreed between the parties, the code recommends, quite specifically, that verification should address the recommendations of Section 3 in respect of limitation of false alarms.

33. Routine testing

Clause 44 of the code deals with routine testing of the system. This clause is the first clause in Section 6 of the code, which bears the generic title 'Maintenance'. This reflects the fact that 'maintenance', as it is defined in the code, comprises the work of inspection, servicing and repair necessary in order to maintain the efficient operation of the installed system; all such inspection need not be carried out by specialists, and, in the case of routine testing, it will normally be carried out by the user.

On occasions, users question the need for the level of routine testing recommended by the code, given that modern fire alarm systems provide a much greater level of monitoring and 'self-checking' than their earlier counterparts, for which recommendations for routine testing were first formulated. It is sometimes suggested that the technical committee responsible for the code have not taken developments in the standard of monitoring into account in the most recent revisions of the code.

In fact, the routine testing recommended in the code is not intended to overlap significantly with the benefits afforded by system monitoring. A closer study of the recommendations of the code in respect of routine testing makes this clear. The testing that is recommended is very basic in nature, and it can be inferred from the recommendations of the code that it really only has two principal functions.

The first of these is to ensure that the system has not suffered some form of catastrophic failure, such as total power failure or major circuit failure. In pursuit of this confirmation, the code recommends that, every week, a manual call point should be operated. The purpose of this test is only to ensure that the control equipment is capable of processing a fire alarm signal, if one occurs, and that it can provide an output to fire alarm sounders. If there is a facility for transmission of fire alarm signals to an alarm receiving centre, it should also be ensured that the signal is correctly received at the alarm receiving centre.

Several points arise from the simple description of the test and its objectives given in clause 44 of the code. First, only one single manual call point need be operated on the occasion of each weekly test. This is less onerous than the equivalent recommendation in the 1988 version of the code, which recommended that, in large systems, several manual call points might need to be tested each week to ensure that all circuits were tested over a 13-week period.

In this sense, the technical committee have taken account of the circuit monitoring found in modern systems, as well as taking account of common complaints from building occupants when, on the occasion of each weekly test, the fire alarm system is sounded several times. The latter practice is, arguably, also undesirable from the point of view of fire safety, since occupants would be unlikely to respond effectively if an actual fire occurred during the period when these multiple tests were being carried out. Indeed, to avoid any confusion between the weekly test and a genuine fire alarm signal, the code now recommends that the duration for which fire alarm sounders should operate at the time of the weekly test should not normally exceed one minute. (In practice, the period could be much shorter than this, but the period of one minute often permits a single person to carry out the test and return to the control panel to silence the sounders.)

A further point to note is that it is not necessary to confirm that all fire alarm sounder circuits operate correctly at the time of the weekly test, or that sound pressure levels are adequate throughout the building. However, as a matter of good practice, the code does recommend that occupants be instructed to report any instance of poor audibility of the fire alarm signal. Correct operation of sounder circuits is addressed during service visits (see Chapter 34).

It should be noted that the code does recommend that there be confirmation, at the time of each weekly test, that the signal is correctly received at the alarm receiving centre. The reason for this is that the signal from the fire alarm system passes through other equipment (i.e. a transmitter), is then transmitted via a signal path that might, or might not, be monitored and is then processed and displayed on yet further equipment at the alarm receiving centre; this introduces potential failure modes beyond those possible in the facilities to warn occupants of the building in the event of fire. In practice, this means that the alarm receiving centre will need to be contacted immediately before, and immediately after, the weekly test, and that, in the case of the latter contact, it be confirmed with the alarm receiving centre that the signal was correctly received; it will be insufficient to simply inform the alarm receiving centre that further calls should be treated as genuine.

The second, but more subsidiary, objective of the weekly test is to make occupants familiar with the fire alarm signal. For this reason, the code specifically recommends that the weekly test should be carried out during normal working hours. It is also recommended in the code that the test be carried out at approximately the same time each week. In systems with staged alarms, incorporating an 'Alert' and an 'Evacuate' signal, the two signals should be operated, where practicable, sequentially in the order that they would occur at the time of a fire. This is to minimize the chance of confusion between the 'Alert' and 'Evacuate' signals. (The author is aware of one case in which some occupants thought that the 'Evacuate' signal, which they heard each week, was a test signal that should be ignored, while the intermittent 'Alert' signal should, if it were ever heard, be treated as indication of a fire!)

In some premises, certain occupants may not work at the time when the fire alarm system is tested. An example would be permanent night shift workers. To ensure that these employees are also made familiar with the sound of the fire alarm system, the code recommends that, in such cases, an additional test(s) be carried out at least once a month to ensure the familiarity of these employees with the fire alarm signal(s).

While the objective of the weekly test is not to test all manual call points at any particular frequency, as a form of 'bonus' the code recommends that a different manual call point should be used at the time of every weekly test. The purpose of this is to capitalize on the test to give some opportunity to identify a defective manual call point. Since, however, this is merely something of a bonus, the code acknowledges that, for example, in a system with 150 manual call points, each manual call point will only be tested by the user every 150 weeks. However, a separate 'long stop' is contained within the recommendations on servicing, which recommend that the switch mechanism of every manual call point is tested at least every 12 months. To ensure the rotation in testing manual call points, the code recommends that the identity of the manual call point used in the weekly test should be recorded in the system log book.

If an automatically started emergency generator is used as part of the standby power supply for the fire alarm system (i.e. the relaxation in battery capacity offered by the code is adopted), there will be a need for routine testing of the generator. The code recommends that, in this case, the generator is started up once each month by simulation of failure of normal power supply and operated on-load for at least one hour, after which fuel tanks should be left filled, and oil and coolant levels should be checked and topped up as necessary.

If vented batteries are used as a standby power supply, a monthly visual inspection of the batteries and their connections should be carried out. In particular, electrolyte levels should be checked. In practice, the use of vented batteries in fire alarm systems is now very rare, but occasionally it occurs in premises that contain large battery banks for other purposes, e.g. some power stations.

34. Servicing

Clause 45 of the code deals with the subject of inspection and servicing of the system. In the context of the code, servicing falls within the scope of the more generic term 'maintenance'. Servicing is defined as the routine process of work on the system (including cleaning, realignment, adjustment and replacement) carried out at predetermined intervals. The code stresses the importance of periodic inspection and servicing so that unrevealed faults are identified, preventative measures taken, false alarm problems identified and addressed, and that the user is made aware of any changes to the building that affect the protection afforded by the system. The last of these points is a particularly important one that, traditionally, has probably not been addressed as well as it should be by fire alarm service technicians.

The periodic inspection and servicing of the system needs to be carried out by a competent person with specialist knowledge of fire detection and fire alarm systems. The code advises that this knowledge should include a knowledge of the causes of false alarms. The person carrying out the work should have sufficient information regarding the system and adequate access to spares.

As noted in the code, servicing will normally be carried out by a contractor. Some large organizations do carry out this work themselves, using in-house staff. However, the code contains something of a 'health warning' in respect of this practice. It is suggested that care needs to be taken to ensure that the in-house personnel have equivalent competence to the technicians of a typical fire alarm servicing organization. This is probably the yardstick that would be applied by the courts if it were ever claimed in civil or criminal law that injury had occurred as a result of inadequate performance of a fire alarm system that, for example, had allegedly been inadequately serviced by the user.

Capability of a fire alarm contractor to service systems is part of the considerations that apply in certification of contractors under the

BRE Certification Scheme, LPS 1014. In addition, within the BAFE Modular Schemes, one module, against which firms can be certificated, relates specifically to maintenance. (There is, presumably, no reason why a large user could not apply for certification of their in-house team under the latter module.)

Perhaps one of the most contentious issues in the drafting of the 2002 version of the code was the frequency at which fire alarm systems should be serviced. Previous versions of the code were definitive on this subject; it was recommended that all systems be serviced every three months. However, this recommendation could be traced back to the days when vented batteries were used as the standby supply, and there was a need for these batteries to be checked at this frequency to ensure electrolyte levels were maintained, etc. Modern 'maintenance-free' batteries used in fire alarm systems do not require this attention and, accordingly, the frequency at which systems should be serviced was subject to reconsideration.

One significant body of opinion was that there is no justification for servicing systems on a quarterly basis, particularly in view of the extent of monitoring incorporated within modern systems. In this connection, it is interesting to note that, for many years, it has been practice to service intruder alarm systems only every six months. Moreover, traditionally codes of practice on fixed gaseous fire extinguishing systems recommended only that these systems were serviced every six months. However, there was also significant opposition to change in the then existing recommendation for three-monthly servicing, often on the part of contractors engaged in fire alarm servicing.

Arguments put forward for maintaining the status quo included the fact that some users pay little attention to the status of the system, which could then be seriously defective, or even totally inoperative, until the time of the next service visit. Also, it was argued that, in premises that are subject to frequent modification, reliance is often placed on the service technician to identify the effect of changes on the fire alarm system. It was argued that, in such premises, extending the duration between service visits would be undesirable. While it would be unfair to generalize, the experience of the author is that, in practice, it is an unfortunate fact that service technicians often fail to identify quite obvious deficiencies that have arisen as a result of changes to the premises, even though it is in their company's interest to do so as the necessary rectification work is then a useful 'small works' revenue earner.

The difficulty in achieving any consensus view on the frequency of servicing is evident in the recommendations of the code in respect of this. The recommendation remains that all vented batteries and their connections should be examined every quarter. (This, of course, might be carried out by competent in-house maintenance personnel.) However, the 2002 version of the code now recommends *periodic* inspection and testing of the system, rather than specifying an exact frequency at which this should be carried out.

The code recommends that the period between successive inspection and servicing visits should be based upon a risk assessment, taking into account the type of system installed, the environment in which it operates and other factors that may affect the long term operation of the system. However, the code does recommend that the period between successive inspection and servicing visits should not exceed six months. If the risk assessment shows the need for more frequent inspection and servicing visits, the code recommends that all interested parties should agree the appropriate inspection and servicing schedule.

The vague nature of this recommendation is, in the opinion of the author, a slightly unsatisfactory aspect of the code. Certainly, it begs a number of questions. For example, who is to undertake this risk assessment? Should it be the user, who, in many cases, may not be competent to make a decision, given that, in effect, even the technical committee responsible for the code could not be more definitive. Should it be one of the parties so far encountered in the various chapters of the guide, such as the supplier of the system, designer, installer, commissioning engineer or the party responsible for verification (if this is carried out)? Some of these parties may not feel competent to undertake this risk assessment, while others might be deemed to have a vested interest. Is the risk assessment to which the code refers the fire risk assessment required by legislation? This will normally be undertaken by the employer, or a party acting on his/her behalf. Those responsible for undertaking fire risk assessments in accordance with this legislation are usually not specialists in fire alarm systems.

Regardless of who carries out the risk assessment, what is actually involved in carrying it out? As noted above, the code refers to three issues that need to be taken into account. The first of these, namely the type of system installed, might have a bearing on the outcome of the risk assessment, according to the sophistication of the system to monitor itself, the complexity of the system and, for example, whether the system is purely manual or incorporates a large number of automatic fire detectors. The environment in which the system is installed clearly has some bearing, as, in an aggressive industrial environment, detectors may need to be changed at the time of each service visit. Other factors that affect the long-term operation of the system are not specified in the code. Moreover, it is not specifically suggested in the code that the risk assessment takes into account the frequency with which changes to the premises are likely to be carried out.

So what does this recommendation mean in practice? Probably, only time will tell, and this will be driven by the requirements of users, guided by others. However, it would seem likely that, in the long term, six-monthly servicing will become the default period, with more frequent servicing only if a well-justified case can be made for this. Indeed, the recommendations of the code would almost seem to discourage users from accepting that more frequent servicing is necessary, as, if the risk assessment deems this to be necessary, the actual frequency does not simply default back to quarterly, but, instead, the code recommends that *all interested parties* should agree the appropriate inspection and servicing schedule.

This would appear to imply that, if the user determines that there is a need for servicing at more frequent intervals than every six months, in order to comply with the code the user would need to approach the fire and rescue authority and, possibly, the fire insurers to obtain agreement as to what the frequency should be. It is most unlikely that either of these parties would be able to offer a greater engineering insight to the appropriate frequency than would be available elsewhere, and the associated bureaucratic process is unlikely to appeal to many users. In any case, the latest guidance documents on fire safety legislation tend to advocate six-monthly servicing of fire detection and fire alarm systems.

Although some disappointment in the disappearance of a specific recommendation for quarterly servicing has been expressed by a number of fire alarm servicing organizations, the situation for such organizations in terms of their revenue earning is not as bleak as it might at first seem. When the work that is to be carried out during service visits is considered, there has been some tightening up and expansion of the recommended work. For example, there is, in the 2002 code, more definitive recommendations regarding the visual inspection that should be made at the time of each service visit to check whether structural or occupancy changes have affected the compliance of the system with the code.

This is just one of 15 checks and tests that the code specifically recommends be carried out at the time of each periodic inspection and test. (There is, however, a suggestion that there might be an omission of certain tests that are declared unnecessary by the equipment supplier if it can be demonstrated that automatic monitoring achieves the same objective as the relevant test.) In addition, as discussed in Chapter 25, the 2002 code contains a new duty for service technicians to scrutinize carefully the system's false alarm record. In some cases, compliance with the code will necessitate preliminary investigation of high rates of false alarms (see Chapter 25).

However, perhaps the major comfort to servicing organizations is that the 2002 code continues to recommend annual testing of all manual call points and automatic fire detectors. The test recommended for each type of detector is a functional test. For example, it would not be sufficient to rely purely on measurement of analogue values at the control equipment of an addressable system (although the code also recommends that these analogue values be checked every 12 months). In practice, much of the time involved in a service visit has always been that associated with testing detectors. (Special arrangements are described in the code in the case of aspirating systems.)

Custom and practice has been that 25% of all detectors were tested at the time of each quarterly visit, so that all detectors were tested on an annual basis. In fact, many users continue with quarterly servicing, so that only 25% of the detectors need to be test operated at the time of each service visit. If six-monthly servicing is adopted, either all detectors will need to be tested at the time of each alternate visit, or 50% of the detectors would need to be tested at each service visit. In addition, the code provides recommendations on other measures that should be carried out on a 12-monthly basis, including a visual inspection to confirm that all readily accessible cable fixings are secure and undamaged, and confirmation that the entire 'cause and effect' program of the system is correct.

Thus, a service visit carried out in accordance with the 2002 version of the code will, for many companies, involve greater time and effort than under previous versions of the code. Moreover, a change from quarterly servicing to six-monthly servicing will certainly not halve the annual service bill; while some reduction in the annual charge might be expected, given the continued need for functional testing of all manual call points and detectors and, for example, the extended work that the service organization might need to anticipate for investigation of false alarm problems, users have probably experienced little reduction in their annual service charges following the publication of BS 5839-1:2002.

35. Repair and non-routine attention

The code uses the term non-routine attention to describe the matters addressed in clause 46 of the code, which comprise the following.

- A special inspection of the system when a new servicing organization takes over responsibility for servicing the system.
- Repair of faults or damage.
- Modifications.
- Actions to address an unacceptable rate of false alarms.
- Inspection and test of the system following a fire.

The code recommends that, when a new servicing organization is appointed, they carry out a special inspection of the system. The user should, therefore, anticipate that, if, as would seem reasonable, this inspection is carried out as part of the first service visit, this visit might be more expensive than subsequent visits. What is the purpose of this special inspection? First, the servicing organization should study existing documentation and ensure that they have sufficient information to service the system effectively in the future.

However, the code also recommends that the new servicing organization should identify major areas of non-compliance with the code; these should then be reported to the responsible person appointed by the user (see Chapter 36). The code acknowledges that classification of a non-compliance as major is subjective, but a list of nine non-compliances that should be regarded as major is given in the code.

A study of this list suggests that this initial inspection must be quite thorough, and whoever carries it out must have a basic knowledge of the recommendations of the code in respect of system design. For example, the code recommends that major areas of non-compliance that should be identified include an inadequate number of call points and inadequate provision of fire detection for compliance with the category of system in question. The code also expects this inspection to reveal any inadequacies in sound pressure levels, non-compliances in respect of standby power supplies, inadequate circuit monitoring, cabling with inadequate fire resistance or support (such that collapse of a significant length of cable could occur in the event of fire), shortcomings in electrical safety, an unacceptable rate of false alarms and changes to the premises that have affected the effectiveness of the system.

In addition, in the course of this inspection, it should be determined whether a suitable log book exists; if there is no such log book, one should be provided by the servicing organization. Given the extensive nature of this inspection, some servicing organizations might feel that it is not appropriate work to incorporate within the first service visit, and it might be considered that a special visit would be required for this purpose.

It might be questioned whether it is reasonable for the code to impose this burden on a servicing organization, every time they take over responsibility for a system. If a special fee is charged for this inspection, which would not be unreasonable, this might even discourage a user from changing servicing organization. It is, therefore, reasonable to question why it was considered necessary to include this special inspection within the recommendations of the code.

One simple reason is that the system taken over might previously have been serviced in accordance with a contract that complied with an earlier version of the code, in which there might have been less emphasis on some of the matters that the 2002 version of the code now recommends be considered at the time of each service visit. Secondly, a change in the servicing organization provides yet further opportunity for a fresh pair of eyes to consider just a small number of key design issues, thereby ensuring that the protection afforded by the system is adequate. Moreover, this special inspection is actually advantageous to a servicing organization itself. First, it may preclude future complaints or allegations of liability against the servicing organization if it subsequently transpires that there are shortcomings in the system that the organization has not identified. Secondly, inevitably, in the case of some systems, the inspection will create the potential for some 'small works' to be carried out by the new servicing organization! It is not, however, implied in the code that all non-compliances with the current version of the code need to be addressed. In many cases, upgrading of the system, or at least certain aspects of the system, will not be justifiable; this is a matter for the user to determine. Whereas, for example, it would be reasonable to expect low sound pressure levels to be addressed, rewiring of non-fire resisting cable throughout an installation is unlikely to be reasonable.

In order to ensure that the system is properly maintained, there is normally a contract with a third-party maintenance organization. The code recommends that, in this case, there should be an agreement for emergency call-out to deal with faults or damage to the system. The agreement should be such that, on a 24-hour basis, a technician of the maintenance organization can normally attend the premises within eight hours of a call from the user. It should be noted that, unless such an agreement exists, the maintenance arrangements do not comply with the recommendations of the code. However, this does not preclude in-house maintenance, to which this particular recommendation does not apply. Moreover, the code acknowledges that the eight-hour response time might not be possible in the case of very remote areas and certain offshore islands. If the eight-hour period cannot be achieved, this needs to be recorded as a variation in the system log book.

To assist the user when faults occur, particularly at a time that the person responsible for the fire alarm system is not available, the code recommends that the name and telephone number of any third party responsible for maintenance of the system should be prominently displayed at the control and indicating equipment.

The code recommends that a great deal of care should be taken when the system is modified, so that the original design is not compromised. The code also recommends that care should be taken that the modifications do not detrimentally affect compliance with fire safety legislation. This might necessitate consultation with enforcing authorities; there might also be a need for consultation with insurers. Thus, the code recommends that responsibility for modification of the system should lie with someone who is competent in at least the basic principles of fire alarm design and is conversant with the code. This does not, of course, preclude this person being a representative of the user or the maintenance organization.

When modifications are carried out, an element of retesting of the system will need to be undertaken. The code stresses that this is particularly true of software-controlled systems. It is an unfortunate fact that, in the case of such systems, minor software changes can give rise to the need for extensive retesting, otherwise it cannot be ensured that software errors have not affected the 'cause and effect' logic of the system. The code recommends a number of specific tests that should be carried out on each occasion that modifications are carried out; these are in addition to the tests of equipment and functions that are already known to be affected by the modifications. It should be noted that, if the modifications involve software changes, part of the test work recommended by the code includes random testing of parts of the system that should not have been affected by the changes to ensure that these have not been affected in error.

In the few years immediately prior to the publication of the 2002 version of the code, fire alarm companies began to offer an arrangement whereby the system configuration could be carried out remotely, via a modem. A similar service had, already, for many years, been offered for modification of computer systems by computer companies. Similar arrangements are often possible in the case of, for example, software-controlled telephone systems.

Concern had, however, been expressed within the fire safety profession that the organization carrying out the modification might not have first-hand knowledge of the system's design principles and the actual circumstances at the protected premises. A simple practical concern was that, for example, the user might, without realizing the implications, request a third party to switch off the smoke sensors of multi-sensor detectors located within escape routes of a Category L system, e.g. as a result of false alarms. Without adequate knowledge of the premises, the firm undertaking the modification might be equally ignorant of the implications of this measure.

This issue was considered very carefully by the technical committee responsible for the 2002 version of the code. The advice given in the code is that, although the modifications may be carried out remotely by the maintenance organization, it will be appropriate for a competent person from the maintenance organization to visit the premises before the modification is carried out, to confirm the validity of the modification and consider its effect on compliance with the code. The advice is also that it might be necessary to visit the premises to undertake certain tests immediately after the modification has been carried out.

Some users and maintenance organizations might regard this advice as unnecessarily onerous and expensive, particularly on every occasion that a sufficiently knowledgeable and competent user requires a minor change to system configuration. However, nothing in the code precludes the post-modification tests being carried out by the user. Moreover, the advice regarding the pre-modification visit is given within the commentary of subclause 46.4; it does not appear within the recommendations of this clause, and so failure to comply with the advice would not constitute a non-compliance with the recommendations of the code. Equally, it would be wise to exercise caution before modifying a system without following this advice.

It should also be noted that the code does have particular recommendations, given in subclause 46.4.3, applicable to modifications carried out remotely. The recommendations are that any person carrying out modifications remotely should have access to current 'as fitted' drawings of the system and to the system configuration, indicating full details of 'cause and effect' logic, available with the system documentation. It is also recommended in this subclause that any person carrying out modifications remotely should be conversant with the code.

Regardless of how the modification is effected, the code recommends that, on completion of the modifications, all 'as fitted' drawings and other relevant system records should be updated as appropriate. It is also recommended in the code that a modification certificate should be issued, confirming that the work has been carried out in accordance with the recommendations of the code, or identifying any variations. A model modification certificate is shown in Annex G of the code. It should be noted that, in the case of this certificate, the certificate should be issued by the person carrying out the modification work; this is as would be expected.

However, completion of the modification certificate requires a second signature, confirming that the modifications have introduced no additional variations from the recommendations of the code, other than those recorded in the certificate. This part of the certificate may be signed by the same person as carried out the modification work, but (probably more commonly) responsibility might, ultimately, rest with another person or organization, such as the user or a consultant acting on the user's behalf. In this case, there will be two different signatures on the model modification certificate, namely that of the person carrying out the work and that of the person ultimately responsible for the modification and its suitability. Where modifications are necessary to address an unacceptable rate of false alarms, the modifications should take account of the guidance in Section 3 of the code. The modifications should not introduce new non-compliances with the code unless these are agreed with all interested parties.

When a fire occurs, it may cause damage to at least part of the system. Accordingly, the code recommends that there be a special inspection and test of the system following any fire. The work involved in carrying out this inspection and test is described in subclause 46.4.5 of the code.

If the system has been disconnected for a long period of time, the code recommends that the system be inspected and tested in accordance with the recommendations of the code for annual system testing. A 'long period' is not defined in the code, and this will, therefore, be left to the judgement of the user and/or, perhaps, the maintenance organization. However, clearly, this clause is intended to relate to, for example, a situation in which the system has been totally powered down in an empty building and is then to become operational on reoccupation of the building.

36. User responsibilities

Section 7 of the code, which comprises only two clauses, is devoted to the matter of user responsibilities. It is not, however, expected that the typical user will purchase a copy of BS 5839-1. However, earlier in the code, it is recommended that appropriate information be provided to the purchaser or user. The organization responsible for the provision of documentation needs to be identified in the fire alarm contract.

Clause 47 of the code, which is the first of the two clauses in Section 7, is founded on the appointment of a 'responsible person'. This term is defined in the code as the person having control of the building and/or premises, whether as occupier or otherwise, or any person delegated by the person having control of the building and/or premises to be responsible for the fire alarm system and the fire procedures. Clause 47 recommends that this person be given sufficient authority to carry out the duties described in that clause, and that this person should normally be the keeper of the documentation described in clause 40 (see Chapter 29). The primary duty of the responsible person is to ensure that:

- the system is tested and maintained properly;
- appropriate records are kept;
- relevant occupants in the premises are aware of their roles and responsibilities in connection with the fire alarm system;
- necessary steps are taken to avoid situations that are detrimental to the standard of protection afforded by the system;
- necessary steps are taken to ensure that the level of false alarms is minimized.

The implications of these objectives relate to the testing, maintenance, keeping of documentation and proper system management described in the earlier chapters of this guide. It is also recommended in clause 47 that the responsible person should ensure that the control and indicating equipment is checked at least once every 24 hours to confirm that there are no faults on the system. It is also the responsibility of the responsible person to ensure that suitable spare parts for the system are held within the premises; the code gives guidance on the nature of these.

Finally, clause 48 provides recommendations regarding the information that should be recorded in the system log book. A model format for the log book is contained in Annex F of the code. As noted in clause 48, a fire alarm system log book might be required to be kept under certain fire safety legislation. In practice, while the latest fire safety legislation is not so prescriptive as to require this, the keeping of a log book is one means of demonstrating compliance with legislation in respect of fire alarm system testing and servicing. It can, thus, form a component of defence against allegations of breaches of the relevant requirements of legislation, or against civil liability.